Leonard Knight Elmhirst

International Explorations
of
Agricultural Economics

A Tribute to the Inspiration of
LEONARD KNIGHT ELMHIRST

———————

Edited by **ROGER N. DIXEY**, *University of Oxford*

———————

The Iowa State University Press, Ames, Iowa, U.S.A.

1964

© 1964 The Iowa State University Press.

All rights reserved.
Composed and printed by
The Iowa State University Press,
Ames, Iowa, U.S.A.

Library of Congress Catalogue Card Number 64–13372

Foreword and Dedication

ONE OF THE MORE IMPORTANT FACTORS in progress is to find people who have the capacity to create something new. Sir Edward Appleton, a British winner of a Nobel Prize, told a very illustrative story when receiving his Prize in Stockholm. At a meeting at Cambridge University when candidates were being selected for a scholarship, one of the Fellows of the College spoke warmly and enthusiastically for one candidate. He concluded with the words: "I think that I can best describe the standard that characterizes this man by saying that when he has said his word on some matter it is also the final word on the matter." To this the Dean of the Faculty remarked: "That may well be so, but I think we should do better to get hold of a young man who says the *first* word on some matter."

Our Founder-President can very well be identified with the young man who says the first word, who takes the initiative. To him, more than to anyone, is to be credited the fact that the International Conference of Agricultural Economists (now the International Association of Agricultural Economists) was founded at the conclusion of the initial conference in 1929, at Dartington Hall, Totnes, England. This book which we now dedicate to him symbolizes, somewhat tardily, the recognition accorded to the young scholar.

For nearly thirty years you, L. K. Elmhirst, have been the President of I.A.A.E. and, since 1958, our Founder-President. Not only have you been the leading personality of the international gathering of agricultural economists in a formal sense, but also you have been an inspiring and encouraging spirit in it. You have spared no effort in trying to bring together agricultural economists from all over the world, and you have certainly succeeded in doing so. However, it is not only as a leader that we sincerely hold you in very high regard but even more as an individual. Your ideas are, and always have been, that all people are created equal regardless of race, creed, natural origin, the language they speak, and the political system under which they live. In the hearts of those members who participated in the activity of the I.A.A.E. in the period around World War II, is forever enshrined your action after the war in gathering your fellow economists once again from whichever side they had fought. No one else has offered so many patient, careful and inspiring efforts of all kinds as you have for the benefit of the I.A.A.E. It is first and foremost to your credit that we, your fellow economists, feel we are brothers and sisters within a great family.

[v]

The publication of this book has been made possible by the very great interest that the members of the I.A.A.E. and kindred organizations have shown in this common enterprise of ours. Subscriptions have been received from all over the world. The fact that the response to our initiative in publishing this book has been so ready and cheerful is certainly a clear manifestation of the esteem our Founder-President enjoys in our sphere. It gives me great pleasure, on the behalf of the I.A.A.E., to express our warm and sincere thanks to all those who have co-operated financially and otherwise in making the publication possible. I also want to thank Mr. Roger Dixey, who volunteered and in a very creditable way executed the demanding editing of the book as well as gave the essays their form. Our appreciation is also directed to the Iowa State University Press which has published the volume.

As we present this book to you, our Founder-President, may we also dedicate ourselves to continuing to strengthen our Association, to keep it as a strong link of communication among the world's agricultural economists, and to maintain it as a living monument to your efforts.

NILS WESTERMARCK
President of the International Association
of Agricultural Economists.

Contents

[*vii*]

International Explorations

of

Agricultural Economics

1

Leonard Knight Elmhirst

J. R. CURRIE

Formerly of the Economics Research Department,
Dartington Hall, England

LEONARD ELMHIRST comes of a Yorkshire family whose history dates from the middle ages and whose traditional calling has been the church, landowning, and the law. His father was incumbent of the Anglican parish of Laxton in the East Riding who as a typical parson *cum* landowner had the twin cares of his flock and the ancestral estate. As a shrewd Yorkshireman he also expected his large family to do their part in conserving the property. Anxious to encourage thrift, he paid by results. His boys were given so much a tail for rats destroyed, and half-a-crown per fifty stobs split by hand out of the hardwood logs cut on the estate. In such ways the virtues of hard work and of service for others were extolled and young Leonard soon added a sense of responsibility to a love of nature and the country-side, especially perhaps of trees and indeed of sound land management. The boys' old governess, Miss M. Glendinning, told the present writer while on a visit to New Zealand in 1955 that her young charge was one of the most observant persons she ever met. She recalled with pleasure an example of his precociousness when a child of only seven or so. Accompanied by his elder brother and younger members of the family they were being conducted on a nature exploration of the woodlands. Their study of plant and animal life was being so disturbed by frolics and fun that Leonard appealed to his governess to send "the little ones home so that we can study the woods without interruption." This illustrates a bent which has remained with him all his life—a determination to know all that can be learnt in any given situation.

[3]

From home at the age of eight he went away to St. Anselm's School at Bakewell to learn under a distinguished naturalist, Mr. Stearn Fox, the headmaster. Later he went to Repton (a public school in the English sense, i.e., an independent boarding school), where he was fortunate to have as one of his chief mentors William Temple, who later became Archbishop of Canterbury. This was the beginning of a long friendship, and although never a blind follower of the enlightened Archbishop, the impact of the latter's liberal philosophy of life and the many discussions arising from it have had a marked effect on Elmhirst's outlook. From Repton he went to Trinity College, Cambridge, where he read History and Theology with the initial intention of following in his father's footsteps.

The teaching of G. Lowes Dickinson (who in later years became a regular visitor to Dartington) began to modify his views. And then came the 1914–18 war. The fact of being invalided in Mesopotamia, where he himself was ministering to the sick, and later in India, changed the course of his career. While he and others were recovering from the worst of their illnesses, he made a special study of Lionel Curtis' attempt to work out a means whereby India could achieve self-government within the British family of nations. This and his previous training and experience led naturally to an interest in social service which became almost the ruling passion of his life. Appositely, his thoughts turned to India's needs in this respect and, typically, he sought to learn of the problems at first hand from the best authorities. By a fortunate chance he found himself lodged during convalescence in the same house as Lionel Curtis himself who, as indicated, was a leading mind on India's problems and future. In fact, he can be said to have been the real architect of the pre-liberation constitution of India which was passed by the British parliament as the Montague-Chelmsford Reform Act. Elmhirst in fact typed the original draft and still has a copy in his possession.

Curtis also introduced him to Sam Higginbottom, a pioneer missionary at Allahabad, a man well grounded in agricultural economics. In 1921, after Elmhirst had taken an agricultural degree at Cornell, Higginbottom brought him into contact with Sir Rabindranath Tagore and his educational work in Bengal. It was for him that Elmhirst started an institute on rural reconstruction, later known as Sriniketan, one of the earliest attempts at community development in the villages immediately around Bolpur in West Bengal. This soon dispelled any doubt that disease and lack of technical knowledge, leading to poverty, lay at the root of the decay of Indian village life. During his stay in Bengal so deep a friendship sprang up between him and the poet that the latter asked him to travel abroad with him as his secretary. This took him to China, Japan, Italy, and South America, where he had a wonderful opportunity of studying the rural scene and learning of each country's problems and aspirations direct from many eminent authorities.

The years of study at Cornell had introduced him to the courses in agricultural economics given by G. F. Warren and W. I. Myers and opened up a whole new international horizon. He made many friends from many countries and came to understand the interdependence of the segments into which selfish nationalism had split the world. It is of more than passing interest perhaps that he graduated from kitchenman at the Cosmopolitan Student Cafeteria to Chairman of the Cosmopolitan Club! This fortunate progress led him in 1920 to a meeting with Dorothy Whitney Straight who had many international interests and friends in foreign countries and, five years later, became his wife. It also crystallized his interest in international affairs and developed that flair which all associate with him in his enlightened approach to social and rural problems.

Leonard and Dorothy Elmhirst are twin souls in their desire to see reason and goodwill prevail, and above all to be of service to others though entirely without condescension. Wealth may be a privilege, they aver, but it is a great responsibility. Therefore, while taking risks in attacking problems of education or rural betterment, the Elmhirsts have always held that the risks must be carefully calculated.

The experiment in rural reconstruction and education, in the broadest sense, which they established in England at Dartington Hall is founded on this philosophy. This is neither the time nor the place to assess its positive results, but there is no doubt about the objectives and motivating forces which surround its planning and guidance. Obviously, much of Elmhirst's experience with Tagore in Bengal, his training at Cornell, as well as his wife's rich background in the world of arts and education in New York, have moulded the design for the establishment and running of Dartington Hall as an institution seeking a practical approach to the wide range of problems, social and economic, which now beset society.

This general picture of the trend of Elmhirst's interests and activities would be incomplete without some further details of the growth of his interests in international agricultural economics. The experience and teaching at Cornell undoubtedly were a dominant influence. Here he was greatly stimulated by the close friendship with many of his colleagues, especially Dr. Warren, Dean Carl Ladd, and Dr. Myers, based largely on their mutual interests. Later these contacts were to prove important. When the Elmhirsts were looking for a suitable site for the research and educational projects they had in mind, Dr. Myers happened to be in Europe surveying the status of agricultural economics. He naturally called on his old pupil and as a matter of direct interest went with him to survey Dartington Hall's possibilities. The decision was then taken that here was the ideal setting for the activities that were envisaged. This was in 1926. Obviously Cornell, and Elmhirst's estimate of the progress being made in American farming, provided the nucleus of the design for the work at

Dartington Hall. He knew the value of the close relations which existed between research at Cornell and the farmers of New York State, largely brought about by the extension service. His natural reaction, both as a scientifically trained agriculturist and as the son of a landowner, was to plan a way by which the owner of the land could help his tenants and other farmers in the area to adopt better methods of farming so as to obtain higher standards of living. Thus, it was laid down that Dartington should experiment with improved methods of agricultural production and take steps to promote the early adoption by other farmers of those which proved successful. This was but one aspect of the project. In order to ensure the fullest use of American experience, he invited Dean Ladd, Head of the Agricultural Extension Service, to spend his sabbatical leave in 1928 at Dartington Hall, to give general advice in relation to agricultural development and to visit other countries in Europe where he could meet the leaders in agricultural economics and related disciplines. The present writer accompanied Dean Ladd on these journeys and found, as Elmhirst had expected, an eagerness everywhere to learn of the development in agricultural economics in other countries. It was also clear that members of the profession would welcome some means of establishing closer contacts with other workers in the subject.

It was from this background that Dr. Warren's original concept of an organization to stimulate research and education in this new field emerged as a plan for an international conference of agricultural economists. The details were incubated at Dartington Hall by Ladd and Elmhirst. This led to the holding of the first conference at Dartington Hall in 1929, which was very much of an experiment. The objectives were twofold: the primary one, possibly, was to see what the reaction of economists from different countries would be when discussing mutual problems and, as a consequence, how far a formal organization could help in developing a bridge between members in the different countries by enabling personal contacts to be established; the second objective was to provide a forum for discussion of the techniques and problems relating to the discipline. All who participated in the meetings were unanimous in agreeing that the aims had been achieved and that steps should be taken to organize a second conference.

In view of the prominent part taken by Warren and his colleagues it was decided to hold it at Cornell. Here the formal basic constitution of the organization was drawn up. Under this, it was unanimously agreed that in making arrangements for future conferences, the time-table and facilities provided should give ample opportunities for economists with mutual interests to meet informally and thereby develop easy and direct contacts.

While the objectives of what is now the International Association of Agricultural Economists are still among Elmhirst's major concerns, he has for many years maintained a very wide interest in other directions, national and international. Personal comfort and selfishness never enter into his calculations. His decisions rest on an acute sense of duty. During the second World War, for example, when invited to lead the joint Anglo-American Commission around the Middle East, he did not hesitate to improve the food situation, not only of the army but of all the countries at the eastern end of the Mediterranean, even as far as Persia. He visited every country to study at first hand the problems and potential of each area. Later, at Minister Richard Casey's request, he went to Bengal as Agricultural Adviser to try to alleviate the famine conditions there. Crossing the Atlantic in response to requests for lectures was another wartime activity not without danger and acute discomfort in those days.

In more peaceful post-war times he has taken part in much public work of social and economic significance. His roots go deep in the educational field. Locally, for a number of years he was a County Councillor for Devon, paying particular attention to education. While the boarding school at Dartington Hall is one of his major interests, he is chairman also of the county school which serves the Dartington parish and of the secondary schools for the Totnes area; he is a member of the Council for Exeter University; he was on the government committee set up to study the place of national parks in the use and conservation of beautiful areas of Britain for public access; and he was president of the English Forestry Society at a time when privately owned woods were in need of reconstruction after being seriously devastated by the demands of two World Wars.

Further afield, at the invitation of the Government of India, he served on the Commission for Higher Education in Rural Areas. Their report resulted in the setting up of a series of rural institutes for higher education, one of which many of those who attended the Conference at Mysore in 1958 had the privilege of visiting.

As president of the International Association of Agricultural Economists, Elmhirst guided its fortunes for more than thirty years, and today as an elder statesman he fills the useful office of Founder-President. He was mainly responsible for the establishment by the Dartington Hall Trust of an Institute of Agrarian Affairs in the University of Oxford, which not only carries on research as reflected in its Journal, but has the responsible and onerous task of editing the triennial proceedings of the Association. He took an active part in the formation and development of the British Agricultural Economics Society, of whose Executive Council he was chairman for more than twenty years and of which he was President in 1949. He pioneered the independent non-party research organization composed of business leaders and scholars, known as P.E.P. (Political and Economic Planning) which not only carries out surveys and research in a wide range of social and economic problems at home but investigates those of international importance, such as the European Common Market. His deep knowledge and interest in public affairs has been acknowledged by leading authorities, as for example by his appointment in 1952 as a member of the Development Commission, a body which deals with a wide variety of problems both social and economic pertaining to rural development in the British Isles. It is a government agency established in 1909 as an independent body to study and foster progressive techniques in the fields of agriculture and fisheries, as well as to encourage the establishment of desirable social organizations in rural areas. He has been an appointed member of the Murray Committee, now the Cohen Committee, and has received honorary doctorates at the Universities of Freiburg in Germany, Bengal in India, and Durham in England. In 1960 he was elected a Fellow of the American Farm Economic Association and, in the same year, an honorary member of the Agricultural Economics Society of the United Kingdom.

All those who have been privileged to work with Leonard Elmhirst admire his remarkable qualities: his humility; his great gift for friendship, so valuable an asset in building up the I.A.A.E.; his tact when presiding over meetings, always encouraging the timid and checking the sophisticated and unruly; his tolerance with the less talented who need his help; his aversion to insincerity and humbug; his rooted antipathy to racial prejudice.

These are some of the qualities which have marked him as a leader and have endeared him to all who know him. A few of his really intimate friends know too of his flair for doing a good deed unobtrusively and unproclaimed.

Long may this volume, a tribute from his many friends, remind him of their gratitude and admiration and be a token of their goodwill.

2

Three Concepts of Agricultural Over-population

RUDOLF BIĆANIĆ

University of Zagreb, Zagreb, Yugoslavia

FROM BEING REGARDED as a problem of under-developed countries only, agricultural over-population has now become a common problem affecting many fields of agricultural policy in most countries—from price policy to structural changes. It has attracted the attention of many students of agrarian policy ever since the first number of the *International Journal of Agrarian Affairs* in 1938 was entirely devoted to it.

In most studies of this phenomenon at least three main concepts can be distinguished: those of consumption, those of production, and those of mobility of population.

I. THE CONSUMPTION APPROACH

From the consumption point of view agricultural over-population may be said to depend on what size of agricultural population an area can support at a certain standard of personal consumption (f_o). The positive surplus above this number we shall consider as agricultural over-population (V). In connexion with this we also use the term population pressure (g) which is a relation between the actual number of agricultural population (A) and the standard number of this population (A_o). Thus we get:

$$V = A - A_o \qquad (1.1)$$

$$g = \frac{A}{A_o} \qquad (1.2)$$

[*9*]

The standard population figure is arrived at by dividing the available aggregate consumption fund by the standard consumption per head.[1]

$$A_o = \frac{F}{f_o} \qquad (1.3)$$

$$g = \frac{A}{F} \cdot f_o \qquad (1.4)$$

Thus the surplus of agricultural population is expressed by the following formula:

$$V = A - A_o = A - \frac{F}{f_o} \qquad (1.5)$$

The agricultural population pressure is greater the larger the absolute figure of that population, and the smaller the aggregate consumption fund put at its disposal, and the larger the standard of personal consumption per head. Thus, if the agricultural population in a country increases, or if its aggregate consumption fund decreases, then agricultural over-population increases too. If in a country the consumption standard of the agricultural population increases, the agricultural population pressure also increases in a positive correlation.

This consumption concept of agricultural over-population is the basis of the whole approach to economic development when it deals with an increase of the standard of living, which is hampered by an increase of population which cannot be matched by an adequate increase of food production. All discussions dealing with the maximum or optimum carrying capacity of an area, a country, or the Earth itself, are linked to this concept of over-population as are also the problems of the population explosion, the hunger line, etc. Maximization of product per hectare is the main policy target.

This kind of pressure of agricultural population can be considered also as an indicator of many other social phenomena, from the decomposition of the institutional framework in which the agricultural population lives, up to political revolts and agrarian revolutions which occur when a level of irreducible consumption is approached which cannot be countered by economic means.

To determine the magnitude of agricultural over-population in connexion with this first concept, three sets of problems have to be elaborated. The first is to define the agricultural population. Here we are taking into consideration the *total* agricultural population. The distinction between the terms rural spatial, and agricultural occupational is important. It opens up a whole set of questions, especially in countries in which agriculture is not only an occupation but

---

[1] We make a distinction here between the level of living and the standard of living in the U.N.O. terminology sense.

still a way of life; where it comprises a great number of additional and auxiliary activities, and other multi-functional family services connected with life on the family holding either as main or accessory occupations.

The second set of problems is concerned with the aggregate consumption fund. At first this fund was assumed to be evenly distributed and proportionate to the agricultural land, and the problem was to find out how much land was necessary to support one person living by agriculture or one consumption unit. As land proved to be an unreliable indicator, the next step was to take volume of production in physical terms (in kind, or food production per head) as a standard measurement of agricultural over-population. The problem of minimum subsistence level (calories, kg., etc.) is the expression of this kind of problem. The next stage was to move from volume to aggregate income in cash and kind, conceiving over-population in terms of average income from agriculture per head of agricultural population. The problem of parity of income between non-agricultural and agricultural population arose as a measurement of living standards.[2]

Further refinement of the over-population concept led to the regional analysis of population distribution, moving also from regional to communal, local or village over-population figures so as to remove the semblance of equal distribution of population over wide areas, thus evening out the surpluses with the vacuums.[3]

A switch from the spatial to the institutional dimension was the next natural step. Agricultural over-population came to be defined according to size of holding assuming the number of people in an area to vary according to the size of the holding, the smaller ones being overcrowded, and the larger ones sparsely populated. The problem became linked with land reform policy bringing about a redistribution of land both locally and regionally, leading to internal migration. External colonization was the obvious extension of this problem.

Soon the concept of over-population by size of holding was replaced by a more accurate standard, that of the size of the income from agriculture per holding per head. Instead of the spatial, the money dimension was adopted measuring the number of people living on agricultural holdings according to the income distribution.

---

[2] J. D. Black as far back as 1938 set the following standard (his second) for agricultural over-population: ". . . population in agriculture which is able to obtain the same returns from its labour and content of living as comparable social classes can obtain in other industries. . . ." "The Problem of Agricultural Overpopulation" *International Journal of Agrarian Affairs*, 1939, Vol. 1, p. 10.

[3] The assumption is still made that income at the personal disposal of the agricultural population is evenly distributed. A more accurate measurement of the total disposable consumption fund would be found by deducting expenditure, i.e., according to the real burden of direct and indirect taxes, debts and other transfers, rent, investments, etc.

Another variant of this concept defined by income standards is the distinction between the internal income achieved on the holding and the off-holding income which again can be intra-local and extra-local. In a stricter sense only internal income, earned on the holding, could be included when counting agricultural over-population. But as the definition of agriculture itself has not only technological elements (raising crops and animals), but also institutional ones (auxiliary and additional activities), the off-holding activities are not easily isolated from the internal ones. In defining agricultural over-population, therefore, the technological factor cannot be separated from the institutional. Here sociology mixes with economics. Therefore, in measuring the subsistence standard it is not only the size of the agricultural income that matters but the number of people supported by the holding, which depends on socio-economic ties, unpaid family labour being more strongly linked to an agricultural holding than is hired labour. In this way agricultural over-population was conceived in several different forms. The division between family farms and commercial farms in the United States of America is one example. Distinction between those who own land in absentia and those who live and work on farms is another example. A third is the problem of peasant labour forces working on latifundia and living on minifundia in Latin America, giving agricultural over-population a specific semi-feudal and seasonal note.

Thus the problem had to be treated not only from the point of view of economic policy but also from that of social policy. Different measures of protection (customs, price policy, homestead, or direct and indirect subsidies) enable the peasant population to remain on land for lack of other opportunities of earning their livelihood where economic considerations alone would not justify their staying. In this respect the family peasant holding plays the role of an institutional reservoir for giving subsistence to marginal agricultural over-population. In the Soviet Union this role is partly played by another institutional form, the kolkhozes as opposed to the sovkhozes.[4] The most articulate socio-economic distinction in analysing agricultural over-population has been made by G. Orlando[5] who distinguishes over-population according to type of holding: people on family holdings, share croppers, proprietor-workers, operators, part-time workers, and labour on capitalist estates.

The third set of problems is that of the standard of consumption

---

[4] Explaining why the time used to produce 100 kg. of grain is 1.8 hours in the sovkhozes and 7.3 hours in the kolkhozes, Khroushchev said: ". . . . In the kolkhozes, parallel to the problem of achieving a high productivity of labour, is the problem of securing work for all members of the collective and achieving incomes under the same conditions of equal effort and input of labour as in the social economy. . . . The sovkhozes are a different affair." *Izvestia.* Dec. 16th, 1958.

[5] G. Orlando, "Metodi di Accertamento Della Disoccupazione Agricola. Italiana." *Rivista di Economia Agraria,* 3. Roma, 1952.

(f_o). This represents a constant magnitude, specially defined. Although in reality it depends on the kind and absolute magnitude of the aggregate consumption fund, for the purpose of the study of over-population it has to be conceived, conceptually, as a constant. Various methods have been used to define such standards of consumption per head or per consumption unit. It was defined either in physical or in money units (income per head), as an empirically or scientifically devised norm, physiological minimum, the hunger line, minimum of existence, number of calories, physical units of food or textiles, etc.

This standard of consumption has been set also in relative terms in relation to the consumption of a previously taken basis, or compared with another country or economic region.[6]

II. THE PRODUCTION APPROACH

From the point of view of production agricultural over-population can be defined as the number of people in excess of a standard number of producers required for agricultural production in a certain area. In this concept only the economically active agricultural population is taken into account (A_e). Maximization of production per producer is its main target.

Of course the most appropriate criterion would be the optimum number of economically active members of the population. But as optima are often difficult to define or even to assess, it is more convenient to adopt other standards.

The Level of Production

The standard agricultural population (A_{eo}) is the active agricultural population of a standard productivity, necessary to achieve a given volume of production in a certain agricultural area.

$$V_e = A_e - A_{eo} \qquad (2.1)$$

$$g_e = \frac{A_e}{A_{eo}} \qquad (2.2)$$

$$A_{eo} = \frac{Z}{z_0} \qquad (2.3)$$

$$A_e = \frac{Z}{z} \qquad (2.4)$$

In this case V_e is agricultural over-population, and g_e is population pressure. Z indicates aggregate volume of production, z stands for actual agricultural productivity of the active agricultural population, while z_0 represents standard agricultural productivity per head (or unit) of such population.

---

[6] The concealed assumptions in this concept are homogeneity of consumption over time, the continuous flow of income and expenditure, etc.

When the first studies of agricultural over-population from the production point of view were undertaken, the density of agricultural population on a certain area *(P)* used to be taken as the measure of over-population (say 1 person per ha. of land). This involved so many concealed assumptions—e.g. that labour requirements are proportionate to the agricultural area—that more precise measurements were soon seen to be necessary. First the agricultural area under various crops (arable land, gardens, meadows, orchards, vineyards, or pastures) was converted into a homogeneous average or standard agricultural area *(Q,* arable equivalent) by using different factors of conversion *(k)* for different crops in order to show the distribution of land by the intensity of cultivation.[7] Next the fertility of land and the intensity of production were added as a specific factor[8] expressed in physical terms (harvest units). A further development was to represent the natural indices of production computed by F.A.O. on the natural unit basis. Colin Clark introduced multiple harvest and the irrigation factor[9] for a (wet or dry) cultivated area.

If we put all these factors together we can develop the following formulas:

$$Q = kP \tag{2.5}$$
$$Z = qQ = qkP \tag{2.6}$$

$$V_e = A_e - A_{eo} = A_e - \frac{qk}{z}P \tag{2.7}$$

$$g_e = \frac{A_e}{A_{eo}} = \frac{A_e}{Z} \, z_0 = \frac{A_{eo}}{qkP} \cdot z_0 \tag{2.8}$$

Following these formulas, agricultural over-population, defined from the point of view of production, is proportionate to the following factors: the larger the numbers of the economically active population; the smaller the agricultural area; the lesser the intensity of crops; the smaller the yield per hectare; and the greater the productivity of labour corresponding to the standard use of the labour force.

It must be emphasized that the pressure of agricultural population increases as labour productivity increases, thus the greater the productivity of agricultural labour the greater also the over-population. On the other hand, such factors as an increase of the intensity of agriculture and increase of yields, as well as an increase of agricultural area, ease the population pressure and reduce agricultural over-population.

---

[7] J. Poniatowski, "Le Problème du Surpeuplement dans l'Agriculture Polonaise." *L'Est Européen Agricole,* 1936. pp. 21–60.

[8] Wilbert Moore, *Economic Demography of Eastern and South Eastern Europe.* League of Nations, 1945.

[9] Colin Clark, *Conditions of Economic Progress.* London, 1953.

Number of People

Labour productivity in this case has been measured as real product per head of persons active in agriculture. But as the population is not homogeneous the next step was to convert it into labour units of equal productivity, bringing women and young and old people to the average working productivity of men.[10] A further step was to take into account not the number of persons, but their working time, thus the personal dimension was transposed into the time dimension.[11] The average working time in terms of work hours then had to be included in the concept of over-population. In this way labour requirements were taken as the standard labour demand, and labour working time at full employment level as the total labour supply. It should be noted that potential, not actual, working time is taken as a measure.

The outcome is that the formula has been transformed from a personal dimension into labour-time supply and demand, i.e. into the maximum capacity of supply, and the standard demand of labour-time. Divided by a standard working day or year the average number of agricultural working population was obtained:

$$V_e = w \cdot a \cdot A_e - w_o A_{eo} \qquad (2.9)$$

$$g_{ew} = \frac{w \cdot a \cdot A_e}{w_o A_{eo}} \qquad (2.10)$$

Here a stands for the conversion factor from the actual number of persons economically active in agriculture into a standard number of homogeneous personal labour units; w stands for the number of working hours at full capacity, and w_o for the requirements of labour hours per person in the same period of time (a year).[12]

The difference between the number of working hours at full employment level and the actual working hours measures the efficiency of labour utilization, which must be taken as a factor in assessing the surplus of agricultural labour. In other words, if labour is used less efficiently then this means concealed unemployment and is not a method of solving the problem of surplus population in agriculture.

Here we come up against the problem of what the full employment of labour is. In order to avoid the complicated question of optimum or maximum use, most students of this problem use relative

---

[10] Here again the skill of an agricultural labour unit is still considered as homogeneous, a rather gross assumption.

[11] This conversion has to be done with caution, not overlooking the indivisibility of the factor "human being," or the relative indivisibility of the agricultural family.

[12] The most complete list of labour intensity coefficients or labour inputs on an international scale is given by F. Dovring, who quotes 19 countries: F. Dovring, *Land and Labour in Europe, 1900–1950*. The Hague, 1956, pp. 398–418.

measures which can be called standard use of labour capacity and
may mean anything from conventional to comparative measurement,
e.g. a standard work day of 8 or 10 hours; a yearly number of work
hours, say 1500, 2500, or 3000 hours per person (with deductions made
for holidays and bad weather); or a standard volume of production
per head per year, etc.[13]

An improvement over this method—closer to the reality of labour
requirements—is to take into account seasonal or surplus requirements over peak seasons of agricultural activity, a demand for labour
which, though sometimes of short duration, is nevertheless indispensable. It can be alleviated partly by working harder and longer hours
in the peak period; by using the labour of housewives, children, old
people, soldiers home on leave, and help from relations in non-agricultural occupations; or by stretching the peaks over longer time
periods.[14] But basically the problem of peak labour requirements is
one of the main problems of agricultural over-population as it involves the problem of the employment of the unused labour force in
inter-seasonal gaps. With regard to this problem some authors
distinguish between seasonal and chronic surplus agricultural population.[15] In the slack seasons there may be quite a large surplus of
labour which none the less may be strained in the peak season so that
at times there may even be a deficiency of labour in agriculturally
over-populated districts. This must be distinguished from a chronic
labour surplus representing the long term (more than a year) surplus
spread over all seasons.

Our formula for over-population changes when both notions of
surplus labour are taken into account as follows:

$$V'_e = A_e - A_{eo} \pm A'_e \qquad\qquad (2.11)$$
$$V'_{we} = w\,A_e - (A_{eo} \pm A'_e)\,(1 \pm a')\,(w_o \pm w') \qquad (2.12)$$

Here A' stands for the additional number of persons, a' for the change
in the conversion factor from physical to standard labour units, and
w' for hours of additional work done in peak seasons. In slack seasons
the sign of additions is negative and the labour surplus is increased.

Thus there is a seasonal change in the numbers of the agriculturally active population, a change in the conversion of persons into
labour units, and a change in work hours.

The seasonal surplus is based on the assumption of the functional

---

[13] F. Dovring, *op. cit.*, pp. 84–98. The level of employment in different European
countries varies from 78 per cent to 50 per cent. If the American standard of employment is used, the span of employment levels moves from 14 to 50 per cent only.

[14] P. N. Rosenstein-Rodan, "Disguised Unemployment and Underemployment
in Agriculture." (Mimeo., Centre for International Studies, Massachusetts Institute
of Technology, Cambridge, Mass., 1956).

[15] A. Pepelasis and P. A. Yotopulos, *Surplus Labour in Greek Agriculture 1953–
1960*. Athens, 1962, pp. 126–38.

indivisibility of agricultural labour at certain periods. But underlying this, there is another concealed assumption: that of the indivisibility of some other factors of production (machines, work animals, size of plots, or irrigation schemes).[16]

Capital in Use

The capital factor in agriculture, which so far has appeared in our analysis only as a concealed assumption that the volume of production is proportional to the capital used, now has to be taken into account. The capital dimension can be included in two different ways: as the intensity of capital (quantity) and the productivity of capital (quality).

By the coefficient of productivity of capital in agriculture we understand the ratio of agricultural product (Z) to agricultural capital (K), i.e. how many units of product correspond to one unit of capital:

$$m = \frac{Z}{K} \qquad (2.13)$$

For capital intensity coefficient we take capital per head of the actually economically active population:

$$n = \frac{K}{A_e} \qquad n_0 = \frac{K}{A_{eo}} \qquad (2.14, 2.15)$$

From the known formula of labour productivity we can deduct expressions of both capital productivity and capital intensity by extending the formula:

$$z = \frac{Z}{A_e} = \frac{Z}{K} \cdot \frac{K}{A_e} = m \cdot n \qquad (2.16)$$

$$z_0 = \frac{Z}{A_{eo}} = \frac{Z}{K} \cdot \frac{K}{A_{eo}} = m \cdot n_0 \qquad (2.17)$$

Thus labour productivity in agriculture is the product of the coefficients of capital productivity and capital intensity in agriculture.

We shall call the optimum productivity of capital that capital which is necessary to employ optimally one unit of the economically active population. The capital intensity corresponding to this capital productivity is the optimal capital intensity (n_0).

If in our formulas we now substitute capital productivity and

---

[16] This point has been brought into the open by Tarlogh Singh in his concept of a "work unit" as the minimum size of family holding for India, dependent on the largest instrument of production (an ox-drawn plough) which occupies 1.5 men. T. Singh, *Poverty and Social Change*, Ch. V, 1945. For further development of this concept see: Government of India. *Third Five-Year Plan*. 1961, pp. 229–38.

capital intensity for labour productivity, we arrive at the following formula of agricultural over-population and its pressure:

$$g_e = \frac{A_e}{gkP} \cdot z_0 = \frac{A_e}{gkP} \; m \cdot n_0 \qquad (2.18)$$

$$V_e = A_e - A_0 = A_e - \frac{gkP}{m \cdot n_0} \qquad (2.19)$$

Thus the greater are the agricultural population, the productivity of capital, and the intensity of capital, the greater is the population pressure.[17]

We reach the conclusion that agricultural over-population from the point of view of production increases with the productivity of labour, i.e. the greater the amount of real capital used per worker, and the greater the productivity of this capital. Thus economic development and technical progress in agriculture do not eliminate, but increase agricultural population pressure.

Let us elaborate this point a little further. Capital intensity *(n)* depends on the quantity of capital and on the number of economically active agricultural persons. But factor *m,* representing the quality of capital, does not depend on the number of persons at all. This factor is brought into the production process from outside, and represents an exogenous and autonomous factor of production.

Productivity of capital determining the quality of aggregate real capital depends on three things: (1) the substitution of labour by capital (labour-saving investment); (2) the capital mix which itself depends on the variety of partial capital productivity coefficients[18] making up the structure of the aggregate agricultural capital; and (3) technical progress itself. Measurements taken of the quality of capital have shown that this first factor of the substitution as such, i.e. replacement of labour by capital, assuming the same volume of production, is

---

[17] Taking 1920 as 100, the active agricultural population decreased in the United States until in 1960 it had fallen to index 53; at the same time the gross product increased to 140, but the cultivated area fell to 90. In the same period the volume of production rose to 151, and the capital to 159. Intensity of capital per man showed an increase of 300, while labour productivity in agriculture increased up to 270. The productivity of capital fell from coefficient 0.38 to 0.34. The density of the active agricultural population fell from 3.7 to 2.2 per 100 ha. Nevertheless the population pressure showed an increase from 2.22 to 3.16 (index 142).

In the U.S.S.R. the active agricultural population fell from 100 in 1939 to 78 in 1959, the gross product increased to 159, the area under cultivation to 131, and the capital invested to 208. The index of the productivity of capital reached 75, the density of active population decreased to index 60, the population pressure rising to 120.

[18] Professor M. Cépède has quoted in his very interesting article on French agriculture the following computed coefficients of productivity of capital investments in agriculture in macro-economic terms: water economy 0.37, building of roads 0.24, consolidation of holdings 2.0, buildings 0.03, electricity 0.13, agricultural machinery 0.08, total 0.16. M. Cépède, "Frankreich." *Berichte über Landwirtschaft,* 175. Sonderheft, p. 113.

of limited importance. The second plays a considerable role particularly from the point of view of short-term changes. But in long-term comparisons technical progress is the most important.[19]

The quality of capital is defined as the ratio of the agricultural output to real capital. Technical improvement of machinery, reduction in costs of building, and improved quality of livestock are obvious cases. But real capital can be misleading. One is struck by the fact that a decrease in real capital is followed by a considerable increase in production, depending on the change of the biological structure of real capital. For example, artificial insemination has decreased the number of bulls but greatly improved the quality of livestock production. The cultivation of hybrid corn implied a small increase in cost out of proportion to the increase in production. Vaccination has increased production of all sorts of livestock; the use of pesticides has had a similar effect on crops.

The next step in clarifying the effect of capital on agricultural over-population would be to distinguish between labour-saving and labour-spending capital investments.

III. THE MOBILITY CONCEPT

Agricultural over-population can be conceived also from the point of view of the mobility of the agricultural population. Agricultural over-population in this concept is defined as the number of people whose productivity of labour is nil, i.e. they could be removed from agriculture in a certain area without lowering the level of production there.[20] The fact that the population is removable is stressed. But the emphasis should really be on the other aspect, i.e. that the population is *removable but does not move*. This raises the questions: Why do not people move to other occupations and places? What are the forces which keep them on the spot? When we ask these questions we are linking agricultural over-population with a whole chain of other economic and extra-economic factors which reveal this phenomenon in its great complexity. This concept is linked to a varied set of problems ranging from seasonal and additional wage employ-

---

[19] Further development and bibliographical references concerning these problems are dealt with in my article on "Threshold of Economic Development." *Kyklos,* Basel, 1962, No. I.

[20] One of the more recent definitions of agricultural over-population which could be classified under this concept is: "The amount of agricultural labour which could have been removed from farms for at least a complete year without any reduction in total agricultural output, taking techniques, crop-mix and the quantities of the other factors of production at their historically given levels (with the exception of a routine reorganization of work force)." The other assumption is that "all labour in excess of peak labour employment can be withdrawn without violating the static conditions . . . [it is] reasonable to expect that the remaining working people will do more work after the change." A. Pepelassis and P. A. Yotopulos, *Surplus Labour in Greek Agriculture, 1953–1960.* Athens, 1962, p. 30.

ment in villages, community development schemes, and co-operative movement, to the conservatism of unmovable peasants and lack of institutional flexibility. Industrialization, building of infra-structure, alternative or heterogeneous occupations, problems of opportunity costs, etc. are added to the *classical* dilemmas of agricultural policies of protection or exploitation, co-operation or commercialization, and conservatism or structural changes in agriculture.[21]

The factors causing agricultural over-population to exist at a certain place and in a certain time can be divided into two main groups: the expulsive and the attractive factors (push and pull factors). Each of these groups of factors can again be divided into two sub-groups according to whether they operate within or outside the observed area, i.e. are endogenous or exogenous factors.

These are the four cases of over-population mobility:

1. Attractive endogenous factors (pull in)

$$(g_1 - \triangle \, g_1) < g_2 \tag{3.1}$$

$$\frac{A_1}{A_{o1}} - \triangle \, (\frac{A_1}{A_{o1}}) < \frac{A_2}{A_{o2}} \tag{3.2}$$

2. Attractive exogenous factors (pull out)

$$g_1 < (g_2 + \triangle g_2) \tag{3.3}$$

$$\frac{A_1}{A_{o1}} < \frac{A_2}{A_{o2}} + \triangle \, (\frac{A_2}{A_{o2}}) \tag{3.4}$$

3. Expulsive endogenous factors (push out)

$$(g_1 + \triangle g_1) > g_2 \tag{3.5}$$

$$\frac{A_1}{A_{o1}} + \triangle \, (\frac{A_1}{A_{o1}}) > \frac{A_2}{A_{o2}} \tag{3.6}$$

4. Expulsive exogenous factors (push in)

$$g_1 > (g_2 + \triangle g_2) \tag{3.7}$$

$$\frac{A_1}{A_{o1}} > \frac{A_2}{A_{o2}} + \triangle \, (\frac{A_2}{A_{o2}}) \tag{3.8}$$

If agricultural over-population exists it means that there is a balance between attractive and expulsive factors (the endogenous and the exogenous). Agricultural population is not on the move—a state of over-population remains. Of course, this state of rest does not mean that varied forces are not in action or that there is no tension among them. What is commonly called the conservatism of the peasants is in fact a state of equilibrium which may have been brought about by many different forces straining and checking each other.

---

[21] For recent data covering most European countries, Cf. European Society of Rural Sociology, *Changing Pattern of Rural Organization*. Oslo, 1961.

If the pressure of the agricultural population of a certain area is marked by g_1 and the pressure outside the area by g_2, then the agricultural over-population situation is expressed by:

$$g_1 = g_2 \qquad\qquad (3.9)$$

$$\frac{g_1}{g_2} = 1 \qquad\qquad (3.10)$$

We can take any of the formulas of the first two concepts of agricultural over-population and compare the corresponding pressures between two areas.[22]

When the equilibrium is upset, movement of population takes place from an area of stronger pressure to one of lesser pressure in the horizontal or vertical sense, thus decreasing agricultural over-population.

There are many varied dimensions in which the factors causing the mobility of population can be classified. We have classified them in four groups according to the above factors and to the following dimensions: demographic, national wealth, capital, employment, income, consumption (standard of living), institutional factors, level of economic development, and productivity of labour.[23]

As an example of an attractive exogenous (pull out) factor we take the movement of population caused by the low price of land, or of better land in an area other than that observed. This has an attractive influence, pulling the agricultural population out from the observed area. On the contrary, if the price of land outside the area is high, the population will not move. The price of land in over-populated districts depends much more on population pressure than on any other factor, including the fertility of the land. Opportunity of employment for the agricultural population in manufacturing industries will also operate as an attractive exogenous factor. Such movement will cease when the differences in the incomes of agricultural and non-agricultural occupations are levelled out, taking all other factors as unchanged.

As an example of attractive endogenous (pull in) factors, we may take any increase of cultivable area (land reclamation, etc.) which will act as a pull-in factor based on changes within the observed area attracting people from outside to move in. A similar effect will be caused by a decrease of population, or by increases of agricultural

---

[22] The general formula used in this concept is:

$$(g_1 \pm \triangle g_1) \overset{>}{\underset{<}{=}} (g_2 \pm \triangle g_2)$$

[23] The most comprehensive description of factors causing mobility of agricultural population is the publication of the International Labour office: *Pourquoi les travailleurs abandonnent la terre.* Génève, 1960.

incomes, or wages caused by better cultivation, or more favourable prices of agricultural products. In order to stop population movement under the influence of these factors, other factors would have to be put into operation. These could be: increased costs of removal, increased taxes or customs duties, greater security of income on the spot, etc.

As expulsive endogenous (push out) factors the following can be mentioned: increase in agricultural population, natural calamities (floods, erosion), or decrease in the volume of production. Among expulsive endogenous factors there is technical progress, i.e. mechanization causing decrease in the demand for labour; increased productivity of labour because of greater skill among workers; and insecurity of income from agriculture.

Some exogenous expulsive (push in) factors impelling people into an area or compelling them not to abandon agricultural occupation are: compulsory or induced agrarian land settlement, vocational training in agriculture, compulsory transfer of workers, compulsory delivery of agricultural products, heavy investment in indivisible fixed capital, heavy indebtedness, etc. All these factors prevent the surplus agricultural population in an area from abandoning it.

It may be asked whether it is rational to expect peasants to work under conditions of marginal productivity equal to zero. One explanation of the fact that they do so is the high rate of irrationality (ignorance, pressure of family and village customs, etc.) which means that the inelastic demand for agricultural produce is matched by an inelastic supply of labour effort. Various group loyalties must also be taken into account (family allegiance, paternalism, collective solidarity of kolkhoz members, etc.). Another approach is to treat labour in agriculture not as a function of wages, or profit, or income, but as a resource. Lack of personal incentive to push out others may be due to semi-feudal exploitation. But there are economic reasons as well. Sometimes in research into economically rational behaviour it is overlooked that comparative, not absolute, advantages of labour are among the main incentives to work. What may be zero in absolute cost terms, may not be zero in comparative cost terms. Peasant logic may be different from economists' logistics.

3

The Role of the Agricultural Economist in the Administrative Field

J. F. BOOTH

Formerly of the Economics Division, Department of Agriculture, Ottawa, Canada

I AM VERY PLEASED *that the Executive of the International Association of Agricultural Economists accepted the suggestion of Canadian colleagues that I be asked to contribute to this project recognizing the many years of devotion and outstanding service to our profession and this Association given by Dr. Leonard K. Elmhirst. My acquaintance with him dates from the Cornell Conference of 1930. It was extended by several visits to Dartington and by attendance at most of the meetings of this body over which he presided for so many years. But it was during his visits to Canada in preparation for the 1938 Conference at Macdonald College and his subsequent war-time tours of North America, on one of which he was accompanied by Mrs. Elmhirst, which did so much to keep the flame of organization burning on this continent, that I came to know him best and to appreciate most fully the worth of the man we are now honouring. It is indeed a pleasure and an honour for me to have a part in this undertaking.*

President Westermarck, in extending the invitation to me to prepare an essay on the agricultural economist in the administrative field, indicated that the reason for the selection was my "activity of long duration in the administrative field." This probably had reference to a rather lengthy association with the Economics Division, Canada Department of Agriculture, but might have included some earlier experience with the Markets Division of the Saskatchewan Department of Agriculture. In any event, these associations are the justification for my acceptance of the invitation and they explain the emphasis on Canadian experience in what follows.

[23]

The President also suggested that the treatment of the subject should embrace the international sphere. To this, Vice-President Edgar Thomas, in a conversation at the Storrs Convention of the American Farm Economic Association, added that some reference to differences in the manner of selecting senior administrative personnel in such countries as Britain, the United States, and Canada and the implications that these differences might have on the responsibilities of economists in the administrative field, would be of interest. In what follows, I have been able, with the help of others, to do a little to meet this suggestion, but I have not, in spite of substantial rewriting, been able to give the subject as much international flavour as I hoped would be the case.

The role of an agricultural economist in the administrative field depends to a large extent upon the type of institution with which he is associated. It will be different in a privately endowed research foundation than in a university department. It will differ again in an economics division of a government department of agriculture. In the latter, the responsibilities and the duties of staff will depend upon the nature of the economy of the country, the organization of its agricultural services, and the distribution of functions between the department and provincial or state departments, universities, and research bodies. This discussion will concern the agricultural economist in government service.

The role of an agricultural economist in a governmental set-up similar to that of Canada will include, in addition to such routine matters of organization, methods, housekeeping functions relating to appropriations, budgeting, personnel, supplies, and equipment (which will not be discussed): (1) the development, supervision of, and participation in research programmes, including publication and extension of results; (2) service and advisory assistance to those responsible in other divisions for the administration of various programmes; and (3) participation in the process of developing ideas and of translating them into legislation, policies, and programmes, which may result in actual involvement with administration, particularly in the early stages. These matters will be considered later.

It should be observed at this stage that in all probability not all of the economists in an economics division will be concerned all of the time with any single function. Some may be engaged in research, others in service, but all are likely to take a hand from time to time with other activities. Some may have had more training in agricultural policies than others and may specialize in this field. Some may emerge as policy analysts and advisers with but little educational background in this field. There is not likely to be a set pattern; roles are likely to be interchangeable, but section heads and the director will be most heavily involved in policy formation and advisory services. This discussion will consider the role of an economist in administration as embracing all of these functions.

THE NATURE OF THE CANADIAN ECONOMY

To set the pattern within which Canadian experiences will be discussed, it seems desirable to comment briefly on the nature of the Canadian economy. Outsiders who have heard only of the government-operated Canadian National Railways, Trans-Canada Airlines, the Canadian Wheat Board, and provincially controlled hydro-electric power, may have the impression that government is more active in the field of business than is the case. Actually, though these and other examples do indicate departure from a strictly laissez-faire type of economy, the predominating character and pattern of operation is that of a competitive society in which freedom of enterprise is still the dominating influence.

This freedom is characterized by thousands of small and large single-unit businesses, and by huge multi-unit combinations such as the branch banking system, wheat pools and other grain handling concerns, meat packing companies, chain stores, oil refineries, and others. Subject only to the restraining influences necessary to ensure desirable operating conditions and to the supervision of restrictive trade practices legislation, business operates on a freely competitive basis. Instances of direct participation by government in the realm of private enterprise have been confined in the main to a fairly limited field in which the public utility aspect predominates or where national or international interests are involved.

While endeavouring to maintain and encourage initiative and freedom of enterprise, Canadian governments have nevertheless recognized their responsibility for helping to provide the economic climate within which these characteristics can operate most effectively. Thus, concern and responsibility for economic and social conditions have been added to the earlier concept of government responsibility for protection of life and property. Governments have used their authority and facilities, including the central banking system, to achieve desirable conditions through adjustments of interest rates, through borrowing, through expansion and contraction of credit, through measures to regulate imports, through taxation, and by other means.

With respect to agriculture, early colonial and provincial legislatures were concerned with measures to protect consumers and encourage trade by the establishment of commodity standards and the provision of inspection services. Recognizing the importance of agriculture, various forms of assistance were provided through boards of agriculture, agricultural societies, and other means, to expand its frontier and to increase its importance as a producer of products for export. With the advent of confederation, the federal government extended these services by the establishment of an experimental farms system and by an enlarged programme of grading and inspection. Quality premiums and other financial incentives were introduced to encourage the output of better quality products.

Supplementing these services in the course of time came protection of plant and animal life, greater recognition of the importance of scientific research, appreciation of the growing importance of economic and social problems, and greater concern for the welfare of farm people as evidenced by Information and Consumers Service Divisions.[1]

Midway through the first half of this century, following the favourable results obtained in marketing Canadian grain during the first World War—results which were associated with federal government control—a number of other incursions by governments into the economic aspects of agriculture took place.

Representative of these were legislation in British Columbia to permit regulation and control of marketing (1927–30) and in various other provinces to regulate the marketing of milk and other products (1932–37), also enactments projecting the federal government into the fields of farm credit (1927), control of the marketing of natural products other than grain (1934), and wheat marketing (1935). Since World War II the federal government has become involved with legislation to support farm prices, to expand farm credit, to provide crop insurance, to assist provinces in a nation-wide programme of agricultural rehabilitation and development (A.R.D.A.), and to renew many earlier pieces of legislation. Price spreads, transportation, and economic affairs have been considered by Royal Commissions.

While these enactments have affected the pattern of development in recent decades and have provided opportunities for agricultural economists, the agricultural economy is still represented by family-operated farms and by business organizations, private and co-operative, which compete with one another in serving farmers. Within this mosaic of private enterprise and enabling paternalism there is scope for individual initiative, and for the ministrations of those interested in economics.

THE SPECIAL RESPONSIBILITIES OF AN AGRICULTURAL ECONOMICS DIVISION

In Canadian government experience, and perhaps in that of some other governments, the tradition of service to farmers was already well established when the economist entered the field. For a century and a

---

[1] J. F. Booth, "Historical and Legislative Background of Canadian Argicultural Development: Introduction, Economic Organization of Canadian Agriculture." Canadian Council, International Conference of Agricultural Economists, 1940.

half, colonial, provincial, and federal governments had been concerned with furthering the development of agriculture and of increasing the efficiency of production and marketing. This had included the provision for agronomists, animal husbandmen, entomologists, chemists, biologists, and market specialists. It was not unnatural therefore that when the agricultural economist appeared on the scene farmers should expect him to devote the knowledge and tools of his trade to their day-to-day problems.

For a time, about 1910 to 1929, the departments of economics at universities and colleges of agriculture considered these matters. The staffs for this purpose were very limited—one or two persons at most institutions.

With the establishment of a Division of Economics in the Federal Department of Agriculture, the services of the economist, including research, were in effect added to the already well established research efforts of workers in the natural sciences. These services were also added, in effect, to the efforts of the colleges and universities in this field, a matter that will be touched on later.

It is important to recognize this service-to-farmers aspect of the federal programme. Dealing with the day-to-day business management problems of the individual farmer—as distinguished from the economic and social problems of the industry of agriculture—is an important and distinctive activity of a Division of Economics. In no other department of government has this responsibility to the individual been quite so clearly established—until recently, at least. Departments such as Labour, Fisheries, and Trade and Commerce are in somewhat the same position. In some departments such service is the responsibility of divisions other than that of Economics. But most departments are concerned mainly or only with matters relating to the public as a whole, as in the case of the Post Office Department, National Revenue, and External Affairs. This special type of personal service to agriculture—in fact, the whole of the service, both personal and industry—is traditional. It is part of our way of life and in no sense attributable to the emergence of agricultural economists. It may be considered an aspect of agricultural fundamentalism, and though the extent of the service in certain respects has declined in recent years as industry and national problems have come more into the spotlight, its significance has recently been enhanced as the need became apparent for information useful in the application of new programmes for credit expansion, crop insurance, and agricultural rehabilitation.

This distinctive characteristic of agriculture's status is something of an enigma to fellow economists in other departments, particularly those in Finance and Treasury Board! One of the Division's problems in administration has been that of acquainting treasury economists with these differences and their significance in terms of appropriations.

Provincial and University Relationships

One of the requirements of administration in a country with several levels of government and divided jurisdiction is that of establishing satisfactory working relationships with these governments and local institutions for the handling of matters of common interest. This was approached in Canada by obtaining an understanding with provincial departments and universities on allocation of responsibility and by an offer to co-operate with any institution desirous of undertaking a useful project on a basis of joint participation. Under this arrangement, the Division has worked with universities and provincial departments on hundreds of research projects. These are handled on the basis of an agreement, formal or informal, setting forth the responsibility of each of the co-operating bodies. The nature and extent of each party's contribution varies; there is no set pattern. Where feasible, an attempt is made to achieve something approaching a dollar-for-dollar matching contribution, but this is not always achieved; the Division's share usually turns out to be the larger part. Contributions take various forms, such as supervision or direction, staff, office accommodation, use of equipment and supplies, provision of transportation, and publication of results. Several provinces have made annual or special financial grants to cover their shares of the costs involved.

Regional field activities of the Division in central Canada are handled by staff based at headquarters in Ottawa, but on occasions staff members have been assigned to provincial institutions in that area. In other parts of Canada, provincial or regional offices are maintained. These regional activities have added variety and scope to the functions of Division economists both in relation to other units of the federal service and in respect to provincial governments, universities, farm organizations, and agricultural business.

Scope of Activities

The role of an Economics Division and of its agricultural economists is likely to be a broad one even where numbers permit of specialization. It, and they, are likely to be concerned with production economics and its various sub-headings; with marketing and trade matters; with consumption and co-operatives; with prices, statistics, and subsidies; with domestic and foreign policies; and with international relations. It may act as a co-ordinating agency for annual reviews of the agricultural outlook and represent the Department in inter-departmental matters.

The functions suggested by these activities fall into three categories: (1) research, (2) service, and (3) policy advisory and development assistance. The distinction between (2) and (3) may become apparent as we proceed.

RESEARCH

As already indicated, the Division fell heir to a programme of research, the counterpart of services already being provided in the natural sciences by the Federal Department. It was in fact to be the Division's primary function, for it will be recalled that in 1929—apart from marketing legislation providing grading and inspection services, and livestock and plant health and quarantine regulations—government had not yet become extensively involved in the economic and social affairs of its people. In the United States of America, the Bureau of Agricultural Economics was concerned with research and with grade standards, inspection, and markets information. The Federal Farm Board—the compromise outcome of McNary-Haugenism—had just been born but was to be followed by other and more far-reaching legislation. In Australia, advanced forms of marketing legislation had already been translated into marketing schemes. In Britain, new marketing legislation was in the offing. Rumblings of dissatisfaction with grain marketing and pressure for new marketing legislation were experienced in Canada.

The decade of the 1930's was a period of substantial expansion for the Division despite the restrictions generally imposed by depression. At the peak of this development which extended into the 1940's, the Division, with the aid of other bodies, was concerned with about 125 major research projects annually in addition to many *ad hoc* service-type undertakings. The largest single project during the period was the economic classification of some fifty million acres of farm land in the open plains area of Saskatchewan and Alberta where acute drought conditions added to the burden of depression and brought major adjustments in farm practices. This project, conducted in cooperation with the universities and provincial departments of agriculture, extended over a ten-year period. An important addition to the research programme of this decade was an association with the development and administration of The Natural Products Marketing Act, 1934–36.

The period of the 1940's was featured by the association of the Division with the war-time programme and with subsequent legislative developments. In this period the Division really won its spurs. The requirements of the war-time economic front plunged the staff into a varied programme of *ad hoc* research and into service in which staff members were assigned to secretarial, administrative, and membership responsibility on the numerous boards and committees serving the war effort. The closing years of the decade brought involvement in international affairs which was to extend and become a featured activity of the Division throughout the 1950's. Since 1957, participation in the development of legislation and policies has been extensive.

In the beginning, the research programme was *farm oriented* as already implied, in contrast with *industry orientation,* in which research is more concerned with industry problems and with policies and programmes.

I am aware that this preoccupation of government with economic research is not universal. In many countries, perhaps most, such activity is undertaken by universities, research institutes, or other bodies. It is often implied, if not suggested, that even though these bodies may receive government financing, their activities are free from the influences that might affect research—economic and social research in particular because of its relationship to the political aspects of government.

In my experience, political considerations have not been a significant factor in limiting research efforts; nor have they imposed embarrassing administrative restraints in the operation of the Economics Division. I doubt if staff members engaged in research are conscious of any such limitations. I am aware that research results have sometimes been embarrassing to the Minister.

It must be added that the kind of research referred to in this respect is that related to the economic problems of the farmer and the industry as a whole rather than to analyses and research pertaining to policy development or administration. The latter is of a confidential nature and may be accompanied by recommendations. It is not normally intended that such information be made public and if it were it probably would undermine relations between economists and those responsible for policy decisions. I well recall an occasion when the Division's background analysis and report on a particular marketing proposal caused the Minister to turn to another Division for help in developing his programme. Months later he again turned to the Economics Division for assistance. Release of the Division's original report would have been harmful both to the programme under consideration and to relations within the Department.

The point is that research on farm and farm industry problems—important as it is to those concerned, and useful as background information for policy consideration—is designed for use primarily at the farm and industry level and is released for that purpose.

' *Shifting Emphasis in Research.* Over the years, an appreciable shift in emphasis on various types of research has occurred. Research by the Economics Division on problems at the farm and local level has declined both relatively and actually. This is due to greater participation in this phase by provincial institutions; also to greatly increased pressure on the Division for research and service on matters of concern to the Federal Department. The result of this combination of circumstances, particularly a greatly increased load of service-type research, has been a decline in longer term basic research—whatever it may be termed—from around 80 per cent of total effort in the 1930's to substantially less than 50 per cent to-day. There is a danger of reaching a point when its scarcity may affect the supply of basic material helpful to the analysis and consideration of policies and programmes.

SERVICE ASPECT OF AN AGRICULTURAL ECONOMIST'S ROLE[2]

The distinction between "service" on the one hand and "analytical and advisory assistance on policy matters" on the other is not clear cut. There are elements of each in the other. The difference may be one of emphasis, but "service" is sufficient to warrant separate treatment.

By "service" I mean the multitude of day-to-day activities that agricultural economists are called upon by other divisions to undertake—the provision of statistical data on this and that subject, probable shifts in crop acreage next year, the calculation of livestock-feed ratios, estimates of pig marketings six months hence, the trend of prices, the effects of increasing or decreasing support prices, preparation of briefing material for delegations, or a statement for use at an international conference—these and many more. This is an important phase of an economist's assignment. Its growth is a sign of acceptance and appreciation which it has taken economists years to obtain; but it has now become so important as to be a major part of the work of an economics division. Much of it is called for by divisions administering marketing legislation, and for that purpose the Economics Division maintains a corps of commodity specialists who work closely with the various divisions. But no aspect of the Department's activities is beyond the compass of the Division's interest, and most if not all Divisions make use of it.

Providing answers in this particular field calls for the building up of large quantities of source material and a good deal of digging which some refuse to dignify with the term research. An answer may take a few hours or a few months, and all of it is useful. Not infrequently demands in this field lead to more fundamental effort. An economist on the service beat may participate also in *ad hoc* and longer range research projects.

THE ANALYTICAL AND ADVISORY SERVICE ON POLICY FORMATION

Participation in the development of legislation[3] and the formation of policies is an important—some would say the most important

---

[2] The term "service" in this section refers to assistance given to those concerned with departmental administration, as contrasted with research and service performed specifically on behalf of farmers.

[3] Contributing to the development of legislation may be the function of an agricultural economics division; drafting the result in language for consideration by legislatures is the task of a legal division or lawyer.

—function of an economics division. But its importance depends upon a number of factors. The Division, its head and senior personnel, must have the confidence of the Minister and senior administration. Unless it has that confidence it will be impossible to render, and obtain acceptance of, unbiased analysis and opinion. Its importance will depend, too, upon the extent that the Minister relies upon his staff for the development of ideas. If he is inclined to seek advice only from his colleagues in Parliament and from farm and business leaders, important as these are, the economists' role will be a minor one.

Professor Edgar Thomas, in the conversation mentioned earlier, said that reference might be made to differences between countries in the manner of choosing administrative staff. He referred particularly to the United Kingdom and Canada. These differences would affect the role of economists, particularly in the part of the field now being considered. In considering this matter, it may be useful to have a look at the division of responsibility for work in this field in several countries.

Division of Responsibility in Several Countries

In Canada, senior administrative posts in technical departments are filled, for the most part, by people trained in the speciality of the department and who, in most cases, have come up through the department. They may have had, or may receive, special short-term training courses in administration which are provided by the Civil Service Commission. But there is no class specially recruited for senior administration and advisory service. This means that the senior advisory assistants to the Minister of Agriculture are likely to be people who have received training in agriculture or in some specialized aspect of agriculture, and who have risen from the ranks. Among these will be agricultural economists. The senior advisory assistants on policy matters in the field of economics will include members of the Economics Division staff.

Much the same sort of procedure is followed in the United States where the senior staff in the Department of Agriculture is largely made up of professional people who have specialized in some branch of technical agriculture. Within this generalization, agricultural economics constitutes one administrative grouping in the Department with two agency components: the Economic Research Service and the Statistical Reporting Service. The Research Service conducts research at various levels of intensity and fields of activity. It conducts research for short-run administrative jobs and long-run basic research. An important element of the research is concerned with analysing and appraising government programmes and operations. But an "attempt is made to keep the Economic Research Service out of politics and out of policy making."[4] However, a staff economists' group, a unit of agri-

---

[4] Willard W. Cochrane, Director, Agricultural Economics, United States Department of Agriculture, in a letter to the author, September 18, 1962.

cultural economics but outside the Economics Research Service which reports through the Director "is regularly concerned with program development and policy issues in the office of the Secretary of Agriculture."[5]

In Britain, where much of the basic research in agricultural economics is done at university centres, with support from the government, the officers at the Ministry of Agriculture, Fisheries, and Food in London who are concerned with economics deal with policy matters including programme analyses. They are also responsible for or associated with such matters as the Annual Price Review, and for analytical work on a wide range of information and problems, including the structure of the industry, farm management and farm incomes, and several aspects of agricultural marketing.

The British Civil Service is also noted for a corps of very able administrators who possess good university degrees, commonly history, but who are not highly trained specialists. These people are found throughout the government service and in high places. They are among the senior advisory group in the various Ministries.

Commenting on a question I raised, J. H. Kirk has said: ". . . as compared with your description of our set-up, there is a rather stronger professional element than you seem to have suspected, but the much larger non-professional element is not a specially trained one, if by that you mean trained to carry out this particular task." He went on to say that advice given to the Minister on agricultural policies in the economics field comes from a committee of senior officials composed of three groups (a) Commodity Chiefs, (b) four or five officials who have a general concern with economics, finance, and marketing, and (c) several professionals who also are custodians and analysers of most of the figures. "Some of those in groups (a) and (b) may happen to have degrees in economics or agriculture but that would be only incidental . . . we have, no doubt, a smaller professional element in our policy decisions than in most countries."[6] I regret that his excellent explanation of this position, which is made at some length, cannot be included because of space limitations.

Australia has a Bureau of Agricultural Economics in the Commonwealth Department of Primary Industry. It engages in a wide variety of research and service ranging all the way from the cost of producing farm products to policy considerations in relation to such matters as the Common Market and trade with China. The Bureau has taken an active part in economic analysis and in providing policy advisory service to the government on important agricultural questions. Economic research pertaining to agricultural matters is also undertaken by state governments, universities, banks, and research institutes.

[5] *Ibid.*
[6] J. H. Kirk, C.B.E., Under-Secretary, Ministry of Agriculture, Fisheries, and Food, in a letter to the author, October 8, 1962.

Referring to the functions of an agricultural economics division, Sir John Crawford states that ". . . the general intention and the bulk of practice is to confine this work to research and advisory service. They would not be concerned in Australia with the drafting of legislation nor with the day-to-day administration policies. They would, however, frequently take part in the necessary inter-departmental committee work for formulating policy, and the leaders of such divisions would be among the senior policy advisers working with Ministers." [7]

On the matter of qualifications for administration, Sir John also states: ". . . the Australian practice is probably between North American and British practice. The general philosophy would be that the man to administer a department or a bureau should have the capacity to administer. If he is also a professional in the field (e.g., health or economics) then so much the better . . . in fact, however, there is a strong probability that the people appointed will have a background in the professional field of some standing and recognized as such."

The consideration that prompted this enquiry into the practices of several countries was the suggestion that the importance of the function of analysing and advising on policy formation as a role of economists in administration would depend on the extent to which economists share this field with an administrative group. In the four Western countries reviewed, it is apparent that there is a substantial professional content in such service.

It is understood that the trend in most countries of western Europe is in the same direction. About the countries of eastern Europe little is known. Before World War II, in Hungary, Czechoslovakia, and Poland the training preferred for this class of service leaned heavily toward law and political science.

In Canada, the Economics Division's first major participation in economic analyses and policy formation came in connexion with the development and enactment of the Natural Products Marketing Act in 1934. The war years brought new responsibilities in this field but the greatest development came after 1945 with the introduction of much new legislation and greater participation of government in the economic and social spheres at home and in agricultural programmes abroad. Price stabilization, deficiency payments, freight assistance, acreage payments, credit policies, crop insurance, agricultural rehabilitation (A.R.D.A.), tariffs, trade, and G.A.T.T., F.A.O., Colombo Plan, O.E.C.D., The World Food Programme, and the Common Market are some of the policies and programmes with which Division economists have been involved.

---

[7] Sir John G. Crawford, C.B.E., The Australian National University, Canberra, in a letter to the author, October 2, 1962.

Policy and Programme Administration

The Economics Division as such has taken no part in the administration of departmental programmes and policies, but members of its staff have been seconded for duty with Royal Commissions and other bodies and have served from time to time—and in recent years more or less continuously—on boards responsible for the administration of certain legislation. Some have headed sections concerned with activities related to the work of the Economics Division. These extramural activities have involved the Division in some supplementary or supporting service. The problems involved and the merits of this policy are worthy of further consideration.

OTHER MATTERS

There are other matters that might be dealt with at some length if space permitted. I shall make brief reference to three of them. The first concerns, and is a plea for, more graduate training as preparation for public service. I would add also the desirability of including in college curricula more courses dealing with agricultural policies and with other matters, domestic and foreign, that relate to agriculture.

The second is a vexing question—whether policy and programme analyses should be accompanied by conclusions and recommendations. On this, I am inclined to the position taken by Strong and others that they should be, assuming the report is not for publication.[8]

My last point is a reference to fragmentation or the splitting up of economics services, a matter that is likely to be faced by all Divisions at some time. The Economics Division, if I may conclude these all too numerous references to it with another example, has had to face this problem on four occasions over the years. Three of these involved the prospect of additional economics services being established within the Department or institutions operating within its jurisdiction. The fourth represented a transfer of a section of the Division to another part of the Department. The arguments put forward by the Division in opposing such action—cost, duplication, advantages of association, and co-ordination of research and policy development—were sufficient to maintain the *status quo*. I believe the position we took is sound.

But there may be a case for the other side. What amounts to fragmentation is occurring elsewhere and those who support it point to over-all expansion and advancement of the role and status of economists. There may also be other advantages. I am sure we have not heard the last of this subject.

---

[8] T. H. Strong, "Using Economic Research in Policy Making," *Proceedings of the Tenth International Conference of Agricultural Economists*. Oxford Univ. Press, 1960.

4

The Application of Production Functions in Economic-Agricultural Investigations

ANATOL BRZOZA

Institute of Agricultural Economics, Warsaw, Poland

THE FOLLOWING REMARKS are a result of the author's investigations into the possibility and suitableness of applying multiple correlation and regression methods, when so-called production functions for analytical purposes are to be deduced.[1] They refer particularly to the most general form: analysing the influence of the so-called production factors (land, capital, labour) on the yield of product (income). The same goes for other applications: fertilizer function, costs function.

In this chapter attention is concentrated on certain methodological problems which seem to have wider significance than the indirect problems mentioned above. They are concerned with interpreting the properties of partial regression coefficients in multiple regression equations. The generally accepted interpretation merely states that the coefficient of an independent variable (partial regression coefficient) indicates how much the dependent variable increases (or decreases) with the unit increase of a given independent variable, assuming that the quantities of the remaining independent variables which influence the dependent variable, are unchanged.

From the purely mathematical point of view, such a definition is quite correct, but it is not fully adequate to the special case of the

---

[1] Anatol Brzoza, "Some Contributions to the Problem of the Production Function on the Peasant Farms." *Zagadnienia Ekonomiki Rolnej,* No. 2, 1962, and "The Application of Regression in the Computation of Organic Costs." *Zagadnienia Ekonomiki Rolnej,* No. 6, 1962.

regression equation. This is because it does not take account of the genesis of the equation in question but limits itself to the final form of that equation. As is well known, the regression equation and in particular the partial regression coefficients are deduced from a set of primary equations appropriate in number. For example, the regression equation:

$$\bar{Y} = a + b_1 X_1 + b_2 X_2 + \cdots + b_k X_k, \tag{1}$$

is deduced from the set of equations:

$$\left.\begin{array}{l} b_1 \Sigma x_1 x_1 + b_2 \Sigma x_1 x_2 + \cdots + b_k \Sigma x_1 x_k = \Sigma y x_1 \\ b_1 \Sigma x_2 x_1 + b_2 \Sigma x_2 x_2 + \cdots + b_k \Sigma x_2 x_k = \Sigma y x_2 \\ \quad\cdot\qquad\qquad\cdot\qquad\qquad\qquad\cdot \\ \quad\cdot\qquad\qquad\cdot\qquad\qquad\qquad\cdot \\ \quad\cdot\qquad\qquad\cdot\qquad\qquad\qquad\cdot \\ b_1 \Sigma x_k x_1 + b_2 \Sigma x_k x_2 + \cdots + b_k \Sigma x_k x_k = \Sigma y x_k \end{array}\right\} \tag{2}$$

and the constant "a" from auxiliary equation:

$$a = \bar{Y} - b_1 \bar{X}_1 - b_2 \bar{X}_2 - \cdots - b_k \bar{X}_k \tag{3}$$

In the set of equations (2) the left-hand side of each equation is the sum of sums of products of deviations of a particular independent variable from its mean value by the corresponding deviations of all remaining explanatory or independent variables taken in turn, each such sum of products being multiplied by the appropriate (unknown) partial regression coefficient b or b_2 or . . . or b_k. The right-hand side is the sum of products of deviations of the appropriate explanatory variable by the deviations of the explained or dependent variable. In other words, the left-hand sides of the equations express interactions between explanatory or independent variables. The right-hand sides express dependences of the dependent variable upon independent variables. For certain values of the partial regression coefficients which we are investigating, both sides of the set of equations become equal to one another.

It is therefore a premise, underlying the extraction of multiple regression equations and of partial regression coefficients, that interdependence occurs not only between the dependent variable and each independent variable but also among the independent variables.

In reality, in most cases (especially in economic analysis) not only the dependent variable is correlated with independent variables, but also particular independent variables are in a higher or lower degree mutually correlated. The set of equations (2) may be transformed into a set as below, directly confirming the thesis above:[2]

$$\begin{array}{l} b'_1 r_{11} + b'_2 r_{12} + \cdots + b'_k r_{1k} = r_{1y} \\ b'_1 r_{21} + b'_2 r_{22} + \cdots + b'_k r_{2k} = r_{2y} \\ b'_1 r_{k1} + b'_2 r_{k2} + \cdots + b'_k r_{kk} = r_{ky} \end{array} \tag{4}$$

[2] E. O. Heady and J. L. Dillon, *Agricultural Production Functions.* Iowa State Univ. Press, Ames, 1961, p. 115.

where respective r represents simple correlation coefficients between particular variables, and b' being so-called standard partial regression coefficient. Standard coefficients may be deduced from simple ones, using the general formula:

$$b'_i = b_i \sqrt{\frac{\Sigma x_i^2}{\Sigma y_i^2}} \tag{5}$$

Standardized partial regression coefficients deduced from the set of equations at (4) and ordinary coefficients of partial regression derived from them by the use of the reverse of formula (5) express how strong is the influence of the given independent variable upon the dependent variable after abstracting from the connexion of the said dependent variable with the other independent variables which are exerting their influence in parallel. It does not denote, however, that a finally deduced value for a particular partial regression coefficient of a given variable is fully independent of correlation between particular explanatory variables. On the contrary, such correlation helps to decide the value of the partial regression coefficients. The pure influence of the given independent variable on the dependent variable will be weaker or stronger in one set of data compared with another, according to the correlations between the remaining independent variables. Thus, the partial regression coefficient does not represent an *absolute* quantity but only a *relative* one.

The above statement is essential not only from the statistical-mathematical point of view, but particularly in the case when the above method is used for the purposes of economic investigations. For example, when the influence is investigated of the so-called production factors (land, capital, labour) on the size of production by means of the so-called production function, the respective partial regression coefficients (or partial elasticity coefficients in the function according to Cobb-Douglas) got from the equation of multiple regression, do not express an influence absolutely independent of each of the above factors, although it might appear, both from the definite form of the equation and from some interpretations placed upon it, that a partial regression coefficient expresses the influence of the given factor assuming that the others do not exert any influence or are equal to zero or do not exist at all.[3] If it were so—to proceed by *reductio ad absurdum*—the production function would be the same in all countries and all times. That it is not so results from the fact that links existing between land, labour, and capital are different in different countries and in different times.

---

[3] A. Brzoza, "Some Contributions to the Problem of Production Functions on Peasant Farms." *Zagadnienia Ekonomiki Rolnej,* No. 2, 1962.

Classical theory of production functions, according to Say, considers the action of each of the above factors in the production process independently and apart from others. Land, irrespective of other factors, brings a rent; capital, profit; and labour, wages. This is nonsense both from the technical and from the economic points of view. The problem of production lies in the combination of these factors. In this process a mutual interaction takes place between the factors of the process. This interaction is expressed by competitive or complementary dependences of factors. To some extent mutual substitutional processes may occur (for technical or economic reasons). Each of the above factors acting independently creates by so doing *environmental* conditions for the activity of the other factors. Is there then any point in a partial examination of the separate action of each factor? It seems there is, providing that consideration be given not merely to the isolated activity of each of the factors but also to their mutual relationship and ratios and to the intensity of alliance of each of the analysed factors with the other factors, all operating jointly in a complex. From a statistical point of view this implies a necessity to pay considerably more attention to correlation and regression coefficients existing between independent variables, which are commonly omitted by the interpretations of the results obtained.

Let us try now to present and justify the above argument by a positive example of investigations carried out on application of multiple regression in computation of unit costs of agricultural products in peasant farms, running agricultural accounting (farm book-keeping) in 1956–57, situated in two regions of Poland: south-eastern and central-western. In the south-eastern region the regression equation between total outlay on the farm and the amount of production of grain, potatoes, sugar beets, milk, cattle, pigs, and eggs was deduced on the basis of individual results of accounting in the group of small farms (3–7 ha.). In the central-western region the relevant equation has been deduced on the basis of similar data obtained for larger farms (over 10 ha.). To avoid misunderstanding it is necessary to stress that in this chapter we do not seek to pass judgement on the results obtained from either the formal statistical or the agricultural economic points of view. We accept a conventional judgement that the data obtained are statistically significant and economically reasonable. In reality, neither assumption is correct, but this does not concern us here and does not prevent our taking advantage of the results of the interpretation of partial coefficients of interest to us.

The results are as follows:

South-eastern region, farms of 3–7 ha.

$$X_1 = 22{,}849 + 312.84X_2 - 41.62X_3 - 73.43X_4 - 1.13X_5 + 21.64X_6 + 11.75X_7 + 1.53X_8 \tag{I}$$

$$R^2 = 0.50; \quad \overline{S} = 8{,}624$$

Central-western region, farms over 10 ha.

$$X_1 = 18,399 - 19.78X_2 + 63.45X_3 - 1.31X_4 + 1.60X_5 + 31.32X_6 + 16.95X_7 + 1.77X_8$$

$$R^2 = 0.87; \quad \bar{S} = 14,389 \tag{II}$$

In these equations: X_1 = total outlay on farm in zlotys; X_2 = grain production in quintals per farm; X_3 = potato production in q.; X_4 = sugar beet production in q.; X_5 = milk production in litres; X_6 = cattle production in kg.; X_7 = pig production in kg.; X_8 = egg production per farm. The figures prefixed to the several X_i, being partial regression coefficients, indicate the number of zlotys by which total outlay will be recovered or reduced if the relevant X is increased by a unit whilst the other X_i remain unchanged.

Let us analyse a little closer the dependencies occurring in the sets of equations and examine how and in what degree they exerted an influence on the values of particular coefficients. First of all, let us investigate the intensity of correlation between particular variables occurring in both equations. The above correlations are illustrated by the appropriate tables of simple correlation coefficients between particular pairs of variables (Tables 4.1A and 4.1B). The above mentioned tables are completed as far as the diagonal only, all diagonal elements being equal to unity. The lower left portion of these tables would be a reflection of the upper right section. We understand that $r_{ij} = r_{ji}$.

As has been noticed before, we are not concerned in this chapter with an analysis of the substance of the above results. Our object now is to draw attention to the extremely complicated relationships which

TABLE 4.1A

	x_1	x_2	x_3	x_4	x_5	x_6	x_7	x_8
x_1....	1.00	0.54	0.25	0.04	0.35	0.47	0.53	0.23
x_2....		1.00	0.54	0.29	0.19	0.34	0.55	0.17
x_3....			1.00	0.01	−0.33	0.10	0.53	0.19
x_4....				1.00	0.15	0.22	0.19	0.03
x_5....					1.00	0.23	0.23	0.16
x_6....						1.00	0.43	0.13
x_7....							1.00	0.12
x_8....								1.00

TABLE 4.1B
SIMPLE CORRELATION COEFFICIENTS BETWEEN VARIABLES,
CENTRAL-WESTERN REGION, 1956–57
(Farms over 10 ha.)

	x_1	x_2	x_3	x_4	x_5	x_6	x_7	x_8
x_1....	1.00	0.48	0.61	0.23	0.76	0.80	0.78	0.60
x_2....		1.00	0.62	0.39	0.39	0.41	0.39	0.28
x_3....			1.00	0.16	0.40	0.48	0.44	0.27
x_4....				1.00	0.35	0.31	0.02	0.25
x_5....					1.00	0.68	0.54	0.52
x_5....						1.00	0.56	0.58
x_7....							1.00	0.47
x_8....								1.00

exist within the frame of the sets of coefficients relating to a particular region and to the strong differentiation which exists between the sets relating to different regions. Often neglected in interpretation is the fact that the partial regression coefficients are, in a way, quantities derived from these mutual relationships; attention is paid to the final result and the coefficient obtained is considered as an absolute and independent quantity. Let us now follow the process of forming the above coefficient.

First of all we must calculate simple regression coefficients on the one hand between the dependent variable and the several independent variables and on the other hand between each independent variable and all remaining correlated independent variables. The results of these computations for both regions under investigation are given in Tables 4.2A and 4.2B.

Each of these tables represents the influence of a given independent variable on the dependent variable and on the other independent variables. For example, following the row b_{12} for the southeastern region, an increase of grain production by one quintal per farm is associated with an increase in total outlay by 428 zlotys. This is but a simple regression coefficient. Behind the growth of outlay by 428 zl. lie not only the influence of increased grain production by 1 q. but also other influences which are not revealed by the simple regression coefficient. What do these influences consist of?

Within the given frame of relationships an increase by 1 q. in grain production causes or, strictly speaking, is associated with increases of 1.4 q. in potato production (b_{32}), of 0.63 q. in sugar beet

TABLE 4.2A

SIMPLE REGRESSION COEFFICIENTS BETWEEN VARIABLES,
SOUTH-EASTERN REGION, 1956–57

b_{12} 428.21 zl./q.	b_{32} 1.43 q./q.	b_{42} 0.63 q./q.	b_{52} 22.79 l./q.	b_{62} 2.84 kg./q.	b_{72} 10.18 kg./q.	b_{82} 9.66 eggs/q.
b_{13} 75.20 zl./q.	b_{23} 0.20 q./q.	b_{43} 0.01 q./q.	b_{53} −1.47 l./q.	b_{63} 0.32 kg./q.	b_{73} 3.63 kg./q.	b_{83} 3.97 eggs/q.
b_{14} 14.63 zl./q.	b_{24} 0.13 q./q.	b_{34} 0.01 q./q.	b_{54} 8.32 l./q.	b_{64} 0.83 kg./q.	b_{74} 1.61 kg./q.	b_{84} 0.80 eggs/q.
b_{15} 2.33 zl./l.	b_{25} 0.002 q./l.	b_{35} −0.0007 q./l.	b_{45} 0.003 q./l.	b_{65} 0.016 kg./l.	b_{75} 0.035 kg./l.	b_{85} 0.074 eggs/l.
b_{16} 44.75 zl./kg.	b_{26} 0.04 q./kg.	b_{36} 0.03 q./kg.	b_{46} 0.06 q./kg.	b_{56} 3.25 l./kg.	b_{76} 0.92 kg./kg.	b_{86} 0.86 eggs/kg.
b_{17} 22.66 zl./kg.	b_{27} 0.03 q./kg.	b_{37} 0.08 q./kg.	b_{47} 0.02 q./kg.	b_{57} 1.48 l./kg.	b_{67} 0.19 kg./kg.	b_{87} 0.38 eggs/kg.
b_{18} 3.27 zl./egg	b_{28} 0.003 q./egg	b_{38} 0.009 q./egg	b_{48} 0.001 q./egg	b_{58} 0.33 l./egg	b_{68} 0.02 kg./egg	b_{78} 0.04 kg./egg

TABLE 4.2B

SIMPLE REGRESSION COEFFICIENTS BETWEEN VARIABLES,
CENTRAL-WESTERN REGION, 1956–57

b_{12} 448.24 zl./q.	b_{32} 1.76 q./q.	b_{42} 1.38 q./q.	b_{52} 58.18 l./q.	b_{62} 3.73 kg./q.	b_{72} 7.59 kg./q.	b_{82} 10.84 eggs/q.
b_{13} 199.05 zl./q.	b_{23} 0.22 q./q.	b_{43} 0.20 q./q.	b_{53} 21.26 l./q.	b_{63} 1.53 kg./q.	b_{73} 3.06 kg./q.	b_{83} 3.69 eggs/q.
b_{14} 59.12 zl./q.	b_{24} 0.11 q./q.	b_{34} 0.13 q./q.	b_{54} 14.69 l./q.	b_{64} 0.77 kg./q.	b_{74} 0.12 kg./q.	b_{84} 2.68 eggs/q.
b_{15} 4.74 zl./l.	b_{25} 0.003 q./l.	b_{35} 0.008 q./l.	b_{45} 0.008 q./l.	b_{65} 0.041 kg./q.	b_{75} 0.07 kg./l.	b_{85} 0.13 eggs/l.
b_{16} 82.71 zl./kg.	b_{26} 0.05 q./kg.	b_{36} 0.15 q./kg.	b_{46} 0.12 q./kg.	b_{56} 11.27 l./kg.	b_{76} 1.21 kg./kg.	b_{86} 2.45 eggs/kg.
b_{17} 36.94 zl./kg.	b_{27} 0.02 q./kg.	b_{37} 0.06 q./kg.	b_{47} 0.004 q./kg.	b_{57} 4.13 l./kg.	b_{67} 0.26 kg./kg.	b_{87} 0.93 eggs/kg.
b_{18} 14.42 zl./egg	b_{28} 0.007 q./egg	b_{38} 0.02 q./egg	b_{48} 0.02 q./egg	b_{58} 2.01 l./egg	b_{68} 0.14 kg./egg	b_{78} 0.24 kg./egg

production (b_{42}), of 22.8 litres in milk production (b_{52}), of 2.84 kg. in cattle production (b_{62}), of 10.18 kg. in pigs (b_{72}) and of 9.66 eggs (b_{82}). Consequently, one may set up the hypothesis that the total effect of an increase in grain production by one unit in the given set of farms consists of both the pure effect of the grain increase and of the sum of the effects of the changes in quantities produced of all those other products which vary in association with grain production.

The above hypothesis is confirmed by a calculation concerning both regions under investigation, presented in Tables 4.3A and 4.3B.

The manner of the above calculation was as follows: from the value of the simple regression coefficient of outlay upon any *given* farm product was deducted a term corresponding to each of the *other* farm products. Each such term was the arithmetical product of the partial regression coefficient of outlay upon the farm product to which the term immediately relates with the simple regression coefficient of that same farm product upon the farm product originally given.

The result so obtained is the partial regression coefficient of outlay upon the farm product initially given.[4]

The above dependence may be expressed by the following formula:

$$b_{12.345678} = b_{12} - b_{13.2....8}b_{32} - b_{14.2....8}b_{42} - \cdot \cdot \cdot \cdot - b_{18.2...7}b_{82}$$

or, substituting the above formula for the simple regression coefficient according to:

$$b_{ij} = \frac{\Sigma x_i x_j}{\Sigma x_j^2}$$

we may rewrite it:

$$b_{12.345678} = \frac{\Sigma x_1 x_2 - b_{13.2...8}\Sigma x_3 x_2 - b_{14.2...8}\Sigma x_4 x_2 - \cdots - b_{18.2...7}\Sigma x_8 x_2}{\Sigma x_2^2}$$

From the set of equations similar to the above or from an appropriate transformation of them it is possible either:

a. to derive the *partial* regression coefficients of the dependent variable when the simple regression coefficients of dependent upon independent variables and of each independent variable upon each of the other independent variables are given, or

b. derive the *simple* regression coefficients of the dependent variable when the partial regression coefficients of the dependent upon each of the independent variables and the simple regression coefficients

---

[4] Partial regression coefficients for particular products are accepted on the basis of regression equations I and II. The results obtained differ slightly from the quantity of partial coefficient in the equation, owing to roundings in the calculations.

TABLE 4.3A

PARTIAL REGRESSION COEFFICIENTS DEDUCED FROM SIMPLE REGRESSION COEFFICIENTS,* SOUTH-EASTERN REGION, 1956–57

b_{12}	β_{32}	β_{42}	β_{52}	β_{62}	β_{72}	β_{82}	$\Sigma\beta_{ij}$	$b_{ij}-\Sigma\beta_{ij}$	$b_{12.3...8}$
428.21	−59.52	−46.26	25.75	61.46	119.62	14.78	115.83	312.38	312.84
b_{13} 75.20	β_{23} 62.57	β_{43} −0.73	β_{53} −1.66	β_{63} 6.92	β_{73} 42.65	β_{83} 6.07	115.82	−40.62	$b_{13.2...8}$ −41.62
b_{14} 14.63	β_{24} 40.67	β_{34} −0.42	β_{54} 9.40	β_{64} 17.96	β_{74} 18.92	β_{84} 1.22	87.75	−73.12	$b_{14.2...8}$ −73.43
b_{15} 2.33	β_{25} 0.62	β_{35} 0.03	β_{45} −0.22	β_{65} 0.35	β_{75} 0.41	β_{85} 0.11	1.30	1.03	$b_{15.2...8}$ 1.13
b_{16} 44.75	β_{26} 12.51	β_{36} −1.25	β_{46} −4.40	β_{56} 3.67	β_{76} 10.81	β_{86} 1.31	22.65	22.10	$b_{16.2...8}$ 21.64
b_{17} 22.66	β_{27} 9.38	β_{37} −3.33	β_{47} −1.47	β_{57} 1.67	β_{67} 4.11	β_{87} 0.58	10.94	11.72	$b_{17.2...8}$ 11.75
b_{18} 3.27	β_{28} 0.94	β_{38} −0.37	β_{48} −0.07	β_{58} 0.37	β_{68} 0.41	β_{78} 0.47	1.75	1.52	$b_{18.2...7}$ 1.53

* $\beta_{32} = b_{13.2...8} \cdot b_{32}$, etc.

TABLE 4.3B

PARTIAL REGRESSION COEFFICIENTS DEDUCED FROM SIMPLE REGRESSION COEFFICIENTS,* CENTRAL-WESTERN REGION, 1956–57

b_{12}	β_{32}	β_{42}	β_{52}	β_{62}	β_{72}	β_{82}	$\Sigma\beta_{ij}$	$b_{ij}-\Sigma\beta_{ij}$	$b_{12.3...8}$
448.24	112.01	−1.81	93.09	116.89	128.56	19.19	467.93	−19.69	−19.78
b_{13} 199.05	β_{23} −4.36	β_{43} −0.27	β_{53} 34.02	β_{63} 47.83	β_{73} 54.80	β_{83} 6.53	135.55	63.50	$b_{13.2...8}$ 63.45
b_{14} 59.12	β_{24} −2.15	β_{34} 8.13	β_{54} 23.50	β_{64} 24.18	β_{74} 2.02	β_{84} 4.74	60.42	−1.30	$b_{14.2...8}$ −1.31
b_{15} 4.74	β_{25} −0.5	β_{35} 0.48	β_{45} −0.01	β_{65} 1.28	β_{75} 1.19	β_{85} 0.23	3.12	1.62	$b_{15.2...8}$ 1.60
b_{16} 82.71	β_{26} −0.91	β_{36} 9.54	β_{46} −0.16	β_{56} 18.03	β_{76} 20.51	β_{86} 4.34	51.35	31.36	$b_{16.2...8}$ 31.32
b_{17} 36.94	β_{27} −0.39	β_{37} 4.07	β_{47} −0.01	β_{57} 6.61	β_{67} 8.08	β_{87} 1.64	20.00	16.94	$b_{17.2...8}$ 16.95
b_{18} 14.42	β_{28} −0.15	β_{38} 1.28	β_{48} −0.03	β_{58} 3.22	β_{68} 4.26	β_{78} 4.07	12.65	1.77	$b_{18.2...7}$ 1.77

* $\beta_{32} = b_{13.2...8} \cdot b_{32}$, etc.

of each independent upon every other independent variable are known.

The most important fact is that this analysis explains essential contents of the partial regression coefficient and shows its genesis. In the above case the statement that the partial regression coefficient tells us how much the dependent variable will increase under the influence of the increase by a unit of one particular independent variable—presuming that the remaining independent variables *remain unchanged* —is not adequate, as in the given framework of relationships a change of the given independent variable is accompanied, as a rule, by the change of all the other independent variables. In essence, partial regression coefficients tell us the amount by which the dependent variable will change when influenced by an increment of a unit in a particular independent variable after discounting the effects upon the dependent variable of all changes occurring simultaneously in the other independent variables.

Thus, the partial regression coefficient is not formed in a static set (as one factor is changing, the rest being unchanged) but, on the contrary, is formed in a dynamic set after elimination of changes due to the influence of other factors. It seems, therefore, that the name: *net regression coefficient* is more suitable than *partial regression coefficient*.

In interpreting the value obtained for a partial regression coefficient it is essential to consider the environment in which it appears and with which the analysed independent variable is connected. Its "net" influence on the dependent variable depends not only upon its inner properties but also upon the attendant circumstances.

In the examples chosen of the influence of production on the amount of expenses on a farm, for two regions of Poland, a characteristic fact appears: that simple regression coefficients between grain production per farm and the expenses on a farm are similar. In the south-eastern region an increase of grain production of one quintal induces an increase of expenses by 428 zlotys; in the central-western region by 448 zl. But in the small farms of the south-eastern region, grain is accompanied by other phenomena and its connexions with other products influencing expenses are different, compared with those in the central-western region. As a result, when the net influence of these phenomena is deducted, the net influence of an additional quintal of grain in the south-eastern region is expressed not by 428 zl. but by 313 zl., and in the central-western region not by 448 zl., but by —20 zl. Considering absolute quantities it is possible to affirm that increased grain production has a much stronger influence on the farm expenses of small farms. Thus, the cost of production per unit computed by the regression method varies according to the phenomena which accompany the production.

5

Advanced Research Methods in Agricultural Economics in Western Europe

GEORGE BUBLOT

University of Louvain, Belgium

WHAT ARE THE FUNDAMENTAL CHARACTERISTICS of research in agricultural economics in the countries of western Europe? What are the most frequent subjects of study and research methods? How are the centres financed? What is their average size? And what do the research workers think of the organization of research in agricultural economics in their respective countries? Such are the questions to which this chapter will try to give concise answers.

Essentially, this will take the form of an analysis of information received, from forty-six foreign correspondents from ninety-three research centres in fifteen countries of western Europe.

By research centres we mean the institutions—private, public, colleges, or universities—which have research in agricultural economics as the only or at least the principal objective of their activity. They include the departments of agricultural economics within universities and agricultural colleges, private research centres subsidized by the state, and the public research institutions directly created by government. Contrariwise, technical research centres, such as those studying the organization and simplification of farm labour, or the rationalization of buildings, national institutes of statistics, extension agencies in farm management, farmers unions, etc. are on principle excluded. The activities of these institutions are more or less closely connected with agricultural economics, but they are not primarily concerned with research in that subject. We exclude also international associations such as the European Economic Community (Brussels), the Organiza-

[*46*]

tion for Economic Co-operation and Development (Paris), the Food and Agriculture Organization (Rome and Geneva), the Confederation Internationale de Techniciens Agricoles (Paris), and similar groups. Except for the F.A.O. these institutions, although they may carry out some studies, do not regard them as main objects of their activities. We cannot be sure that this elimination is justified; it is based entirely on the statements collected. On the other hand, we have not been able to use all the information from all the research centres in every country. This is especially true of the large countries such as Italy, and to a smaller degree France and Germany. The results are summarized under four main headings:

1. The methods of financing, and the average size of the centres,
2. The subjects of research,
3. The methods of research, and
4. Personal remarks concerning the organization of research.

THE METHODS OF FINANCING AND THE AVERAGE SIZE OF RESEARCH CENTRES

Table 5.1 shows the distribution of the 93 centres among the 15 countries. The largest number are sponsored by the State. This un-

TABLE 5.1

METHODS OF FINANCING AND AVERAGE SIZES OF THE RESEARCH CENTRES
(Situation, Jan. 1, 1963)

| | Number of Centres | Number of Centres Sponsored by | | | Average Sizes | | | |
| | | | | | Financial | Number of people | | |
	Number of Centres	State or gov-ernment	College or uni-versity	Private societies	Annual budget *	Graduate *	Other	Total
					(dollars)			
Austria.....	6	1	4	1	..	....	6	7.3	21.6	28.9
Belgium....	9	8	1	..	9	22,000	9	2.3	5.0	7.3
Denmark...	4	2	2	..	2	43,200	4	6.7	1.5	8.2
Finland.....	4	..	2	2	4	27,275	4	4.5	2.2	6.7
France.....	12	10	4	4	..	....	..	....	....	....
Germany...	14	10	4	2	6	29,400	8	7.7	7.0	14.7
Greece.....	2	..	2	..	2	1,333	2	2.0	1.5	3.5
Italy.......	7	3	3	3	5	86,700	7	4.5	3.5	8.0
Netherlands.	1	1	..	1	1	910,800	1	40.0	270.0	310.0
Norway.....	2	2	..	..	2	167,500	2	25.0	13.0	38.0
Portugal....	6	3	..	3	6	75,333	6	11.0	11.0	22.0
Spain......	4	4	..	1	3	15,220	4	23.5	4.5	28.0
Sweden.....	5	3	1	..	3	65,000	4	5.0	3.5	8.5
Switzerland.	1	1	..	..	1	11,500	1	....	....	5.0
United Kingdom.	16	10	10	..	12	91,975	16	10.8	10.4	21.2
Total......	93	58	33	17	56	72,495	74	8.9	11.4	20.1

* Number of answers for which data are available.

derlines their fundamental character: their direct or indirect connexion with a university, involving a tight institutional link and a
continual co-operation between higher education and research, this
last being mostly entrusted to professors.

This is not general, however. In some countries, such as the
Netherlands, Belgium, Sweden, Denmark, and Norway, the State has
recently taken an active part in research, either by creating a specialized institute, or by organizing a department of research. Frequently
this gives rise to important institutions, to which large grants are
made as in Norway and the Netherlands. Apart from these exceptions,
research is generally as widespread as university education itself,
though the various centres are of very modest size whether measured
by the annual budget or by the number of people employed.

THE SUBJECTS OF RESEARCH

It is difficult to distinguish between the different particular research subjects; each project, because of the multiple aspects of the
problems investigated, may have several. In spite of this difficulty and
always on the basis of the information received, we have summarized
in Table 5.2, by country, the principal programmes of the different
centres. The general trend is clear: farm management, and the problems of the economics of agricultural production generally, have been
the principal subjects of research for a long time and still are the most
frequent. In the past this type of research was local, empirical, and
based on regional interest. It has been associated, so far as research
methods are concerned, with the use and analysis of book-keeping
leading to budgeting and, more recently, to the more refined methods
of programme planning and linear programming.

The study of the problems of farm management corresponds to an
autarchic and self-contained structure of the farms which prevailed in
the past, either in a region or a country. But continuous development of market economy evidently raised questions of marketing. It
is not surprising to see marketing the most frequent subject for research after farm management (41 out of 243). The broadening of
the research project has thus paralleled the broadening of agricultural
economics. These two sets of problems have many connexions with
agricultural policy and land economics which is why we meet these
subjects fairly frequently. Finally, various aspects of production and
demand, analysis of supply and demand, rural sociology, and economic
problems in developing countries, show a great expansion of research
though the actual projects are still very limited in number.

This evolution of the subjects of research discloses the fundamental anxiety of the agricultural economist to make important contributions to the solution of actual problems. His energies seem to
be spent in two directions: to attend to the needs of agriculture, and
to apply adequate methods to satisfy them. On the average, each centre

TABLE 25.2

PROGRAMMES OF RESEARCH
(Situation, Jan. 1, 1963)

	Number of Centres (A)	1	2	3	4	5	6	7	8	9	10	11	12	13	Total (B)	Average Per Centre (B/A)
Austria	6	1	1		1	2	1	1	1		2		1		11	1.8
Belgium	9	5	1	2		4	1								13	1.4
Denmark	4	3		1	1	1		1		1	1				9	2.3
Finland	4		2	2		2	1		1		1				9	2.3
France	12	6	1	2	1	3	2	2	3	1	4		3		28	2.3
Germany	14	5			3	5	1	8	3	6	1	2	1	1	36	2.6
Greece	2	2				2	2				2				8	4.0
Italy	7	4			2	6	1	6	6						25	3.6
Netherlands	1	1				1	1		1		1				5	5.0
Norway	2	1			1	1	1	3	1			1			9	4.5
Portugal	6	3	2			2	1			1	1				10	1.7
Spain	4	2		1	1	2	1		1	1		1			10	2.5
Sweden	5	2	2	1	1	2	1		3		1	1	1		15	3.0
Switzerland	1	1	1							1					3	3.0
United Kingdom	16	8	8	2	2	8	1	5	5	4	2	2	2	3	52	3.3
Total	93	44	18	11	13	41	15	26	25	15	16	7	8	4	243	2.6

1. Farm management
2. Agricultural production economics
3. Agricultural co-operatives and agricultural co-operation
4. Analysis of supply
5. Agricultural marketing, international trade
6. Analysis of demand, consumption
7. Agricultural policy
8. Land economics
9. Agrarian aspects of economic development, historic development
10. Rural sociology
11. Comparative studies (interregional, international)
12. Statistics: area, production, forecasting
13. Underdeveloped countries

TABLE 5.3

METHODS OF RESEARCH USED
(Situation, Jan. 1, 1963)

	Number of Centres (A)	1	2	2a	2b	3	4	5	6	7	8	Total (B)	Average Per Centre (B/A)
Austria...........	6	2	2			1	1	1	3		3	13	2.2
Belgium..........	9	3	3			2	8					16	1.8
Denmark.........	4	1	3	3	2	3	1		1	1	1	15	3.8
Finland..........	4	1				2					2	6	1.5
France...........	12	4	6	2	2	2	1		7	1		21	1.8
Germany.........	14	2	3	3		4	2	3	4	1	4	28	2.0
Greece...........	2	6	2			2	2	1	1	1	2	12	6.0
Italy.............	7	1	1			3	3	1	1	1	6	23	3.3
Netherlands......	1	2	2	1	1	1	1	1	1		1	8	8.0
Norway..........	2	6	3			2		1		1	2	12	6.0
Portugal.........	6	1	2			2	2	2	2	2	2	18	3.0
Spain............	4	2	2			4	3	2				14	3.5
Sweden..........	5	1				4	1	1	2		4	17	3.4
Switzerland......	1			1	2		3					2	2.0
United Kingdom..	16	8	6	1	2	6	3	1	6	2	9	44	2.8
Total...........	93	41	37	10	7	38	29	14	28	9	36	249	2.7

1. Book-keeping and cost accounting
2. Linear programming
2a. Programme planning
2b. Budget planning
3. Regression and correlation analysis
4. Statistical methods
5. Macro-economic models
6. Models
7. Factor analysis
8. Surveys

has 2.6 research subjects. This shows the close interdependence of the problems rather than the dispersion of the research activities.

THE METHODS OF RESEARCH

When research methods are not directly related to the fundamental sciences, there is a rather close connexion between the subjects and the methods of research. (See Table 5.3.) Thus, when farm management is the most important subject of study, the methods of study most frequently met are accounting, programme planning, and budgeting. They are suitable methods for farm management and unsuitable for market or demand analysis.

The evolution of the research methods used has undoubtedly followed the course of the fundamental sciences: mathematics, pure economics, and their derivatives: mathematical statistics, econometrics, and operational research. And the more a method rests on a fundamental discipline, the more general is its use in economics. Linear programming can be applied to many other problems than those of farm management; in the same way, regression analysis is suitable in every branch of research in agricultural economics. This explains why the growing use of the quantitative and refined methods of linear programming, regression analysis, statistical methods, etc. is so fruitful in research. Factor analysis is relatively little used; on the other hand, the word *model* is used with vague and rather general meaning.

We must here point out that the designation of a method by one and the same word may hide the fact that there are very many ways to apply it and very different refinements in its use. For instance, the easiest application of linear programming is to solve the simple problem of maximization or minimization, such as the determination of the optimum plan for a farm. But the method can be applied also in national planning and economic development, as on stochastic models. In the same way, regression analysis varies in its applications from a free-hand curve to the more complex aspects of structural equations of demand and supply (system of the simultaneous equation), and to the consideration of the problems of auto-correlation or multi-collinearity. To repeat, a research method called by a single name may be used in many different ways. Finally, we should say that as research methods derive more and more from the fundamental disciplines so they have broader and broader fields of application.

In that respect, a regional analysis is very difficult. It is only possible for a researcher to use modern research methods if he has reliable statistical data at his disposal. This explains why the Scandinavian countries, just as Germany and the Netherlands, have made great advances in the use of refined research techniques. Perhaps it is true that higher scientific education and reliability of statistical data are two correlated aspects of economic growth, which involves a more and more quantitative approach to the problems of life. But it is

TABLE 5.4

PERSONAL REMARKS AND SUGGESTIONS ABOUT RESEARCH AND TEACHING IN AGRICULTURAL ECONOMICS
(Situation, Jan. 1, 1963)

	Answers Received	Question I			Question II			Question III						Question IV						Question V				
		No ans.	Yes	No	No ans.	Yes	No	1	2	3	4	5	6	1	2	3	4	5	6	1	2	3	4	5
Austria	2	2			1		1	2						1			1			1	1			
Belgium	2			2			2		2								1		1		2	1		
Denmark	1	2		2	1					1			1		2				1	2		2		
Finland	4	2	2	2	1		1	2		1				2			1			1			1	
France	2	2	1	2	3	2	1	6		1	2			2	2	2	2				1		1	2
Germany	6		1	1		1	1		2	1				1			1			3	1	1		1
Greece	2	1	1	2	2		2	1							1		4			1	1			
Italy	4		1			1	1	1	2		2		1		2					1		1	1	
Netherlands	1		1	1			1									1	1				1			
Norway	2		1	1	1				1						1						1		1	1
Portugal	1	3			2			3						3		1	1		1	2				
Spain	1	1	1		1	2		1				1		1						1		1	1	
Sweden	4					2				3	3	4	1			1	1	3	1				1	
Switzerland	1																							
United Kingdom	13	5	2	6	5	2	6	3	1	3	3	4	2	3	4	3	4	3	2	4	8	1	4	
Total	46	19	10	17	18	8	20	21	8	6	5	5	5	14	11	7	16	3	2	16	16	7	9	4

TABLE 5.4 (*continued*)

Question I. Do you think that the training of the research workers in your country is sufficient for the needs of the research?

Question II. Is the teaching of advanced methods of research sufficient in the agricultural colleges?

Question III. What are the main deficiencies, if any, in the training of research workers in your country?
1. No answer. 2. Lack of postgraduate studies and specialization. 3. Deficiencies in mathematics. 4. Deficiencies in economics. 5. Deficiencies in statistics. 6. Others: problem solved; does not apply; lack of funds to develop research in wider field; there are deficiencies but advanced methods are taught in the 6th year.

Question IV. What do you think about the organization of agricultural economics research in your country?
1. No answer. 2. Good organization—quite good organization. 3. Improving. 4. Lack of co-ordination. 5. Too little independence for research work. 6. Others: Lack of capable men between the leader of the research centre and young graduates; lack of space to work; insufficient government support for the establishment of long-time research programmes and for keeping the research workers for several years.

Question V. Other suggestions and remarks concerning co-operation between the research centres of the European countries.
1. No answer. 2. Creation of a European association for agricultural economists; creation of a regional section of I.A.A.E. 3. Need for European *colloquia*. 4. Need for better co-operation and more interchange within Europe. 5. Others: there are already many international meetings; the publication of research programmes is needed; still very insufficient; very desirable at present; need for more independent research with regard to group interests; or financial agencies to guarantee full objectivity in the reports of their researches.

[53]

equally true that the researcher without sufficient data has no incentive to improve his research methods; the variability of the final result is influenced much more by the accuracy of the basic data than by the refinement of the method. Thus as Earl O. Heady[1] conveniently points out: "It is less the range and power of the tools and more the lack of data, and limitations in its forms, which prevent the useful and productive application of research. The data of observation and the more refined tools are technical complements in the sense that the value or magnitude of the product which they can generate depends on the extent or presence of both. Inadequate and shabby data cannot be transformed by powerful mathematical techniques into a product of useful predictions and coefficients."

PERSONAL REMARKS CONCERNING THE ORGANIZATION OF THE RESEARCH

Table 5.4 summarizes the answers to certain questions put to our foreign correspondents about the organization of teaching and research in agricultural economics in their countries.

The following features appear very clearly. Many correspondents find that the training of the research workers in their countries is insufficient (10 yes, 17 no). The origin of these deficiencies can logically be found in the educational systems seeing that a majority think that teaching is deficient (8 yes, 20 no). The answers to Question III give more information about the nature of the deficiencies: the lack of post-graduate studies and the deficiency in the basic sciences—mathematics, economics and statistics—are the most frequent. Although this represents the view of the majority, the answers to each question are very different even between correspondents in a same country. This does not mean that when all the correspondents of a country found the training of the researchers insufficient, the absolute level of the scientific education of the researchers in that country is necessarily less satisfactory than in a country where the correspondents answered Questions I and II affirmatively. In fact, each answer is mainly a personal opinion.

So far as Question IV is concerned, some correspondents find that the organization of research in their countries is good or improving. Among the greater deficiencies, the lack of co-ordination is often regretted. So far as Europe is concerned, the need for more contact and more co-operation between centres is affirmed, either by creating a European association of agricultural economists (16 answers), or by providing for exchange between centres (9 answers), or by the institution of European colloquia (7 answers).

---

[1] Earl O. Heady, "The Agricultural Economist and His Tools: Research Methods," *Proceedings of the Eleventh International Conference of Agricultural Economists*. Oxford Univ. Press, London, 1963.

6

National Commodity Stabilization Schemes: Some Reflections Based on Australian Experience

KEITH O. CAMPBELL

University of Sydney, N.S.W., Australia

IN THE PAST TWENTY YEARS, the stabilization of agricultural prices has loomed increasingly large as an objective of public policy, both nationally and internationally. Interest in administrative measures directed to this end reflects a growing concern about the effects of price fluctuations on the fortunes of primary producers and indeed of some entire economies. More recently attention has been centred on the possible contribution of price-stabilization measures to the advancement of under-developed economies. The United Nations Organization has sponsored several studies into the practicability of schemes for international compensatory financing and there have been advocates of a much wider network of international commodity agreements than exists at the present time. Simultaneously, there has been evidence of a renewed examination of the potential role of domestic commodity stabilization schemes in mitigating price fluctuations in developing countries.

The discussion of national price stabilization schemes which is to be found in the literature is usually of a generalized nature and predominantly laudatory in tone. One forms the impression that nothing but good can come from governmental measures designed, as Swerling has put it, ". . . to siphon off a part of agriculture's windfall gains as a reserve for rainy days." One suspects that such favourable reactions are a result of preoccupation with the fiscal and monetary implications of such schemes and of a tendency to discount the political and administrative problems associated with their operation. The purpose of the present chapter is to examine certain aspects of farmer-financed stabilization schemes in the light of Australian experience over the greater part of two decades. Price-stabilization schemes are difficult to evaluate objectively at any time, since their precise aims, particularly as regards the degree of price stability sought, are typically ill-defined. Moreover, any judgement about them necessitates a subtle balancing of efficiency, stability, and growth as objectives of economic policy and raises questions of equity and economic freedom.

The Australian stabilization schemes, of which the wheat-stabilization scheme is the archetype, are not concerned solely with export sales, as are many schemes in the under-developed countries. It is true that the provisions for taxing producers' returns in periods of high prices, and holding such sums in stabilization reserves for subsequent price-support activities, apply to the export phase of operations, but in the Australian case the Treasury is specifically required to underwrite price supports to a substantial extent if the stabilization reserves become exhausted. The scheme also covers sales to domestic consumers which take place at a specified price that is independent of overseas price movements. The domestic price fixed initially is adjusted annually in accordance with movements in production costs. The price so determined is also, for all practical purposes, the price guaranteed to growers. Leaving aside complications introduced by the International Wheat Agreement, the Australian wheat-stabilization scheme, therefore, consists of a familiar two-price arrangement, with provision for stabilization operations with respect to export sales.

Claims by the Australian Government that such a scheme is price stabilizing rather than protectionist in nature are attributable to the existence of the stabilization fund provisions and to the fact that, in the early years of the scheme, the domestic price was far less than (at one stage, one-third of) the prevailing overseas market price, thus providing an example of what the Haberler Committee called anti-protection. However, between 1956 and 1963, the scheme became progressively more protectionist in nature—in the sense that the domestic support price was consistently in excess of the export price—and after 1960 the Federal Treasury was forced to engage in price-support operations on a considerable scale. This illustrates the inherent difficulty of making a clear distinction between the price-stabilizing and the price-raising activities of governments in the manner that the Haberler Committee attempted to do. Legislative amendments in November 1963 included a 9 per cent reduction in the support price, but this was matched by a 50 per cent increase in the quantity of export wheat qualifying for the price guarantee. Without a radical change in the present pricing arrangements, it is difficult to see how the Australian wheat scheme can honestly be described as a price-stabilization scheme in the strict sense. This experience with the wheat-stabilization scheme virtually duplicates the history of the dairy-stabilization scheme almost a decade earlier.

In Australia as in other primary producing countries, the principal motivation for the adoption of stabilization schemes in the early post-war period was as a domestic defence against the destabilizing influence upon the economy of cyclical instability of prices on world markets. Leaving aside output fluctuations of weather origin, price fluctuations on overseas markets are an important determinant of the level of agricultural income and indeed of national income in many primary producing countries. From a fiscal point of view, what happens when stabilization funds are accumulated in a boom is comparable with the deflationary effects of a budget surplus. They tend, at least in part, to offset the inflationary consequences of a balance-of-payments surplus in the country concerned. A reverse mechanism takes place in a recession. In essence, the government imposes forced saving during periods of favourable export prices so as to permit dissaving in export recessions.

The question immediately arises whether other types of fiscal and monetary measures would not accomplish the same purpose as stabilization funds and perhaps do it more effectively. The answer, I believe, must be given in the affirmative at least in those countries with well-developed taxing procedures and monetary systems. The answer is less clear cut and may, in fact, be in the negative in the case of under-developed countries, where income taxation, if it is in existence, is largely ineffective. In such cases export taxes may be the only practical alternative.

In the more advanced open economies, it would seem preferable to rely on the progressive nature of the tax structure, counter-cyclical tax policy, and monetary controls. Using such techniques it should be possible to stabilize aggregate disposable income—not solely the disposable income arising from export production. Such an approach would have the added advantage of avoiding interference with resource adjustments in response to changing economic conditions—a major drawback of the commodity-based scheme as we shall see. On the other hand, the stabilization fund has the virtue of being of the nature of a built-in stabilizer and does not call for the same amount of political courage and financial discipline as general counter-cyclical policy—if the rules can be determined in advance and adhered to.

But even the use of stabilization funds calls for a considerable measure of fortitude if they are to achieve what is claimed for them. To adhere to a stabilization scheme in boom times, when alternative short-run opportunities look attractive, is especially difficult for an under-developed economy. In more advanced countries, governments have to stand up to the pressure of organized farmer groups, who always become restive when the size of the stabilization funds starts to grow. In both Australia and New Zealand, governments have been forced by farmer pressure to modify their stabilization-fund arrangements substantially as a consequence of the mounting size of the stabilization reserves. In the Australian case, the amount that may be accumulated in the wheat-stabilization fund is no longer discretionary, a specific modest upper limit of £A20 million, and more recently £A30 million, having been set. Pressures of this kind led earlier to the introduction of the *revolving fund* principle whereby the stabilization fund, when it is at or near the maximum, is turned over regularly by making current collections of tax and simultaneously returning to farmers the proceeds of earlier collections. This is done in order to ensure that the reserve funds represent as far as possible the contributions of the current population of wheat growers and reflect their current scales of output. One effect of this procedure is that the net intake into the fund in a given year may be zero or even negative. In such cases the scheme loses all pretence of having counter-cyclical properties.

Clearly, the over-all effect of stabilization funds on a country's economy depends on the number and significance of the country's exports which are covered by schemes of this kind. The stabilized product must represent a significant part of the country's trade, or a battery of schemes must be in operation for different export commodities, if the dampening or stimulating effect of stabilization-fund operations on the country's economy is to be significant. New Zealand has thus been much better placed than Australia to reap fiscal benefits from its price-stabilization schemes. A considerable fillip was given to the New Zealand economy by virtue of the stabilization reserves held in 1956 and 1957. The disbursement of these is estimated to have increased the gross income of dairy farmers by 15 per cent and their net income by 30 per cent in the two years in question. At the same time, the distribution of these reserves did add further pressure to the adverse balance of payments existing at that time. In Australia, with its much more diversified economy and less extensive schemes, the effect of intake into and disbursements from the stabilization funds on the over-all economy have been virtually imperceptible.

Whatever the theoretical potentialities of commodity-stabilization schemes, their usefulness as counter-cyclical devices depends ultimately on the acumen and independence of the administrators of such schemes, where some degree of discretion is allowed in the interests of flexibility. In cases where the *modus operandi* of the scheme is established in advance by legislation, its success in accomplishing the results sought depends vitally on the powers of prophecy vouchsafed to those responsible for establishing the rules. The Australian example quoted earlier is a classic example of the latter type of situation. In this case a set of rules was established only after tough negotiations with farmer organizations. Subsequent attempts to alter the rules to take account of emerging developments in supply and market conditions have generally been resisted by farmers, since the proposed changes almost inevitably have gone counter to their immediate interests.

The basic decisions to be taken on the management of such schemes include (1) the rate at which the stabilization fund should be accumulated and disbursed and (2) the extent to which contact should be maintained with the trend of overseas prices. Perhaps the major problem in practice is that of distinguishing a cyclical price decline from a long-term irreversible shift in demand. Since the dangers of an ill-judged and ill-timed policy can be worse than no scheme at all, some writers have recommended mechanical formulae usually involving some sort of moving average. The suggested formulae of Bauer and Paish, arising out of their examination of the operations of the West African marketing boards, are the best known of this type. But mechanical formulae, even moving averages, have considerable short-comings in a dynamic world, and in no way meet some of the other objections to these schemes. Such formulae are apt to produce rather sluggish responses to price changes (particularly secular ones) and they rarely take into account factors other than the price of the product in question—factors such as changes in the general price level in the country concerned and changes in the prices of competing products. There would seem to be good reasons, therefore, for giving considerable discretion to the administrators of stabilization funds. However, such administrators should be required to keep producer prices in reasonable contact with market trends. In other words, the stabilization objectives of the scheme should be defined in advance. Whether such a degree of discretion is feasible in a particular political context is, of course, an entirely different matter.

Any consideration of stabilization schemes raises questions of the justification of compulsory saving, particularly when it is aimed at a specific class of the population. Why, it may be asked, cannot the individual producer be trusted to save part of his boom-time cash receipts for use in adverse times? Why must a paternalistic government intervene?

This is a difficult question for the protagonists of stabilization schemes to answer, especially if there is any doubt as to the social benefits of any particular scheme. The usual justification for government intervention is based on a belief that farmers are perverse and even imprudent in their savings and investment behaviour. It is claimed that farmers in regions subject to price instability are not disposed to save in times of boom prices or bountiful seasons against less auspicious times. But even in low-income countries (where one tends to discount the possibility of entrepreneurs taking a long view), there is evidence that the larger operators, at least, are aware of the cyclical problem and take steps to meet it. Observations of the behaviour of commercial farmers in more advanced countries suggest that the extent of private adaptation to the exigencies of a fluctuating income situation is much greater than is commonly believed. In particular, farmers do not readily adjust their consumption expenditures in line with income fluctuations. Moreover, there is always a possibility that those entrepreneurs who do not save, but spend their windfall gains almost immediately (for instance, in acquiring some additional assets), are in fact adopting a more rational policy from a long-run standpoint than they would be by holding liquid assets. This would be particularly so if the monetary system in a country is none too stable. In my view, there is much to be said for allowing a farmer to make his spending decisions in the light of his own particular circumstances rather than subjecting him to a system by which he is required to save by government fiat.

The contribution of commodity stabilization schemes in mitigating the problem of income instability in agriculture is circumscribed by virtue of their preoccupation with price variations. Yield fluctuations, in semi-arid areas particularly, can on occasions be as serious a source of disturbance to farm incomes as price fluctuations. A specific decision to concentrate on price rather than income stability could not be questioned, were it not that the mechanics of some price-stabilization schemes do actually aggravate income instability arising from variations in output. Under the provisions of the Australian wheat-stabilization scheme, for example, the stabilization tax, being an excise tax independent of yield, represents a higher proportion of net income in a year of short crop than in a year of a large crop. Moreover, when the stabilization fund is actively operating, year-to-year fluctuations in yield could give rise to considerable divergences between individual growers' tax contributions and their subsequent receipts from price-support activities. This particular trouble is intensified to the extent that a rapid turnover of the stabilization fund is encouraged for the other reasons mentioned earlier. In addition, where, under a two-price scheme, the domestic price is less than the export price, the farmer may receive a lower average price per bushel for a short crop than a bumper crop. Considerations such as these suggest that farm income instability needs to be looked at in a much broader context than price alone.

Perhaps the major criticism which can be launched against commodity-stabilization schemes as they are operated in the world today is their adverse effect upon resource allocation. This can be viewed in a national context or at the farm level. Taking the national viewpoint and assuming that a country desires to maximize its foreign exchange earnings, is it in the country's own best interests to institute price-stabilization schemes in respect to its export crops? The answer is no, if production is at all responsive to price and if the country's production represents a small proportion of total world trade in the commodity in question. A stabilization scheme tends to restrain production when export prices are high and to discourage contraction of production when export prices are low. With a stabilization scheme in existence, a country's foreign exchange earnings are therefore likely to be lower over the course of the business cycle than otherwise. Moreover, if the country's exports represent a significant proportion of total world trade, these production trends may actually accentuate the cyclical movement of prices on world markets. Consequently, it may be more prudent for a country wishing to maximize its export proceeds to allow the volume of exports to increase as much as possible when overseas prices are favourable and let it decline when export prices become less attractive, particularly if the price behaviour of alternative rural products is not highly correlated with the price of the commodity subject to the stabilization scheme.

A more precise answer to the question requires, of course, an examination of the elasticity of export supply of particular commodities with respect to price. If supply were completely inelastic, then there would be no adverse effect. But, by and large, the quantities of commodities moving in international trade do respond significantly to price movements. This applies not only to crops with short production periods such as wheat, but also, to some degree, to plantation crops such as rubber. On the question of supply response under stabilization schemes, it is instructive to compare the growth of wheat production in Australia with that in North America during the decade after World War II.

It can be argued, of course, that high temporary prices may lead to future over-production and therefore that stabilization of prices is likely to bring about a more economic pattern of production over time, but again the problem arises of distinguishing, *ex ante,* between a short-term change in demand and a long-term structural change. It may well be true that stabilization measures tend to minimize adjustment problems in particular industries, to the extent that temporarily high prices become embedded in the cost structure of the industry in question. Costs of wheat production in Australia in the early post-war period, for instance, were well below North American levels, but the cost differential has been steadily narrowing ever since. In one sense, then, it can be said that the maintenance of more stable prices may lead to lower production costs in the long run. But it must also be remembered that upward price and income movements have some favourable effects in the direction of causing farmers to adopt new technology and this may ultimately be cost reducing.

The adverse effects of stabilization schemes on resource allocation become especially evident when a country elects to put one, or only a few, of its commodities under such a scheme, while allowing the prices of other commodities (which are closely related to it in demand or production) to fluctuate freely in accordance with export price movements. In practice, most commodity-stabilization schemes are operated in complete disregard of the prices of competing products. This problem of inter-commodity price relationships is well illustrated in the case of the Australian wheat scheme. When wool prices rose unfettered during the Korean boom, wheat plantings were reduced about 25 per cent primarily because wheat prices were stabilized. Exactly the opposite trend occurred between 1958 and 1963, when wool prices were relatively less attractive than those in the stabilized wheat industry. As a consequence the area of wheat harvested in Australia increased by about 60 per cent in this period thus increasing substantially the price-support commitment of the Government.

Similarly, on the demand side, the grain-livestock economy in Australia has, on occasions, been thrown seriously out of gear, because wheat was priced unduly low relative to competing coarse grains. The Australian Wheat Board at one stage was forced to place quantitative restrictions on the volume of wheat made available for livestock feeding, in order to ensure that the volume of wheat exports was maintained. A more recent complaint, as the domestic price of wheat has risen above export parity, has been that wheat can no longer be used as a feed grain in livestock industries competing on export markets.

Sometimes it is claimed for stabilization schemes that they actually improve resource allocation in an industry by virtue of reducing price uncertainty. Although such schemes do tend to reduce the amplitude of price fluctuations, most of them do not provide anything approaching price certainty to producers. This is certainly true of the Australian wheat scheme. Providing a little more certainty with respect to the price of one product in a multi-enterprise situation does little to improve the state of the farmer's over-all knowledge, though it may lead to increased production of the commodity with the lower price risk. Whether this represents a superior allocation of resources is another question.

Commodity stabilization schemes need also to be examined from the standpoint of growth and development. It can be argued that under-developed countries cannot afford to sterilize any windfall gains from export booms in stabilization reserves—that the pressing need for imports of equipment to aid development, as well as for consumer goods, is too great. To these countries, the holding of reserves represents a real cost in terms of abstinence. There is the added risk that the terms of trade may not remain constant and that the money held in stabilization reserves will not have the same purchasing power at a later date. Moreover, if export earnings are used for investment immediately, this may, in itself, assure a higher level of disposable income in the next recession.

Stabilization schemes also have important implications as regards investment and growth in particular industries. It is often presumed by the protagonists of such schemes that, if the price of an agricultural commodity is stabilized, investment in that industry will proceed at an even rate over time. This, I would submit, is not the nature of the investment process in agriculture. Moreover, it is wrong to assume that price fluctuations always act as a deterrent to investment in agriculture. The contrary may, in fact, be the case.

It is clear that when a stabilization tax is applied to an industry during a boom, there will be a reduction in the volume of investment. In many instances, investment will probably be reduced to almost the full extent of the amount put in the stabilization reserve. But it would be rash to expect that an increase in farm investment of comparable magnitude would occur during a price recession even though producers' prices are supported from the stabilization reserve at that time. The general economic climate might well discourage entrepreneurs even though they be in a stabilized industry. In other words, the volume of investment may be higher in aggregate under fluctuating incomes than if the same aggregate income is received at a more steady rate. This is a proposition which cannot readily be proved, but it is a matter of great importance to countries endeavouring to achieve rapid economic development and it merits some detailed research. Certainly not enough is known at present about farmers' investment behaviour for us to be at all certain that if rural investment is discouraged at one point in time, it can be induced by government action at another point in time when the economic climate is less favourable.

Commodity stabilization schemes do have income-stabilizing potentialities which are understandably attractive to under-developed economies. However, Australian experience raises doubts whether their advantages in this direction, at least in advanced countries, outweigh their disadvantages in disrupting the resource-allocating function of market prices and their tendency to inhibit economic growth. In such economies problems of economic stability can usually be taken care of more efficaciously through other fiscal devices which have less adverse side-effects on the rural industries. Admittedly the extent of the side-effects varies from scheme to scheme. Much depends on the specific provisions of the particular scheme, the relation of the stabilized price to the free market price, the elasticity of supply, and whether similar schemes operate for competing products.

Given the variety of forms of public policy with respect to agriculture which are blessed with the name "stabilization scheme," and the variety of circumstances in which they are operated, it is patently impossible to make any sweeping judgements about them. However, there is clearly a need for more rigorous examination of the assumptions about rural production and investment behaviour upon which many of these schemes have been based. It needs also to be recognized that in the real world such schemes are particularly vulnerable to political interference and administrative ineptitude, and this tends to reduce substantially any potential usefulness they may have as techniques of economic policy.

7

Tasks and Results of International Co-operation in Agricultural Economics

C. von DIETZE
Freiburg University, Federal Republic of Germany

H. C. AND A. D. TAYLOR'S *Story of Agricultural Economics* [1]* begins with the economic thinking aroused by the agricultural depression of the 1890's. Henry Taylor himself set an example for international co-operation in agricultural economics. He completed his
training in Great Britain and in Germany before becoming the first
professor of agricultural economics in a United States land-grant institution and writing the first American textbook on this subject.
Throughout his life he remained in close contact with agricultural
economists in many countries all over the world.

Similar personal relations with foreign economists go back many
years. Adam Smith, before publishing *The Wealth of Nations,* got
in touch with the physiocrats in France. Generally, with or without
meeting their foreign colleagues, economists have made ample use of
their publications. Apart from these two forms of individual international co-operation, organized forms have come into being only since
the beginning of this century, most of them between governments and
their delegations. As distinct from such organizations, the International Association of Agricultural Economists is composed principally
of individual members.

For a clear understanding of the modern sense of agricultural
economics, it will be helpful to see what the term *oeconomia* meant
up to the 18th century. Deliberately, I use this Greek word in its Latin
spelling. For I want to explain its sense during the centuries when

---

* Numerals within brackets indicate references at the end of the chapter.

Latin was the common language of European scholars. To them, a human household was a *microcosmos* whose order had to reflect the design God had conceived for the whole *macrocosmos*. For this design, since the days of Tertullian, the term *oeconomia* was used. Neither Cato, in the second century B.C., nor the writers of the middle ages or of the 17th century, considered a country household to be absolutely self-sufficient. But they were far from thinking or advocating that it should be organized according to the chances of markets. J. J. Becher, a famous Austrian author of the 17th century, had in mind an *Oeconomia ruralis et domestica* including a prayer book and a cookery book. [2].

Since the 18th century, agriculture has been looked upon as interwoven into a national or even a world-wide division of labour requiring a continual adaptation to market conditions. Later, agricultural economics in a modern sense came into being as a branch of science which has to deal with the economic problems facing individual farmers in their business, as well as with the measures of governments affecting agriculture. On a national basis, societies or academies were created for an exchange of ideas and experiences. But international co-operation was left to the initiative of individuals.

Adam Smith's system of economic thought including his views on agrarian problems spread to many countries. In Germany, Ch. J. Kraus [3], friend and colleague of Immanuel Kant at the University of Königsberg, handed it over to the rising generation of the Prussian administration. As late as 1896, A. Meitzen conceived his work on *Agrarpolitik* [4] on Smithian lines, using even headlines reminding us of the "discouragement of agriculture" [5]. Albrecht Thaer, at the beginning of the 19th century, informed his country of the agricultural ideas and methods with which he had acquainted himself in England before publishing the *Grundsätze der rationellen Landwirtschaft* [6], by which he became the father of agricultural economics in Germany. W. Roscher, though one of the inaugurators of the historical school of economics as opposed to the classical school of Adam Smith and his followers, in his *Nationalökonomik des Ackerbaus* [7] demonstrated a wonderfully comprehensive knowledge of English and French agricultural and economic literature. But nothing is known of his personal relations with economists in Great Britain or France. In comparison with Roscher, A. Buchenberger, in his important work *Agrarwesen und Agrarpolitik* [8], made little use of foreign publications. He combined great experience in agricultural administration with valuable research work and a scholarly approach to the problems. But the problems had already become so manifold and complicated, and the literature had grown so enormously, that any one man had great difficulty in knowing all the national authors on his subject, much less the foreign writings.

This difficulty was greatest with the authors writing in a less accessible language, such as Finnish, Swedish, Danish, Dutch, or even Italian. Unfortunately, the influence agricultural economists exercised on the concepts and teaching of their colleagues in foreign countries, so far, have been investigated only in a few directions. The Taylors, in the *Story of Agricultural Economics* [1], have traced the British or German background of United States economists merely occasionally. To S. v. Frauendorfer we owe an instructive book on the development of agricultural economics in Italy [9]. The big volumes which he and H. Haushofer have published on *Ideengeschichte der Agrarwirtschaft und Agrarpolitik* [10] confine themselves to German-speaking countries. We are fortunate to have a study of the development of *Agrarpolitik* in Hungary [11]. A similar study for Norway is on the way. It would be most interesting and valuable to see on which background the conceptions of agricultural economics have been developed in other countries, such as Japan or India. But an internationally comprehensive story of agricultural economics has not yet been written. Only one more instance of the influence which individual scholars in agricultural economics have received and exercised in the vast international field may be given.

M. Sering became a leading *Agrarpolitiker* after having studied and analysed *Die Landwirtschaftliche Konkurrenz Nordamerikas* (1887) [12]. Up to 1914, he was almost fully engaged in national land tenure and price problems. Of course he remained in personal contact with many foreign economists. But it was his work in explaining and fighting the international agricultural depression of the early twenties [13] which gave him the greatest impulse to renew and to expand international co-operation. So, when the International Conference of Agricultural Economists was founded in 1930, Sering became one of its vice-presidents. In his domestic work he had already ceased to act according to a *bon mot* of F. Aereboe, the most influential reformer of *Landwirtschaftliche Betriebslehre* [14] in Germany, who said that a good scholar in agricultural economics wants no more than an enlightened head and a girl secretary. Sering also took great interest in the growing work of organized co-operation in agricultural economics.

The first institution of that kind was the International Institute of Agriculture at Rome, founded in 1905 on the initiative of the American Granger, D. Lubin. Forty governments, amongst them all the Great Powers, became members of the Institute from the beginning. It embarked on collecting and publishing statistical and technological data, and agricultural legislation. Its Year-books, Reviews, and Monthly Bulletins became an indispensable source of information. A few years before it ceased to exist, it reached the climax of its contributions towards raising the standard of agricultural economics by publishing a most valuable book, *World Trade in Agricultural Products. Its Growth; its Crisis; and the New Trade Policies*

[15]. Unfortunately, this admirable publication, owing to the out-break of World War II, did not raise as much interest and appreciation as it fully deserved. The authors were Miss L. Bacon (from the United States) and F. Schloemer (from Germany).

The tasks of the International Institute were taken over by the Food and Agriculture Organization (F.A.O.) of the United Nations which has considerably extended its activities [16]. Though its economics department is not so large as the technical department, it comprises a great number of agricultural economists from a good many of the 104 (1962) member states. The *Production* and *Trade Yearbook*, the annual reports on *The State of Food and Agriculture,* the *Bulletins* and *Studies* give an enormous amount of valuable information. The special land tenure and settlement branch is also worth mentioning. From it member governments can get experts on land reform or advice on land tenure legislation.

Meanwhile, governments also joined in promoting international co-operation in agricultural economics for certain parts of the world, within the frame of organizations created for a far greater range of economic problems, particularly for Europe. The United Nations' Economic Commission for Europe (E.C.E.) at Geneva has, in its agriculture division, a joint E.C.E./F.A.O. secretariat. Other important instances are the Organization of European Economic Co-operation (O.E.E.C.) and the European Economic Community (E.E.C.). All of them make use of the statistical and other information presented by the F.A.O. So do the contracting parties to the General Agreement on Tariffs and Trade (G.A.T.T.).

The E.C.E./F.A.O. secretariat [17] entrusted one of its early studies to "an independent scholar of outstanding qualifications." The contracting parties to the G.A.T.T. [18], in 1957, commissioned four well-known experts (R. de Oliveira Campos from Brazil, G. Haberler from the United States, J. Meade from England, and J. Tinbergen from the Netherlands) to report on trends in international trade. In most cases, the publications are prepared within the branches of the various international organizations concerned.

Within the O.E.E.C. (since 1961: O.E.C.D.) [19], the European Productivity Agency has a special agricultural department. It takes its share in performing the general tasks of the O.E.E.C., i.e. to act as a clearing house for the exchange of scientific experiences, as a study centre and as a "brains trust." The plans and programmes for its studies have to be approved by the delegates of the member governments. Up to 1955, the greatest weight was given to technical problems suitable for raising agricultural production. Since then, economic problems—such as marketing agricultural products—and agricultural policies have found increased consideration. Of this change the publications [20] give good evidence, particularly the reports on agricultural policies in Europe and North America.

The E.E.C. having embraced agriculture and trade in agricultural products, and having started a common agricultural policy, was bound to organize the co-operation of agricultural economists in the member countries. Quite a number are permanently engaged in the European Commission at Brussels, others are invited for special tasks. The reports of the Commission show a high degree of common agreement in evaluating the agricultural situation and its prospects, and in making proposals for common agricultural policy. Such differences of opinion as exist between the member governments (e.g. as to the future level of grain prices) are not based, as a rule, on different conceptions of agricultural economics. The common agricultural policy has to do not only with markets and prices, but also with improvements of the agrarian structure. So have the reports of the Commission [21]. Thus, common tasks of far-reaching, most practical importance bring about a co-operation between agricultural economists much closer than is found in other international organizations which have to bear fewer actual responsibilities. That has a clearly perceptible, favourable influence on the interchange of views, and on the mutual understanding of conceptions and methods. Such an understanding can be expected, of course, essentially between economists of the western world. Conditions for its development are most favourable not only where the economists are united in a common responsibility for advocating agricultural policies, but also in an association which is perfectly independent of governments.

When, in 1930, the International Conference of Agricultural Economists adopted its constitution at Cornell, it was the first organization of international co-operation in this field consisting of individual members, not of delegates. Since then, other international associations based on individual membership have arisen, e.g. the European Society of Rural Sociologists. A good many persons are members of both. For the International Conference (now the International Association) of Agricultural Economists has, from the beginning, had a wide understanding of its object. The Constitution mentions not only "fostering development of the science of agricultural economics," but also "the improvement of economic and social conditions relating to agriculture and rural life."

For achieving such a far-reaching object it was necessary, first of all, to find qualified members from all important countries, to get them to meet each other, and to help them to understand each other. When the late Vice-President, G. F. Warren, presented the Cowbell to the President, he said that the tongue of this bell was the only one all the members of the International Conference could understand. These words applied not only to the multitude of languages, but also to the lack of a common scientific terminology in economics which was to be felt between economists of every single country, and all the more in international discussions. Important terms, such as "Agrarverfassung" or "Agrarpolitik," "Land Tenure" or "Agricultural Policy," "Bauer" and "Peasant" cannot be translated without changing their meanings. Even the words "Agricultural Economics" are used with quite different understandings of their range. Attempts to secure an unmistakable mutual understanding by carefully elaborated, obligatory definitions such as the *Handbook of Definitions and Methods* of the E.C.E./F.A.O. secretariat [17], could be useful for statistics and for some purposes of limited range. But for the wide and heterogeneous field of the International Conference, they could bear little fruit. The Conference, quite successfully, followed the device: *primum vivere, deinde philosophari*. Its *Proceedings* show a remarkable improvement achieved by close personal contacts and common work.

The first conferences produced a good many papers without systematic coherence, and frequently the discussions were at cross purposes. But after 1934 a noticeable development took place. Well-prepared papers were devoted to a few main topics of general importance.

Each of the last three conferences had only one main theme. The headings show a progress towards tackling problems which require a high degree of common background, as the following brief summary may show:

1934: The international depression and the measures to combat it.
Social and economic aspects of farm organizations.

1936: Relations of agriculture to industry and the community.
Relations of land tenure to the economic and social development of agriculture.
Farm organization with special reference to the needs of technical, industrial, and economic development of agriculture.

1938: The social implications of economic progress in present-day agriculture.
Land tenure and social control in the use of land.
Farm labour and social standards.
International trade in relation to agricultural development.

1947: The movement of farm population.
The flexibility of land tenure, capital, and credit systems to meet technical, economic, and social developments.
Effectiveness of market mechanism for adjusting farming to public need.
The place of state buying and selling in free world trading.
The human satisfaction of rural work and rural living.

1949: Diagnosis and pathology of peasant farming.
Agricultural co-operation and the modern state.
The spread of industry into rural areas.

1952: The economics of population and food supplies.
Long-term objectives in land tenure.

1955: The problems of technical change in agriculture.

1958: Agriculture and its terms of trade.

1961: The role of agriculture in economic development.

The *International Journal of Agrarian Affairs,* edited on behalf of the International Conference, has become important for preparing the conferences. The publication of several articles pertinent to the theme of the 1961 Conference, in good time before its opening, was particularly useful.

The progress made in finding an adequate scientific standard for doing justice to all the problems discussed has been acknowledged in the literature reviewing and evaluating the proceedings [22]. Such progress could not have been achieved without the very existence of the International Conference. Moreover, the spirit in which it was founded and guided had a decisive share in the results of this kind of international co-operation.

The International Conference provided a platform for personal relations between agricultural economists from all parts of the world. In innumerable cases it led to sincere friendship which survived political tensions and hostilities. It was the basis for continuing the work of the Conference after World War II.

No doubt, the principle of individual membership was and is essential. It is in danger where agricultural economists do not speak and act on their own responsibility but on behalf of governments or political parties. Of course differences of political views and of philosophy will always exist, and it would be ridiculous to condemn or to overlook them. They will certainly affect the ideas and the programmes for which agricultural economists stand. But in co-operation in a scientific field the members must be able to trust each other's sincerity and veracity.

Anyhow, some common values and convictions are indispensable for satisfactory results in international co-operation. "Fostering development of the science of agricultural economics" is not an end in itself. Certainly it was not so for the Founder-President of the Conference when he planned and when he guided this organization. For him, as we all felt and as he manifested in his presidential addresses a good many times, international co-operation in agricultural economics has to serve humanity. It is a genuinely ethical motive which prompted his acts and his attitude. The International Conference could and will do valuable work so far as such an ethical impulse was and will be effective.

This experience may be considered in regard to the old conception of *oeconomia* as a subdivision of ethics. Modern scientific methods have more or less banned the ethical aspects from the discussion of economic problems. But they cannot deny the fundamental importance of ethics for human life. Even co-operation in solving purely economic problems, though serving the development of science by eliminating all non-economic aspects, depends on the acknowledgement and the observance of ethical obligations.

REFERENCES

1. Taylor, H. C. and A. D., *The Story of Agricultural Economics in the United States, 1840–1932,* Iowa State Univ. Press, Ames, 1952.
2. Brunner, O., "Die alteuropäische Ökonomik." *Zeitschrift für National-ökonomie,* Bd. XIII, Wien, 1952.
3. Kraus, Ch. J., *Staatswirtschaft,* Bd. 1–4, 1808.
4. Meitzen, A., "Agrarpolitik im engeren Sinne." In: G. v. Schönberg, *Handbuch der Politischen Ökonomie.* 4. Aufl. Bd. II, Tübingen, 1896.
5. Smith, A., *Wealth of Nations,* Book III, Chap. II, 1776.
6. Thaer, A. D., *Grundsätze der rationellen Landwirtschaft.* Berlin, 1809–12
7. Roscher, W., *Nationalökonomik des Ackerbaus und der verwandten Ur-produktionen* (Bd. II, des System der Volkswirtschaft). Stuttgart, 1859, 14. Aufl. Stuttgart, 1903.
8. Buchenberger, A., *Agrarwesen und Agrarpolitik* (A. Wagner, *Lehr-und Handmuch der Politischen Ökonomie,* Dritte Hauptabteilung, Zweiter Teil). Leipzig, 1892–93.
9. v. Frauendorfer, S., *Agrarwirtschaftliche Forschung nd Agrarpolitik in Italien.* Berlin, 1942.
10. ———, and Haushofer, H., *Ideengeschichte der Agrarwirtschaft und Agrarpolitik im deutschen Sprachgebiet.* München, Bonn, Wien, 1957–58.
11. Schriffert, A. M., *Agrarpolitik als Wissenschaft in Ungarn.* Dissertation, Jena, 1933.
12. Sering, M., *Die Landwirtschaftliche Konkurrenz Nordamerikas in Gegenwart und Zukunft.* Leipzig, 1887.
13. ———, *Agrarkrisen und Agrarzölle.* Berlin und Leipzig, 1925. "Internationale Preisbewegung und Lage der Landwirtschaft in den aussertropischen Ländern." *Berichte über Landwirtschaft:* N. F. Sonderheft 11. Berlin, 1929.
14. Aereboe, F., *Allgemeine Landwirtschaftliche Betriebslehre.* Berlin, 1917.
15. Bacon, L. B., and Schloemer, F. C., *World Trade in Agricultural Products. Its Growth; its Crisis; and the New Trade Policies.* International Institute of Agriculture, Rome, 1940.
16. Newiger, N., "Die FAO und ihr Beitrag zur Lösung des Welternährungs Problems," in *Das Weltagrarproblem.* H. 77 der "Offenen Welt." Köln und Opladen, 1962.
17. Publications of the E.C.E./F.A.O. Secretariat:
    Growth and Stagnation in the European Economy. Geneva, 1954.
    A Handbook of Definitions and Methods. Geneva, December, 1956.
    Output, Expenses and Income of Agriculture in some European Countries. 3. Reports. Geneva, 1953 to 1958.
    Towards a Capital Intensive Agriculture (4th Report on Output, Expenses and Income in Agriculture, Part I and II). Geneva, 1961.
    Review of the Agricultural Situation in Europe at the End of 1960. Geneva, 1961.
    European Agriculture in 1965. Geneva, 1961.
18. Publications of the G.A.T.T.:
    Trends in International Trade (The Haberler Report). Geneva, October, 1958.
    Deutsche Ausgabe:
    Entwicklungstendenzen im Internationalen Handel. Berlin, 1959.
    International Trade 1961. Geneva, September 1962.

19. Krohn, H.-B., "Gedanken über die Tätigkeit internationaler Organisationen auf dem Gebiet der angewandten agrarwirtschaftlichen Forschung." *Berichte über Landwirtschaft.* Bd. 36, Hamburg u. Berlin, 1958.
20. O.E.E.C.: Reports on Agricultural Policies in Europe and North America.
   1. Report: *Agricultural Policies in Europe and North America.* Paris, 1956.
   2. Report: *Price and Income Policies.* Paris, 1957.
   3. Report: *Agricultural Policies in Europe and North America.* Paris, 1958.
   4. Report: Vol. I: *Further Problems in Agricultural Policies.* Paris, 1960.
            Vol. II: *Problems in Dairy Policy.* Paris, 1960.
   5. Report: *Trends in Agricultural Policies since 1955.* Paris, 1961.
21. Krohn, H.-B., and Schmitt, G., *Agrarpolitik für Europa.* Agrarwirtschaft Sonderheft 15. Hannover, 1962.
   Th. Dams, "Daten und Überlegungen zur Agrarstrukturpolitik in der Europäischen Wirtschaftsgemeinschaft." In: *Forschungs-und Sitzungsberichte der Akademie für Raumforschung und Landesplanung.* Bd. XX: "Die Landwirtschaft in der Europäichen Wirtschaftsgemeinschaft," 3. Teil. Hannover, 1962.
22. *Cf.* for Germany:
   Schimanski, Fr. W., *Wesen und Bedeutung der bäuerlichen Familienwirtschaft in den Arbeiten der Internationalen Konferenz für Agrarwissenschaft.* Freiburger Dissertation, 1951.
   Niehaus, H., "Probleme der Bauernwirtschaft im internationalen Urteil." *Berichte über Landwirtschaft:* N. F. Bd. 30, Hamburg u. Berlin, 1952.
   v. Dietze, C., "Agrarwirtschaft und Agrarverfassung," *Agrarwirtschaft,* 1953. Dams, Th., "Landwirtschaft und technischer Fortschritt." *Berichte über Landwirtschaft:* N. F. Bd. 33, Hamburg und Berlin, 1955.
   Weinschenck, G., "Die Landwirtschaft und ihre Terms of Trade." *Agrarwirtschaft,* 1959.
   Ringer, K., "Die Rolle der Landwirtschaft in der wirtschaftlichen Entwicklung." *Berichte über Landwirtschaft:* N. F. Bd. 40, Hamburg und Berlin, 1962.

8

The Agricultural Economist and Peasant Farming in Tropical Conditions

DAVID T. EDWARDS
Economics Department, University of the West Indies
and
A. M. MORGAN REES
Agricultural Economics Department, North of Scotland College of Agriculture, Aberdeen, Scotland

"There is much to be done to make the peasant ideal a reality and to give it a sound economic base. . . . The problem is basic . . . in agriculture over most of the world."
—L. K. Elmhirst, President's Address to the International Conference of Agricultural Economists, 1949.

PEASANT FARMING IS CHARACTERIZED by the following features: small scale of operations; heavy reliance on human labour provided mainly by the peasant and members of the family, and assisted in some systems by animal and mechanical power; use of traditional ("backward") techniques and a strongly conservative attitude towards innovation; individual rather than co-operative or collective cultivation of land; and a significant concentration on production for home consumption.

The huge area bounded by the tropics of Cancer and Capricorn is estimated to include 53 per cent of the world's land capable of supporting the production of major food crops,[1] and contains a wide range of natural conditions.[2] Thus, of the approximately 16.8 million square miles of land capable of producing major food crops in the tropics, about 5.3 million have such low rainfall as to present an ex-

[1] Merrill K. Bennett, "A World Map of Food Crop Climates," *Food Research Institute Studies*, Vol. I, No. 3, Nov. 1960, p. 294.
[2] John Phillips, *The Development of Agriculture and Forestry in the Tropics: Patterns, Problems and Promise*, Faber & Faber, London, 1961.

[73]

tremely high hazard to food crop production, another 3.7 million suffer from the other extreme hazard of heavy rainfall and flood, while the remaining area of 7.8 million have a supply of rainfall which is neither excessive nor inadequate.[3]

The varied natural, social, and economic conditions encountered within the tropics have combined to produce extremely varied systems of food production. Within the tropical areas of the Americas, Africa, Asia, and Oceania the systems vary from the most primitive food collecting to highly scientific mechanized farming. Many of the food production systems do not fall within the class *peasant farming.* Examples of some of those excluded are: food-gatherers of various kinds, nomadic herders, co-operative and collective farming systems, plantation agriculture, and ranching. The peasant farming which remains is itself diversified. This may best be illustrated by reference to a number of examples of peasant farming.

The extensive use of land in some systems of shifting cultivation, such as the Chitimene system of Northern Rhodesia in which one peasant family gradually works over about 200 acres of land,[4] may be contrasted with the intensive and continuous use of a few acres of land by the Asian peasant growing rice under irrigation. Some peasant farmers, including many in the West Indies, concentrate heavily on the production of crops for export and buy much of their food, while peasants in some parts of Africa, for instance the Barotse, are much closer to being purely subsistence farmers. Most peasant farming systems employ primitive hand methods of cultivation, but some systems (e.g. Plateau Tonga maize growing) employ some ox-drawn or mechanical equipment, while others have rapidly adopted modern techniques as, for example, in growing cotton in the Gezira.

Although difficult to measure in quantitative terms, the importance of peasant farming in the tropics is indisputable in relation to the population it supports, the resources it employs, and the output it produces.[5]

*   *   *   *   *

There follows a brief review of the history of agricultural economics in relation to tropical agriculture and the peasant farmer; a discussion of the characteristics of the peasant farmer and his farming insofar as they create field problems for the agricultural economist, and an appraisal of the performance of peasant farming; and, finally, a consideration of the future of peasant farming and of the agricultural economist in the tropics.

A chapter such as this calls mainly for the use of bold strokes on a

[3] Bennett, *op. cit.*
[4] Pierre Gourou, *The Tropical World.* Longmans, Green & Co., Ltd., London, 1958, p. 38.
[5] V. D. Wickizer, "The Smallholder in Tropical Export Crop Production," *Food Research Institute Studies,* Vol. I, No. 1, Feb. 1960.

large canvas, though some parts of the picture need more detailed attention. Naturally, the discussion draws on the personal knowledge and experience of the authors (in Central Africa and the West Indies) as well as on studies by other workers. The considerable volume of work undertaken by agricultural economists in India and work in the former Dutch, Belgian and French colonial territories is not directly discussed, though the chapter has relevance for peasant farming throughout the tropics and even in the under-developed countries of the temperate regions.

THE DEVELOPMENT OF AGRICULTURAL ECONOMICS IN RELATION TO TROPICAL AGRICULTURE WITH PARTICULAR REFERENCE TO BRITISH EXPERIENCE

The fostering of the development of agriculture in the tropics by the colonial powers can be attributed, in its earlier phases, largely to the planter and to private enterprise. The twentieth century, however, has seen a major contribution being made in this field by the public service. With the opening up of areas which offered little attraction to European planters, it became apparent that agricultural development could best be fostered through the indigenous peasant farmers. Thus, in order to encourage the development of peasant farming in the tropics, a public agricultural service came into being. The first appointment of a director of agriculture in a British colonial territory was made in 1896,[6] and during the period from the turn of the century to 1914 most of the larger British colonial territories established departments of agriculture, in some cases the new establishments being based on the expansion of existing botanic gardens. However, staffs were small and often were composed largely of unqualified officers. It was only after World War I that attention was focussed on the fact that an almost virgin field for economic development was constituted by the mass of peasant farmers in the tropical territories. An increase in the agricultural staff was recommended by a committee appointed to examine and report on the agricultural services of the colonies.

Although it was appreciated that agricultural science had much to contribute to the development of peasant farming in the tropics, the growth of departments of agriculture during the inter-war years was often impeded by financial difficulties. In 1935 the unified Colonial Agricultural Service and Colonial Veterinary Service came into being covering both field staff and specialist research staff who possessed university qualifications. By 1939 the number of posts in these two services was 379 in the Colonial Agricultural Service and 125 in the Colonial Veterinary Service.[7] After World War II, with the

---

[6] See: G. B. Masefield, *A Short History of Agriculture in the British Colonies.* Oxford Univ. Press, London, 1950.

[7] Masefield, *op. cit.*

awakening interest in colonial development and with more funds being available for agricultural development and research, there was an increasing demand for trained agriculturists and specialist officers. Thus, "whereas between 1925 and 1945 a total of 314 graduates in agriculture, horticulture and natural sciences received post-graduate training and were appointed to the Colonial Agricultural Service, in the 12 years 1946 to 1958 more than 450 were recruited, trained and appointed."[8]

A parallel can be drawn between the tropics and the temperate countries in relation to the development of agricultural economics. The study of agricultural economics in the temperate countries has been of only recent growth, the main foundations having been laid in the United States at the beginning of this century. In Great Britain, agricultural economics as a recognized field of activity is even younger, and it is only since the founding of the Institute for Research in Agricultural Economics at Oxford in 1913 that the subject has been accorded recognition at the academic level. The general agriculturist and specialists in the various agricultural sciences made their appearance long before the agricultural economist came on the scene in the temperate countries. The same is true of the tropics.

The vast majority of officers who were appointed to the Colonial Agricultural Service were general agriculturists; some were specialists, but it was extremely rare for the speciality to be agricultural economics. Most graduate recruits in the agricultural field were given two years post-graduate training, the first year of which was usually spent at Cambridge, and the second at the Imperial College of Tropical Agriculture in Trinidad. The personnel of the Colonial Agricultural Service generally had received little training in agricultural economics and farm management, while the number of officers who were recruited specifically as agricultural economists was extremely small. It is unlikely that by 1955 the cumulative total exceeded one dozen. Some departments of agriculture have never employed specialist agricultural economists, while others have generally relied upon a single specialist to serve the needs of a large country. Amongst those territories where specialists in this field have been employed are Kenya, Malaya, Northern Rhodesia, Uganda, British Guiana, and Jamaica. It is only in very recent years that relatively large numbers of agricultural economists have been employed in any territory. Thus, in Jamaica the Ministry of Agriculture and Lands now has a complement of eighteen agricultural economists and statisticians.[9]

It is surprising perhaps that a greater interest in the economics of tropical agriculture did not develop earlier, especially as there were signs of awakening interest from time to time. Even as early as

---

[8] G. W. Nye, "Training for Colonial Agricultural Services," *Span.* Shell International Chemical Co., Ltd., London, April 1959.

[9] The only other Department employing a large number of agricultural economists in a British colony, or in a newly independent or emerging British territory, is the Federation of Rhodesia and Nyassaland, where the Department primarily serves non-peasant agriculture.

1929 the chairman of the Agricultural Economics Committee of the Empire Marketing Board wrote:[10] ". . . it is clear that while the study of agricultural economics in the Empire is still relatively undeveloped, there is a growing appreciation of the potential advantages to be derived from the development of the science along sound lines."

The paucity of trained agricultural economists in tropical territories has often led the general agriculturist to do work which more normally would be considered that of the specialist agricultural economist. Thus the general agriculturist in the tropics has had to turn his attention to the collection of background information; the undertaking of surveys; the provision of statistical and intelligence data; the investigation of economic problems; the economic evaluation of development projects; price-fixing; and particularly to problems in the field of marketing, generally without the assistance of specialist advice from an agricultural economist. Masefield[11] considered that there has always been the tendency for the work of the Colonial Agricultural Service to become clogged with the supervision of marketing at the expense of the stimulation of production. To combat this problem some territories established marketing or produce departments which, in certain instances, recruited trained agricultural economists. Until relatively recently the lack of expert advice in agricultural economics was not made good by the advice of economists in the general administration of the territories, for even in the few cases where economic advisers were present, they often lacked knowledge of agricultural economics.

Even when a tropical territory has made provision for an agricultural economist on its establishment, it has often been difficult to persuade specialists to forsake the known, familiar conditions and problems of the temperate countries for the unknown ones of the tropics. A case can be cited of a territory where over a period of ten years the established post of agricultural economist was filled for only five years, owing to recruitment difficulties. All too often the professional agricultural economist working in the developed, temperate countries has shown a lack of interest in the problems of tropical agriculture and of peasant farmers in these areas. This widespread lack of interest is illustrated by the following examples. Of the 164 papers which appeared in the Journal of Proceedings of the (British) Agricultural Economics Society between 1928 and 1952[12] only one, entitled, "Agricultural Development in the British Colonial Empire,"[13] could be said to be on tropical agriculture. Again, although certain university

---

[10] F. L. McDougall, Preface to *The Survey Method of Research in Farm Economics*, by J. P. Maxton. Empire Marketing Board, H.M.S.O., London, Jan. 1929.

[11] Masefield, *op. cit.*

[12] Edgar Thomas, Presidential Address, "On the History of the Society," *Journal of the Proceedings of the Agricultural Economics Society*. Vol. X, No. 4, March 1954.

[13] Sir Frank Engledow, "Agricultural Development in the British Colonial Empire," *Journal of the Proceedings of the Agricultural Economics Society*. Vol. VII, No. 4, 1948.

institutions in the temperate countries—such as the Institute for Research in Agricultural Economics, Oxford, the London School of Economics, and a number of European and American centres—have attracted research students in the field of agricultural economics from overseas, the amount of research on tropical agricultural problems undertaken by agricultural economists resident in the temperate countries has been strictly limited. Out of a list recently published of research projects at United Kingdom agricultural economics departments, only 7 out of a total of 205 related to tropical agricultural topics.[14]

Some indication of the numbers of agricultural economists actually working in the tropics can be gained by an examination of the lists of members of the major agricultural economics societies. In 1962 out of a total of 582 members of the (British) Agricultural Economics Society, only 36 had postal addresses in tropical countries.[15, 16] Individual membership of the American Farm Economic Association stood at 646 in 1928, 888 in 1939, and at 3,237 in 1961. For the same years, individual membership located in Central America, South America, Asia, Africa, Hawaii, and Puerto Rico stood at 23, 11, and finally at 327. However, of the 327 members referred to above, whereas 210 were listed in Asia, only 17 were located in Africa. In addition to the individual members, there were 301 *Journal* subscribers (i.e. institutions and organizations) located in the under-developed or tropical areas in 1961, out of a total of 956.[17] On March 31, 1962, the Indian Society of Agricultural Economics had 407 individual members and 122 institution members.[18] Of the individual membership of the International Conference of Agricultural Economists which in 1957–59 numbered 685, only one-sixth were located in tropical countries.[19]

Some discussion has taken place over recent years relating to the training in agricultural economics of students from the under-developed countries.[20] Nicholls[21] has suggested that in the United States ". . . with less than ten doctorates a year being awarded to agricultural economics students from the under-developed countries, our profession is as yet hardly more than scratching the surface in making our own

[14] *Digest of Agricultural Economics*. No. 20, Oxford. April, May, June, 1962.

[15] *Journal of Agricultural Economics*. Vol. XIV, No. 4, Dec. 1962.

[16] *Journal of Agricultural Economics*. Vol. XV, No. 1, May 1962.

[17] *Journal of Farm Economics*. Vol. XLIII, No. 4, Part II, Nov. 1961.

[18] *Indian Journal of Agricultural Economics*. Vol. XVII, No. 1, Jan.-March 1962.

[19] *Proceedings of the Tenth International Conference of Agricultural Economists*. Oxford Univ. Press, 1960.

[20] See, for example: Kenneth A. Parsons, "U. S. Training for Foreign Students in Agricultural Economics." *Journal of Farm Economics*. Vol. XXXIX, No. 2, May 1957.

[21] William H. Nicholls, Presidential Address, Forty-ninth annual meeting of the American Farm Economics Association, "Higher Education and Agricultural Economics: A Critical Appraisal." *Journal of Farm Economics*. Vol. XLII, No. 5, Dec. 1960.

contribution to one of the world's vital training needs." During the post-war period a number of overseas universities and university colleges have been established in the tropics. A number of these have faculties of agriculture, and some teaching and research in agricultural economics has been developed. It is reasonable to assume that these institutions will in time encourage a greater volume of research into the economics of peasant agriculture in the tropics. One can also look forward to the time when persons indigenous to the tropics will be trained in agricultural economics within the tropics instead of in temperate conditions. This will be a considerable advance over the old system of expatriate training, which in any case has not succeeded in the past in supplying the required output of trained agricultural economists.

The Food and Agriculture Organization of the United Nations has provided training for many persons at its training centres in agricultural economics and statistics.[22] Again, the International Co-operation Administration (now the Agency for International Development) of the United States government and private foundations such as the Agricultural Development Council, Inc., of New York[23] have also played important rôles in meeting training needs in the field of agricultural economics in the tropics. In addition to their interest in the field of training, various international organizations, governments of developed countries, and private foundations have provided technical assistance in the field of agricultural economics by the provision of teams of experts or of single consultants. In particular, the tropics have benefited in recent years from the technical assistance of agricultural economists made available under the aegis of the United Nations, particularly by the Food and Agriculture Organization, and the International Bank for Reconstruction and Development.

THE STUDY OF THE PERFORMANCE OF PEASANT FARMING IN THE TROPICS: PROBLEMS AND FINDINGS

Investigating Peasant Farming

The characteristics of peasant farmers and of their farming systems present serious difficulties in the collection of data by agricultural economists. Some of the problems would be greatly mitigated if the agricultural economist were personally acquainted with the systems under study or if the systems had been the subject of previous study. Even so, many difficult problems would remain. Few records are kept about the operations of peasant farming, either by the peasants or by public bodies. This places the burden of providing information on

---

[22] See: Mordecai Ezekiel, "Ten Years of F.A.O. Statistics and Economics Training Centres." *Journal of Farm Economics.* Vol. XXXIX, No. 2, May 1957.
[23] See: *Annual Report of the Council on Economic and Cultural Affairs, Inc. 1961,* New York.

the peasants' judgement and on their recollections, and on what the investigators can see for themselves.

Unfortunately, the widespread natural suspicion of strangers and the lack of interest in and appreciation of the purpose of the research, unless overcome, limit the co-operativeness of the informants. From the point of view of the investigators, the strangeness of the agriculture and the complicated layout and use of land present formidable problems. Before looking at the complications it will be convenient to mention the problems posed by the fact that peasants and research workers tend to differ in their definitions and processes of thought. For example, peasant communities tend to make only limited use of the established official measures of weight, volume, distance, area, and time. Many commonly used measures appear, at first, to be of indeterminate magnitude. For example, quantities of products are quoted in heaps, bundles, and kerosene tins.[24] Conceptual problems are often encountered in relation to rights of ownership and control of land, crops, and livestock and their products. Customary patterns are sometimes not only complicated, but also varied. The total or limited knowledge of the informant's language is another severe disadvantage. The use of interpreters bridges the gap with varying degrees of adequacy.

Not least of the problems are those stemming from the physical features of the land and its use,[25] allied to the nature of the farm business and other related features. The sheer problem of reaching the areas of peasant farming may be formidable owing to difficult topography and poorly developed systems of communication.[26] The crops and livestock under the control of one farmer are not infrequently scattered widely and are probably difficult to identify without his help. Produce is reaped from widely dispersed trees, some being wild, and from fields which are often so irregular in shape as to be extremely difficult to measure accurately. The measurement of the extent of individual crops may be further complicated by the practice of intercropping, while the estimation of production is rendered more difficult by irregular and incomplete harvesting. Yields, even within a small area, are often highly variable owing to the irregularity of rainfall. Many systems of peasant farming are remarkably diversified, especially in relation to their scale. A system may involve a large number of dif-

---

[24] For a discussion of some measures used for agricultural produce in a particular peasant economy see: Sidney W. Mintz, "Standards of Value and Units of Measure in the Fond-des-Negres Market Place, Haiti," *Journal of the Royal Anthropological Institute of Great Britain and Ireland.* Vol. XCI, Part I, Jan. to June 1961.

[25] A valuable discussion of the problems of estimating land use and production under tropical conditions is given in: K. E. Hunt, *Colonial Agricultural Statistics: The Organisation of Field Work* (Colonial Research Publications No. 22). H.M.S.O., London, 1957.

[26] It is sometimes necessary in Jamaica for a peasant on hillside lands to secure himself by means of a rope while cultivating his land.

ferent crops, in some cases as many as twenty or more, albeit on a very small scale. One crop enterprise may comprise no more than a few trees.

The pattern of disposal of the products of the system and their valuation may be far from simple for reasons connected with payment in kind, home consumption of much of the produce, and because of social obligations. The practice of other members of a peasant's household to farm jointly with him and by themselves, makes the tangle even more formidable. It is no exaggeration to say that the concept of a farm may be quite inapplicable to some peasant farming systems.

The agricultural economist, although attempting to stick to his last, soon recognizes and comes to accept the close identity of the farming system with the household activities, and indeed with the peasant's whole life.[27] Recognition of this close relationship is necessary whether the agricultural economist is attempting to gain entrée to the communities of which the peasant farmer is a part, to collect information about the individual farm, or to understand the farming system. For instance, he has to accept the extra-economic valuation of livestock which are sometimes kept for religious reasons or prestige. In the tropics the distinction between peasant farming as a way of life and as a business has emerged only to a limited extent.

In referring to the difficulties of obtaining information about peasant farming there is a danger of giving two misleading impressions: on the one hand that there is no real difference in the problems of getting information from, say, a family farm in Britain or America and from a peasant farmer in the tropics. As the above review has tried to indicate, however, there are important differences both of kind and of extent. Nor does the prospect of diminishing unfamiliarity of the agricultural economist with peasant farming systems, both by virtue of the increasing volume of research and the production of a growing number of local agricultural economists, reduce the problems which have existed and still exist. On the other hand it would be misleading to suggest that it is virtually impossible to obtain any semblance of the truth about the economics of peasant farming through the impenetrable obstacles which surround it. With patience, persistence and ingenuity it is possible to obtain the information necessary, as reference to some of the studies undertaken illustrates. (A select list is given at the end of the chapter.)

Assessing the Performance of Peasant Farming

In assessing the typical agriculture of shifting cultivations in the tropics, Gourou writes:[28] "It takes great pains to respect the natural

---

[27] The problem is well brought out in a recent paper. See: George Dalton, "Traditional Production in Primitive African Economies." *Quarterly Journal of Economics.* Vol. LXXVI, No. 3, Aug. 1962.

[28] Gourou, *op. cit.*, pp. 32, 33.

equilibrium and to interfere as little as possible with the slow, delicate processes by which the soil succeeds in maintaining itself and in keeping a certain degree of fertilization in the special circumstances imposed by the tropical climate . . . . This agricultural system is perfectly rational and manages year after year to produce the food needed for human nourishment. The disasters brought on by agricultural methods which have taken no account of the treasures of wisdom and experience accumulated in the old tropical system are a sufficient proof of the latter's value."

Many authorities would be in substantial agreement with Gourou's views and would probably arrive at similar judgements about many other systems of peasant cultivation in the tropics. They might feel, however, the need to emphasize the real limitations of the systems, owing to their low productivity and consequent inability to support a high population density (under the pressure of which they tend to destroy the fertility of the soil) or any population at a high level of living, judged by the standards of the economically advanced economies. Judgements such as these need to be accompanied by an economic appraisal of the performance of peasant farming. It is not necessary for the peasant to be an "economic man" or his farming to be independent of other parts of the community's life for this to be both possible and useful.

The characteristics of the peasant farm which are of interest to the economist are: a relatively small area under cultivation at any one time; relatively very high applications of labour per acre; generally low investment in and expenditure on off-farm (and particularly manufactured) inputs—most of the capital being in the form of land and its improvements, crops and livestock, and simple structures and tools; yields per acre are generally low;[29] and output per worker is low.

The economic performance of tropical peasant farming can be judged by various standards. One approach is to ask: How well does a peasant farming system achieve the objectives of the peasant, in the light of his resources, and under the conditions in which he operates? It would obviously not be sensible to judge peasant farming's performance on the basis of the assumption that peasants are only concerned to maximize profits and that they have control of unlimited resources. Realistic assumptions would recognize quite limited resources and objectives which commonly place great importance on security and conformity to community norms. The approach implied here is one which does not judge the capacity of peasant farming systems as against other kinds of farming systems, but assesses the performance of peasant farmers under the conditions in which they operate. Applying this criterion, one can say that peasant farming in the past has gener-

---

[29] Aggregate output per acre may be reasonably high under some inter-cropping systems. See D. T. Edwards, *An Economic Study of Small Farming in Jamaica.* University College of the West Indies, Jamaica, 1961.

ally been able to satisfy the relatively simple demands of the peasants. It has also generally represented a rational response to the environment.

Another approach is to examine the historical success or failure of peasant farming. Has it, over a period, proven itself capable of withstanding economic and physical vicissitudes? One is led to a not unfavourable assessment of it in the tropics in terms of its viability and adaptability. It has been able to adjust itself to the introduction of a money economy and to the production of cash crops for market. In many instances new crops and new techniques have been introduced successfully, while the system has been able to survive natural hazards and violent price fluctuations for export crops. In fact, peasant farming in the tropics has exhibited a similar resilience to that displayed by peasant farming in temperate regions.

A third approach is to enquire into the scope for improvement in typical tropical peasant farming systems. Various economic studies which have been conducted point to the variations in efficiency which occur within the same farming system and indicate the tremendous scope which exists for improvement. The same conclusion could be drawn from comparisons of different farming systems in the tropics, and from comparisons of peasant farming systems with larger scale plantation systems occurring under similar natural conditions. These conclusions indicate a real potential for the improvement of technical and economic efficiency of peasant farming in the tropics.

CONCLUSIONS

Hailey, writing in 1938, stated that the African peasant farming economy was almost everywhere in a state of change and that a series of factors were contributing to the break-down of the old framework of social and economic life.[30] Today the pace of change has become even more rapid. Economic, technological, social, and political revolutions have been under way and the peasant farming structure in the tropics has been subjected to greater pressures than ever before. Some of these pressures relate to a changing institutional framework such as that resulting from the break-down of the tribal system and the introduction of individual land ownership. It is not until barriers, such as the form of agrarian structure, have been removed that development and innovation have an opportunity to flourish.

The various economic, social, technical, and institutional changes which are taking place are the products of internal and external pressures. The population explosion, leading to increasing pressure on land; the demand for rising standards of living; the development of non-agricultural activity; the growth of internal markets, particularly in urban centres; the expansion of world demand for tropical agricul-

---

[30] Lord Hailey, *An African Survey: a study of problems arising in Africa south of the Sahara.* Oxford Univ. Press, London, 1938, p. 1431.

tural products; and the increasing competition for outlets on the world market—represent only some of the pressures that have been exerted on the structure of peasant agriculture in the tropics. Fortunately, while these and other pressures have arisen, greater opportunities have also been present to provide some degree of solution. In particular, the greater application of science to the problems encountered and the more widespread diffusion of knowledge have facilitated change.

These changes have resulted in an urgent need for an accelerated movement of tropical peasant farming towards commercial agriculture—away from the subsistence economy and from farming as a way of life towards an orientation of peasant farming as a business geared to a cash economy. This transition is important not only for the sake of the peasant himself but also for assisting in the economic growth and development of other sectors of the national economy and of society as a whole.[31]

Although it would be wrong to suggest that economic principles do not apply to peasant farmers in a non-monetized subsistence economy, the need for economic advice becomes more pressing as well as more obvious with a change towards commercialization.[32] It is as a catalyst in helping to achieve a smooth transition from a backward to a modern economy, and in assisting to maintain the economic viability of the tropical peasant once the transition has been achieved, that the agricultural economist has a vital role to play in the future.[33] Advice is needed both at the level of government policy and at the grass-roots, farm-management level for the assistance of the extension worker. The scope of the agricultural economist has widened as a result of the changes enumerated earlier and he is afforded unusual opportunities for assisting in the development of peasant agriculture in the tropics.[34] Economic advice has to be backed up by an increasing volume of field research. Many of the research studies which have been undertaken into the economics of peasant farming, although they have been essen-

---

[31] The important role of agriculture in relation to the over-all development of the economy is brought out by Bruce F. Johnston and John W. Mellor. "The Nature of Agriculture's Contribution to Economic Development," *Food Research Institute Studies,* Vol. I, No. 3, Nov. 1960.

[32] Today it has become increasingly unnecessary to discuss such issues as whether or not peasant farmers are economically responsive. See: W. O. Jones, "Economic Man in Africa," *Food Research Institute Studies,* Vol. I, No. 2, May 1960.

[33] For a discussion of the need to change beliefs, habits, and institutions and the painful situations which arise during the transition when economic growth is being introduced into societies which have existed at low levels of economic stagnation, see: W. Arthur Lewis, *The Theory of Economic Growth.* George Allen and Unwin, London, pp. 431–35, 1960.

[34] Pasto has drawn attention to the range of opportunities which include participation in development programmes involving radical reorganization of land use and settlement patterns. See: K. Jerome Pasto, "The Role of Farm Management in Underdeveloped Countries," *Journal of Farm Economics,* Vol. XLIII, No. 3, Aug. 1961.

tially descriptive, have provided a useful broad framework of general information, but the need will arise for an increasing number of studies of a more analytical type and with a greater orientation towards the solving of problems.

In conclusion, one can agree with Clayton who has written:[35] "Research into the economics of tropical, peasant farming can be ascribed to a handful of economists and agriculturalists who have worked in isolation and usually with limited resources. Their efforts nevertheless have provided a firm foundation of knowledge on which to base future inquiry." The need for more agricultural economists to serve peasant farming in the tropics is clear. Fortunately, the value of the work so far has won increasing recognition, and this augers well for the future contributions which they can make.[36] It is to be hoped that the international challenge posed to agricultural economists by work in this field will be accepted more readily in the future than it has been in the past.[37]

REFERENCES

(A select list of field studies into the economics of peasant farming conducted by agricultural economists in the tropics.)

Division of Economics and Statistics, Ministry of Agriculture and Lands, Jamaica. *The Economic Organisation of Small-Scale Sugar Cane Farming in the Rio Minho Valley of Upper Clarendon, 1958.* Kingston, 1960.

——, *The Economic Organisation of Small-Scale Sugar Cane Farming in the Rio Minho Valley of Upper Clarendon, 1959.* Kingston, 1961.

——, *The Economic Organisation of Small-Scale Farming Based on Citrus, Ground Provisions and Livestock. Brokenhurst, Manchester, 1958–59.* Kingston, 1962.

——, *The Economic Organisation of Small-Scale Farming in the Brokenhurst Area of Southern Manchester, 1959–60.* Kingston, 1962.

——, *The Economic Organisation of Small-Scale Farming Based on Banana, Coconut and Cocoa. Highgate Area, St. Mary, 1958–59.* Kingston, 1962.

——, *The Economic Organisation of Small-Scale Sugar Cane Farming in the Rio Minho Valley of Upper Clarendon. (An Identical Sample of Farms.) 1958–60.* Kingston, 1963.

Edwards, D. T., "An Economic Study of Agriculture in the Yallahs Valley Area of Jamaica," *Social and Economic Studies,* Vol. III, Nos. 3 & 4, Dec. 1954.

——, *An Economic Study of Small Farming in Jamaica.* University College of the West Indies, Jamaica, 1961.

Galleti, R., Baldwin, K. D. S., and Dina, I. O., *Nigerian Cocoa Farmers. An Economic Survey of Yoruba Cocoa-Farming Families.* Oxford Univ. Press, London, 1956.

---

[35] E. S. Clayton, "Research Methodology and Peasant Agriculture," *The Farm Economist,* Vol. VIII, No. 6, 1956.

[36] See, for instance: *Report of a Conference of Directors and Senior Officers of Overseas Departments of Agriculture and Agricultural Institutions Held at Wye College, Kent, September 1958.* Misc. No. 531, Colonial Office, London, 1958.

[37] See: Lawrence Witt, "Towards an International Dimension in Agricultural Economics," *Journal of Farm Economics,* Vol. XLI, No. 2, May 1959.

86   *Edwards* and *Rees* / Jamaica

Haswell, H. R., *Economics of Agriculture in a Savannah Village*. Colonial Research Studies, No. 8. H.M.S.O., London, 1953.

Hill, Polly, *The Gold Coast Cocoa Farmer. A Preliminary Survey*. Oxford Univ. Press, London, 1956.

Huggins, H. D., "An Economic Survey of Farming in East Demerara," *Agricultural Journal of British Guiana*, Vol. VIII, No. 3, 1937.

———, "An Economic Survey of Rice Farming in West Demerara," *Agricultural Journal of British Guiana*, Vol. XVIII, No. 2, 1941.

———, *An Economic Survey of Dairy Farming in East Demerara*. Department of Agriculture, British Guiana, 1943.

Jolly, A. L., *Peasant Farming in the Bejucal Area of Trinidad*. Government Printing Office, Trinidad, 1945.

———, *An Economic Survey on the La Pastora Land Settlement, Trinidad, May 1944–45*. Government Printing Office, Trinidad, 1946.

———, *Peasant Farming in Two Districts of the Oropouche Lagoon, June 1944–45*. Guardian Commercial Printery, Trinidad, 1949.

Parisinos, C. C., Shepherd, C. Y., and Jolly, A. L., *Peasant Agriculture, An Economic Survey of the Las Lomas District, Trinidad*. Government Printing Office, Trinidad, 1944.

Rees, A. M. Morgan, *An Economic Survey of Plateau Tonga Improved Farmers*. Government Printer, Northern Rhodesia, 1958.

———, and Howard, R. H., *An Economic Survey of Commercial African Farming Among the Sala of the Mumbwa District of Northern Rhodesia*. Government Printer, Northern Rhodesia, 1955.

Shepherd, C. Y., *Peasant Agriculture in the Leeward and Windward Islands*. (Publishers not specified), 1945.

9

Resource Use and Productivity in Portuguese Agriculture

FERNANDO ESTÁCIO

Centre for Studies in Agricultural Economics,
Gulbenkian Foundation, Lisbon, Portugal

IN AN ATTEMPT TO STUDY resource use and productivity in Portuguese agriculture we have applied the method used by Bhattacharjee for world agriculture "through the fitting of a single-equation production function to the data of agricultural inputs and outputs for selected countries of the world."[1] This was made possible through having cross-sectional data for the eighteen provinces of our country in 1957.[2] We believe that the theoretical objections to the validity of expressing the input-output relationship in agricultural production of a single country by a single equation are removed, since one similar function could be justified "for the agriculture of the world wherein the different countries are like the farms within a nation." In the present chapter, the different provinces of our country take the place of farms in the usual studies for which agricultural production functions are fitted. However, we must recognize that the problems of aggregation involved in such a global type of function lead us to use the greatest caution when interpreting the results.

[1] Jyoti P. Bhattacharjee, "Resource Use and Productivity in World Agriculture," *Journal of Farm Economics.* Vol. XXXVII, No. 1, pp. 57–71, Feb. 1955.

[2] E. Castro Caldas, and M. S. Loureiro, *Niveis de Desenvolvimento Agricolano Continente Português.* Centro de Estudos de Economia Agraria du Fundação Calouste Gulbenkian, Lisbon, 1963.

THE PRODUCTION EQUATION

The single equation used in this chapter to explain agricultural output from a group of resource inputs will be of the Cobb-Douglas type,

$$Y = A \, X_1^{b_1} X_2^{b_2} \cdots X_n^{b_n}$$

or, in logarithms,

$$\log Y = \log A + b_1 \log X_1 + b_2 \log X_2 + \cdots + b_n \log X_n.$$

The advantages of this type of function are well known and its discussion has no place here. It must be noted only that, by fitting such a function, our main purpose is to calculate directly the elasticities of production and the marginal productivities of the different inputs.

The Dependent Variable

The dependent variable Y in our production equation stands for Portuguese agricultural output in its broader sense, that is to say, it includes not only crop, pasture, and livestock production but also forest, fishing, and wildlife production. Really, as Lamartine Yates pointed out for Portugal, "important sidelines for some farmers are cork from the forest and, on the coast, fishing." [3] On the other hand, almost all the farms of the north mountainous part of the country must be considered as mixed agriculture and forestry and, in the south, cork production and a very peculiar swine production associated with holm-oaks and cork-oaks must be included in farm production. It is therefore difficult to split up inputs and outputs between agriculture and forestry.

The Independent Variables

Statistical data of people employed in general agricultural occupations in each province were utilized as the human resource input, measured by X_1 in the production equation, merely by reasons of availability. In fact, for well-known reasons, this is not an accurate measure of the labour really used in agriculture, especially where under-employment occurs as it does in some parts of our country. Data on the quality of human resource, such as managerial and entrepreneurial ability, are not available and so were not considered in our equation, though the influence of human resource may change whenever quality can be introduced.

The natural resources used in agriculture are land and climate. In order to measure land as a single input we must find a system of

---

[3] P. Lamartine Yates, *Food, Land and Manpower in Western Europe*. Macmillan & Co., Ltd., London, 1960, pp. 130–31.

weighting land classes according to their different types of utilization which correspond to wide variations in productivity. The most important land classes to be considered in our case are arable land, vineyards, olive yards, and forests. The acreage of natural pasture is not significant as is generally the case in Mediterranean countries owing to unfavourable climatic conditions. Statistical data concerning the average productivities of these classes of land are available expressed in gross incomes. It is possible, therefore, to convert the different categories of agricultural land into "standard agricultural land" by using those productivities as weights. This will be the independent variable X_2 in the equation.

Turning to climate, conditions are quite different from the north to the south of the country. To each province, a weighted input based on the *Thornthwaite climate index* is expressed by the variable X_3. Material resources, such as fertilizers, livestock, and tractors, for which statistics are available, are considered as a measure of inputs that can be grouped under the wide designation of capital resources.

The variable X_4 measures only the input of chemical fertilizers in an aggregative way; the consumption of manure and natural fertilizers was left out since accurate statistical data are not available. As

TABLE 9.1

STATISTICS OF AGRICULTURAL OUTPUT AND AGRICULTURAL RESOURCE INPUTS
IN DIFFERENT PROVINCES OR DISTRICTS

Provinces or Districts	Agricultural Output Y	Population in Agriculture X_1	Standard Agricultural Land X_2	Climate Weighted Index X_3	Fertilizers X_4	Productive Livestock X_5	Tractors X_6
	(million escudos)	(000)	(000 hectares)		(million escudos)	(000 units)	(million escudos)
Aveiro	748	68.6	248.9	65.80	45.47	105.5	3.5
Beja	1,030	78.1	1,029.3	19.71	63.58	138.4	136.2
Braga	736	87.8	205.5	79.80	19.31	119.4	2.2
Bragança	607	55.1	368.7	43.03	38.32	96.4	4.7
Castelo Branco	567	58.9	537.8	50.83	13.31	128.4	11.3
Coimbra	696	77.8	336.4	52.76	56.73	95.1	5.3
Evora	941	54.7	740.7	27.21	48.24	123.1	76.2
Faro	723	61.3	422.2	23.52	35.85	45.9	21.1
Guarda	566	60.4	310.1	46.19	35.86	102.2	2.8
Leiria	786	71.2	367.0	49.96	50.80	79.8	11.5
Lisboa	872	78.1	358.0	25.92	48.81	55.5	101.6
Portalegre	845	50.6	594.3	26.48	38.10	123.4	44.3
Porto	928	88.8	194.0	74.47	33.27	112.7	4.2
Santarém	1,341	104.5	740.1	37.13	65.66	99.7	75.9
Setúbal	706	46.7	458.3	23.85	33.04	57.3	60.5
Viana do Castelo	429	54.8	112.0	80.00	8.70	96.0	1.7
Vila Real	630	79.0	262.3	62.83	20.06	86.1	2.2
Viseu	903	106.6	400.0	66.43	17.57	134.5	1.0

TABLE 9.2
VALUES OF THE REGRESSION COEFFICIENTS AND MEASURES OF THE RELIABILITY OF THE PRODUCTION EQUATIONS

	Symbol of Coefficients	Values of Coefficients in Different Production Equations			
		I	II	III	IV
Population in agriculture: X_1	b_1	0.558533*	0.633023	0.670683	0.631235*
Land (standard agricultural land): X_2	b_2	0.211074†	0.156882	0.053428	0.042630
Climate weighted index: X_3	b_3		−0.102767	−0.234978	0.002303
Fertilizers: X_4	b_4	0.164722†	0.141717	0.146893	0.120153§
Productive livestock: X_5	b_5			0.149469	0.128637
Tractors: X_6	b_6				0.082615‡
Sum of the coefficients	Σb_i	0.934329	0.828855	0.785495	1.007573
Constant term (in log)	a	1.057317	1.262537	1.371546	1.080092
Constant term (in real units)	A	11.411053	18.303797	23.526087	12.025208
Correlation coefficients	$\bar{R}$	0.889	0.894	0.902	0.926
	R	0.875	0.870	0.869	0.894
Standard error of estimation	$\bar{S}$	0.057160	0.058172	0.058473	0.053133
Standard error of coefficients:	1	0.133133	0.170789	0.176186	0.161467
b_1	2	0.072984	0.106105	0.153821	0.139892
b_2	3		0.143300	0.201947	0.222734
b_3	4	0.070521	0.078549	0.079155	0.073320
b_4	5			0.160833	0.146566
b_5	6				0.043953
b_6					

* Significant at 1 per cent level
† Significant at 5 per cent level
‡ Significant at 10 per cent level
§ Significant at 16 per cent level

to livestock, it is necessary to separate productive livestock from work stock or draught animals. The former includes cattle, sheep, goats, pigs, and poultry and the latter, horses and mules. In fact, it must be noted that in Portugal, as in many other countries, some kinds of livestock are utilized for multiple purposes. This is particularly important in respect to bovines which are slaughtered after being used for several years as draught animals and very often also as milk producers. In this case they have been included in the productive livestock input. A standard unit of measurement for livestock has been used. The conversion factors for the different kinds of livestock are: 0.8 for milk cows and cattle older than 2 years; 0.7 for cows of mixed function (milk, draught, and beef); 0.5 for calves, steers, and sows; 0.35 for boars; 0.25 for sheep; 0.20 for goats; 0.15 for pig weaners; 0.10 for suckling pigs; 0.07 for ewe lambs; 0.01 for poultry. In our production equation only productive livestock are considered and will be measured by X_6, independent variable.

Table 9.1 shows the data referring to the seven variables considered above, that is, the values of outputs and resource inputs for each of the eighteen provinces.

The Multiple Regression Equations

The four multiple regression equations of Y on different combinations of X_i resource inputs, worked out in logarithms of the values of the variables, are denoted by columns I, II, III, and IV in Table 9.2 which presents the values of the regression coefficients, coefficients of multiple correlation, standard errors of estimates, and standard errors of the regression coefficients. From this table it is easy to find out the combination of resources corresponding to each production function. It is also easy to see from Table 9.2 that equation IV seems the most reliable. In fact, the adjusted coefficient of multiple correlation is the highest and the standard error of estimate is the lowest for this combination of inputs. However, from the point of view of the reliability of the values of the regression coefficients, combination I, in which the three coefficients are significant at the 5 per cent level, is also interesting. Moreover, it can be seen that combination I is next after combination IV so far as reliability is concerned. So, to establish conclusions, we shall rely on these two combinations, but chiefly on the second one (IV). The corresponding production equations are as follows:

$$Y = 11.411 \ X_1^{0.558} \ X_2^{0.211} \ X_4^{0.165} \tag{I}$$

$$Y = 12.025 \ X_1^{0.631} \ X_2^{0.043} \ X_3^{0.002} \ X_4^{0.120} \ X_5^{0.129} \ X_6^{0.083} \ . \tag{IV}$$

THE PRODUCTION-ELASTICITIES OF THE INPUTS

As is well known, in production equations of the Cobb-Douglas type the values of the regression coefficients measure the elasticities of production in respect to each input variable. The regression coefficients corresponding to the production functions are given in Table 9.2. From this table and using equation I, we see that 1 per cent increase (or decrease) in the active agricultural population, other input variables remaining unchanged, results in a 0.558 per cent increase (or decrease) in agricultural output. Similarly, a 1 per cent increase (or decrease) in standard agricultural land will result in an increase (or decrease) of 0.211 per cent in net agricultural output, while a 1 per cent increase (or decrease) in fertilizer consumption will increase (or decrease) agricultural output by 0.165 per cent. Similar conclusions concerning resource inputs considered in equation IV can be drawn from Table 9.2.

Table 9.2 shows that b_2 and b_4 coefficients, relating respectively to standard agricultural land and fertilizers, fall from equation I to equation IV by the same amount as the values of b_5 and b_6, relating respectively to productive livestock and tractors, enter into combination IV. That is to say, fertilizers, livestock and tractors together contribute to agricultural output in equation IV by about the same amount as land and fertilizers in equation I. Moreover, as tractors and productive livestock appear in equation IV as new variables, the value of b_1, relating to population, goes up. This seems to show that tractors and livestock increase the production elasticity of manpower, but decrease elasticity of land and fertilizers. This conclusion, however, must be regarded with caution as it is merely based on the changes of the values of the regression coefficients in two different combinations of inputs, owing, possibly, to inter-correlation among variables.

The values of the regression coefficients also show that in Portuguese agriculture at large, active population, measuring manpower input, has the highest elasticity of production. Capital resources, such as fertilizers and livestock inputs, come next followed by tractors. Finally, natural resources, i.e., land and climate, especially climate, present much lower elasticity coefficients. It is important to point out, however, that no valid conclusions can be drawn from this in regard to economic efficiency in the use of these resources. Concerning the significance of the regression coefficients, we admit, according to Anderson[4] that a variable should be dropped only when there are no strong logical grounds for including it in the equation, even if the level of significance of the corresponding regression coefficient suggests that the latter equals zero. In other words, we admit that the best estimate of the regression coefficient is still the one obtained from the

---

[4] Cf. Earl O. Heady, and John L. Dillon, *Agricultural Production Functions.* Iowa State Univ. Press, Ames, 1961, pp. 210–11. See also: Anderson, R. L., in *Fertilizer Innovations and Resource Use.* Iowa State Univ. Press, Ames, 1957, pp. 187–206.

TABLE 9.3

MARGINAL PRODUCTIVITIES OF DIFFERENT ITEMS OF INPUT

Items of Input	Marginal Productivity (in 1,000 Escudos Per Year) Using Equation	
	I	IV
Population in agriculture	6,088	6,884
Land	426	87
Fertilizer consumption	3,786	2,753
Productive livestock		1,018
Tractors		5,737

data. This is specially important in the case of the livestock coefficient in equation IV.

The values of the coefficients show, too, that Portuguese agriculture is in a stage of diminishing returns in respect of the use of the six inputs included in our production equation when separately considered. But if we consider the sum of the coefficients in equations I and IV, close to 1, we come to the conclusion that returns to scale are constant. This being in accordance with the research in other countries,[5] the implications are obvious and have already been pointed out. If average returns to manpower in agriculture must be increased, as seems desirable, it will be necessary to increase either all the inputs simultaneously, or only the inputs other than manpower, keeping the human labour input at lower levels.

MARGINAL PRODUCTIVITIES

In order to draw conclusions about the effects of additional amounts of inputs, we have to base our comments on the marginal productivities of the different items of input. In the case of this function, the marginal productivities can be easily calculated from the production equations through the first derivatives of output in respect of each input. The values of marginal productivities presented in Table 9.3 have been calculated at the geometric mean level of the different variables, which is the most accurate estimate when a Cobb-Douglas function is utilized as Heady and Dillon[6] have pointed out.

From Table 9.3, and using equation IV, we can say that agricultural output will increase by 6,884 (1,000 escudos) as the population input is increased by 1 unit (1,000 persons employed in agriculture) and, similarly, by how much it will increase as each of the other inputs is increased by 1 unit.

Figures presented in Table 9.3 emphasize the wide variation of

---

[5] Bhattacharjee, *op. cit.,* pp. 66–67; Earl O. Heady, *Economics of Agricultural Production and Resource Use.* Prentice-Hall, 1952, pp. 349–81.
[6] Heady and Dillon, *op. cit.,* pp. 589–93.

marginal productivities of resource inputs and show also that human labour is the input that presents the highest marginal productivity, followed by tractors, fertilizers, productive livestock, and finally land. This ranging of inputs according to their marginal productivities is quite different from the one presented by Bhattacharjee[7] in respect of world agriculture at large, i.e., fertilizers, tractors, human labour, land and livestock.

Some comments are called for about the interpretation of the figures of elasticities of production and marginal productivities given in Tables 9.2 and 9.3. As already stated, conclusions must be drawn cautiously and we should not ask more of the adopted method than it can perform. First, it must be noted that these figures relate to only one year; the available input variables were estimated for 1957. The figures show the proportions or the amounts by which Portuguese agricultural output at large is expected to increase as a result of one additional unit of each input. This has no bearing on the increase expected in any one province. In each particular province the increase depends on its particular agricultural production pattern. Our conclusion can be of only general character, referring as it does to all the provinces together. The additional output will average out according to the estimated figures. Secondly, ". . . the production equations do not imply any causal relationships between the inputs and the outputs. They merely express a historical pattern of association established in the provinces considered. The variables we are dealing with are macro-economic variables and do not, as such, measure the same things that these physical magnitudes stand for in micro-economic study of production functions."[8] Thus, for instance, the independent variable X_4, relating to fertilizer consumption, ". . . stands, in all probability, as a measure of a complex of inputs which can be described under the capital invested in agriculture, with which it is undoubtedly intercorrelated."[9] Further, the productivity figures for this variable do not express necessarily the increase in output as the direct result of the increase of one unit of fertilizers, but also that resulting from a multiplier effect of other items of input highly correlated with fertilizer consumption, such as irrigated crops, improved seeds, pesticides application, cultural practices, etc.

Another important point concerns the price levels used for output and some of the inputs. Our basical data are for 1957. If a change in the price relationships occurs, our production equation may lose part of its reliability. Finally, it must be said that the results presented in Tables 9.2 and 9.3 are chiefly indicators of the relative positions of production elasticities and marginal productivities of the different inputs, rather than an exact estimate of them; it is only on this basis

[7] Bhattacharjee, *op. cit.*, pp. 66–67.
[8] *Ibid.*, pp. 67–68.
[9] *Loc. cit.*

TABLE 9.4

ANNUAL RATES OF GROWTH OF INPUTS AND AGRICULTURAL OUTPUT IN PORTUGAL
BETWEEN 1957 AND 1959

Items of Input	Production Elasticity Coefficient	Rate of Growth (Per Cent Per Year) of	
		Inputs	Agricultural output
Population in agriculture............	0.631	−1.15	−0.73
Land............................	0.043	0.00	0.00
Climate.........................	0.002	0.00	0.00
Fertilizers.......................	0.120	8.00	0.96
Productive livestock................	0.129	3.00	0.39
Tractors........................	0.083	18.00	1.40
Total.....................			2.11

that they may be useful for purposes of agricultural policy recommendations.

GROWTH OF PORTUGUESE AGRICULTURAL OUTPUT

The annual rate of growth of Portuguese agricultural output can be calculated by means of production equations from the annual rate of growth of each of the inputs included in them. As is well known, this calculation can be done by multiplying the rate of growth of each of the inputs by the corresponding production elasticity coefficient and adding them together. Statistics of population active in agriculture are available and, according to them, it may be assumed that it is decreasing at an annual rate of 1.15 per cent. Standard agricultural land, as a weighted measure of land resource input, will increase significantly only if a significant new acreage is devoted to the highest productive activities, such as irrigated crops or vineyards. However, this is not happening, so the rate of change of this variable has been assumed to be zero. Climate, for obvious reasons, has also been assumed to have no annual rate of change. According to statistical data for the year 1957–58 and 1958–59 on fertilizer consumption,[10] the annual rate of increase of fertilizer input in Portugal may be reckoned at about 8 per cent; statistical data for the years 1957–58[11] enable us to set the annual rate of change of tractor input at about 18 per cent. Unfortunately there are no accurate data on the annual rate of change in the numbers of livestock. However, from an estimate for the period 1940–53[12], we feel justified in assuming

---

[10] O.E.E.C., *Fertilizers, Production, Consumption, Prices and Trade in Europe and U.S.A.* (9th Study 1957–60.) Paris, 1960.

[11] I.N.E., *Estatística Agrícola.* Lisbon, 1959, pp. 42–43.

[12] Presidência do Conselho, *Relatório Final Preparatório do II Plano de Fomento.* (II) *Agricultura, Silvicultura e Pecuária.* Imprensa Nacional, Lisbon, 1958, pp. 18–19.

that this input will increase at an annual rate of about 3 per cent. These annual rates of change of input levels make it possible to estimate the corresponding expected annual rate of growth of Portuguese agricultural output between 1957 and 1959 presented in Table 9.4.

From this table we may infer that the agricultural output of the provinces of Portugal taken together was increasing at an expected average annual rate of 2.11 per cent between 1957 and 1958. This is in line with the general assumption adopted by Lamartine Yates[13] for western Europe.

In the same period the total population of the country was growing at an annual rate of about 0.7 per cent. Thus, it seems possible to assume that the rate of growth of Portuguese agricultural output is above the minimum necessary to match the general population increase in the country. Such a conclusion, however, loses part of its optimistic aspect when we think of it in terms of *per capita* rate of increase in connexion with the present correspondingly low level of *per capita* index. In fact, computing this rate from the above, it is possible to infer that the *per capita* agricultural output in respect of active population in agriculture is expected to increase at about 3.3 per cent annually, which means doubling in somewhat less than 30 years.

It seems that, in spite of indispensable caution when interpreting the figures obtained in our analysis, some interesting policy implications concerning Portuguese agriculture at large can be drawn from this analysis.

---

[13] Yates, *op. cit.*, pp. 158–59.

10

Plantation Agriculture and Economic Development in Ceylon

T. JOGARATNAM

University of Ceylon, Ceylon

PLANTATION AGRICULTURE REPRESENTS a comparatively recent development in Ceylon. As in most other under-developed countries, the traditional system of peasant agriculture is characterized by small and often uneconomic holdings, primitive methods of production, and low levels of productivity. Plantation agriculture, on the other hand, is a form of large-scale cultivation that utilizes considerable amounts of capital and labour in the production of crops primarily meant for export. As a large-scale system of commercial agriculture, it is not only different from but considerably in advance of the traditional system of subsistence farming. The rapid development of the plantation system, since its introduction into Ceylon in the early decades of the nineteenth century, has contributed considerably towards the economic development of the country. At the same time, it has brought in its train several problems, especially in its relationship to the rural economy. In this chapter, an attempt is made to consider some of the effects of the growth of the plantation industry on the rural economy in particular and its contribution to economic development in general.

The development of plantation agriculture in Ceylon dates back to the time when the British gained control. Though Ceylon had long been famous for her spices, and this had brought the Portuguese and Dutch to her shores, there had been no organized cultivation as such. Even cinnamon, in which Ceylon had a virtual monopoly prior to the nineteenth century, was mainly gathered from the jungles where it grew wild. The Dutch, who had ousted the Portuguese and taken possession of the coastal tracts in 1695, found this method of cultivation so unsatisfactory that a few sporadic attempts were made to open up plantations.[1] These did not make much progress, however, and it was not until after the arrival of the British and the passing of the control of the entire Island into their hands in 1815 that the plantation system began to make headway. By then cinnamon had lost its monopolistic position and trade was declining. But another crop, coffee, was becoming attractive, and Ceylon was found well suited for its cultivation.

The Dutch had attempted to foster the cultivation of coffee, but it was found to thrive only at high elevations which were not under their control. This difficulty was overcome with the arrival of the British. The conquest of the Kandyan Kingdom in 1815 gave them control over the entire Island. The British gave all possible encouragement to coffee cultivation such as abolishing the export duty on coffee in 1825 and waiving the land tax on coffee plantations for a period of twelve years beginning in 1829. Despite such incentives, coffee still remained a smallholders' crop, being confined for the most part to the small gardens surrounding peasant homes. The few attempts made to open up plantations did not prove successful. Difficulties of transport and the preference given to West Indian coffee in the British market made things difficult for the planter. The situation changed in 1835 when the duties on Ceylon and West Indian coffee were equalized. Also, with West Indian costs showing a sharp increase owing to the abolition of slavery, the Ceylon product suddenly found itself in a competitive position. This was further strengthened by the steadily increasing demand for coffee in the European market.[2] Coffee cultivation in the Island soon began to attract the attention of (foreign) investors.

The interest created in coffee production was so great that it is usual to refer to developments in the early 1840's as the "coffee mania." The area expanded rapidly, and within a period of about thirty years more than 300,000 acres of virgin jungle land had been cleared and brought under coffee. This rapid growth was reflected in the demand for land. Sales of crown land which stood at only 146 acres in 1833 shot up to over 78,000 acres in 1841. In all, a total of 258,072 acres of crown land were disposed of during the period 1833–43. The coffee mania was at its height in the early 1840's and, though land sales subsequently did not reach the earlier levels, the coffee industry continued to expand. It is estimated that during the period 1833–86 more than 1.1 million acres of crown land were disposed of at very

---

[1] See: Lennox A. Mills, *Ceylon Under British Rule, 1795–1932*. Oxford University Press, 1933.

[2] I. Vanden Driesen, "Coffee Cultivation in Ceylon." *The Ceylon Historical Journal*, July 1953, pp. 31–61; and October 1953, pp. 156–72.

nominal rates, and of this, nearly 230,000 acres were sold during the four years 1840–43.[3]

There is no direct statistical information on the area under coffee and the role of the plantations in this development. All available evidence, however, tends to show that coffee owned and operated by the British played by far the major role.[4] The early pioneers in the field of plantation agriculture were the British government officers and military men stationed in the Island. Once the success of coffee cultivation was assured there was a steady inflow of capital from the United Kingdom. Thus, the governor of the Island during the period 1841–47 estimated the inflow of British capital to be well over £100,000 a year during his time.

The industry reached the height of its development by 1870 but its subsequent decline was as rapid as its ascent. Within a decade or so it lay in ruins, the plants having succumbed to a fungus disease. Such a catastrophic fall, however, did not mean the end of the plantation system. In the frantic search for new crops, the planters came upon two that were new to the Island, tea and rubber. They also started organizing coconut cultivation, which had long been a smallholders' crop, on a plantation basis. Tea, rubber, and coconuts in a small way, took over from coffee, and the plantation system continued to develop rapidly. (See Table 10.1.)

Tea, which accounted for scarcely 1,000 acres in 1875, expanded rapidly thereafter and by 1900 had come to occupy more than 400,000 acres. Rubber was introduced only around 1900 and it came to occupy another 400,000 acres within the next twenty-five years. Tea, rubber, and coconut continued to expand steadily despite unstable prices in the twenties of the present century. With the onset of the great depression of the 1930's, however, Ceylon's export products suffered a steep decline in prices. Attempts made at the international level to arrest this decline culminated in the International Tea Agreement of 1932 and the International Rubber Regulation Agreement of 1934. Though the agreements were primarily intended to restrict acreages, the plantation crops in Ceylon had almost reached the limit of their expansion as very little new land was available. The expansionist phase in the history of the development of the plantation industry thus came to an end.

Within a period of about a hundred years, more than a million acres of jungle had been developed and brought under plantation crops. This had been achieved by the large-scale inflow of foreign capital and foreign labour. The rapid spread of the plantation system, with its emphasis on large-scale methods of cultivation involving

---

[3] I. Vanden Driesen, "Plantation Agriculture and Land Sales Policy in Ceylon— The First Phase 1836–1886," Part I. *The University of Ceylon Review*, Jan.–April 1956.

[4] I. Vanden Driesen, *op. cit.*, pp. 43–44.

TABLE 10.1

Area Under Plantation Crops, 1875–1958*

(In acres)

Year	Coffee	Tea	Rubber	Coconut
1875	249,604	1,080	. . . .	n.a.†
1885	167,677	120,628	. . . .	550,300
1900	. . . .	405,405	1,750	846,000
1914	. . . .	486,536	168,178	973,500
1925	. . . .	440,000	438,950	881,000
1938	. . . .	555,452	604,111	1,100,000
1948	. . . .	555,083	655,108	1,070,950
1958	. . . .	572,706	664,836	1,070,000‡

* Source: *Ceylon Blue Book (Series) 1875–1925*, Colombo: Government Printer, Ceylon. *Statistical Abstract of Ceylon (Series) 1938–1958*, Dept. of Census and Statistics, Govt. Publications Bureau, Colombo.
† Not available.
‡ 1954 figures.

the heavy use of capital and labour and producing primarily for the export market, was of tremendous significance to the future course of an economy that was still largely feudal in character. The paddy economy of the isolated and self-contained village was now overwhelmed by a virile commercial agriculture serving the export markets in Europe. Plantation agriculture, being the main factor responsible for the break-up of the feudal organization, contributed in a large measure towards the transition from a feudal to a modern economy.

Nothing served to break down the traditional isolation that characterized a feudal economy so much as the system of roads and railways that developed alongside the growth of the plantations. An adequate system of transport was a necessary condition, in fact, for the development of the plantation industry, and the insistent demands made by planters for more and better roads could not be ignored by a government that was becoming increasingly dependent on coffee for its own finances. Even as early as 1850, coffee accounted for more than a quarter of the total revenue of the Island.[5]

The few roads that existed at the time the British arrived were restricted to the larger towns and to a broad tract running along the coastal areas. The British set about building more roads to connect the towns for military reasons and a road to Kandy was undertaken in 1820 and completed in 1832. With the development of the plantations, however, the road policy of the government changed. The construction of roads was now undertaken primarily with a view to helping planters to transport their produce to Kandy. Very soon the

[5] I. Vanden Driesen, "Some Trends in the Economic History of Ceylon in the 'Modern' Period." *The Ceylon Journal of Historical and Social Studies,* Jan.–June 1960, pp. 1–17.

Kandyan areas, where most of the plantations were located, came to be covered with a network of roads. By 1860 more than 3,000 miles of roads, either wholly or partly macadamized, had been constructed and most of them served the plantation areas.[6] This represents a substantial achievement when it is remembered that they were mostly in the hill country running along steep gradients and crossing innumerable streams and rivers.

Roads did not solve all the transport problems of the planters. The mode of conveyance by road, the bullock cart, was found to be slow and costly and the demand arose for quicker transport. The construction of a railway was undertaken from Colombo to Kandy, and the first railway in Ceylon was completed in 1867. With the development of the roads and railways came the postal and telegraph facilities which served not only to bring the different parts of the Island together but also linked it with foreign countries. The rapid development of internal transport served to highlight the inadequacy of the port of Colombo in moving the produce of the plantations to the western markets. The provision of a satisfactory harbour was undertaken, and the construction of the port of Colombo was completed in 1882.

While the rapid expansion of the plantation industry served to break down the isolation of the economy and opened it to modernizing influences, it had an unsettling effect on the village economy. The expansion of coffee cultivation brought with it a greatly increased demand for land and labour. The government, in its anxiety to foster the growth of the coffee industry, embarked on a land sales policy that was to have lasting repercussions. Much of the land that was suitable for coffee lay in the jungles of the recently occupied Kandyan Kingdom. Under traditional usage jungle land could be periodically cultivated by what was known as the *chena* system—a form of shifting cultivation, with the land being allowed to revert back to jungle after a couple of seasons. The government was quick to see the consequences of such claims to jungle land and brought in legislation requiring legal title to chena lands.

The Crown Lands Encroachment Ordinance of 1840 thus had the effect of depriving peasants of their needs of forest lands for chena cultivation and pasturing cattle. The denial of a legitimate source of income created such strong resentment that it was an important factor leading to the rebellion against British rule in 1848. It was quite easily suppressed and the interests of the planters were safeguarded. But the peasants were left with only the valley bottoms in which to eke out a living. The rapid extension of the acreage under coffee had other effects. The indiscriminate felling of forests led to a good deal of soil erosion and silting up of tanks and rivers, thereby impoverishing

---

[6] G. C. Mendis, *Ceylon Under the British.* Colombo: The Colombo Apothecaries Co., Ltd., 1944, p. 58.

TABLE 10.2

INCIDENCE OF LANDLESSNESS IN PLANTATION DISTRICTS IN CEYLON

Districts	Land Area	Area Under Planta- tions*	Agricul- tural Families, Landless†	Agricul- tural Families Owning Less Than 1 Acre of Land†	Av. Size of Paddy Holding‡
	(acres)	(per cent)	(per cent)	(per cent)	(acres)
Kandy.	584,912	41	19	59	.59
Matale.	493,040	13	38	74	.55
Nuwara Eliya.	303,360	44	42	72	.65
Badulla. . . . . .ˑ.	2,076,880	7	23	75	.75
Ratnapura.	800,320	20	32	56	1.06
Kegalle.	410,880	31	21	47	.79
Ceylon (total).	15,997,904	9	26.3	54.1	1.17

* *Census of Agriculture, 1952*, Government Press, Ceylon, 1956.
† *Report of the Survey of Landlessness, Sessional Paper XIII, 1952.*
‡ *Census of Ceylon*, 1946, Ceylon Government Press, 1948.

the peasants further. Faced with uncertain titles to land and diminishing yields, many of them took the easy way out and sold their lands
to the planters, creating a class of landless peasants. Much of the
present day problem of landlessness and poverty amongst the peasants
of the Kandyan areas can be traced to the development of the plantations. An indication of the extent of landlessness in the plantation
districts is given by the Report on the Survey of Landlessness, 1952.
While the incidence of landlessness amongst agricultural families
amounted to 26.3 per cent for the Island as a whole, the figures were
very much higher for some of the plantation districts. (See Table 10.2.)
While the development of the plantations led to the appropriation of land to which the peasants had a traditional claim, it could
not provide any relief by affording alternative avenues of employment. The plantation industry owed its development mainly to foreign capital and foreign labour and the Ceylonese as such played only
a very small part. The role of British capital at the height of the
coffee mania has already been referred to. British capital continued to
flow into Ceylon despite the coffee crash and was largely responsible
for the opening up of the tea and rubber plantations. Thus by the
1930's it was estimated that about 80 per cent of the plantations under
tea and more than 50 per cent under rubber belonged to British
companies.[7] Since World War II however, there have been signs of
a withdrawal of British capital. The Census of Agriculture, 1952, reported that 50 per cent of the acreage under tea on plantations and
38 per cent of the acreage under rubber on plantations were owned by

[7] Lennox A. Mills, *op. cit.*, p. 253.

foreign companies or non-citizens. It should be noted here that 80 per cent of the acreage under tea and 50 per cent of the acreage under rubber were in plantations, the rest being in smallholdings belonging mainly to Ceylonese. Coconut, with more than 80 per cent of the acreage being in smallholdings, was almost entirely Ceylonese owned.

It is true that the rapid expansion of the coffee industry created a tremendous demand for labour. But the peasant was too much tied to his land and village to be induced to seek employment in the plantations for a money wage. The age-old system of service tenure was abolished in 1832, and it was hoped that this would release labour for the plantations. Such labour however was not forthcoming and the planters were forced to turn to south India to meet their requirements. Thus began the large-scale importation of southern Indian labour. The annual rate of entry varied from around 30,000 in the 1840's to about 100,000 by the 1880's depending both on the economic conditions prevailing in south India and on the state of the plantation industry in Ceylon.[8] While some of this labour returned home, most eventually settled in Ceylon.

Today the Indian labour population numbers nearly a million, about 88 per cent of whom are employed in the tea plantations, the rest in rubber. Although the employment of Ceylonese labour on plantations has increased of late, 75 per cent of the workers on plantations are of Indian origin.[9] Such a large concentration of foreign labour in certain areas of the Island, the plantation districts, has given rise to a number of problems. It has prevented the absorption, on any large scale, of the indigenous rural population on the plantations. An important channel by which the development of the plantation industry could have benefited the peasant sector was thus cut off. With increasing population and rising unemployment, it has naturally created a good deal of resentment amongst the local population. The fact that the Indian labour population has preserved its separate racial identity—speaking a different language and following different religion, customs, and habits—has served to worsen the situation. This so-called Indian problem is reflected in the citizenship laws passed by a national government soon after the attainment of independence. A large majority of the Indian labour population was denied citizenship status.[10] It is also reflected in the proposed legislation to limit all future employment in the plantations to Ceylon nationals.

While the development of the plantation industry has given rise to a number of problems, it has come nevertheless to occupy a predominant position in the economy of the Island today. It represents

---

[8] I. H. Vanden Driesen, *op. cit.*, pp. 7–8.
[9] *Statistical Abstract of Ceylon, 1959.* Dept. of Census and Statistics, Govt. Publications Bureau, Colombo.
[10] Under the Indian and Pakistani Residents (Citizenship) Act No. 3 of 1949, only about 132,000 individuals were registered as citizens. (From *Ceylon Administration Reports.*)

TABLE 10.3

ANNUAL EXPORT AND IMPORT TRADE OF CEYLON*

Year	Total Value of Exports of Ceylon Produce	Exports of Tea, Rubber, and Coconut as Per Cent of Total Exports	Total Value of Imports Into Ceylon	Imports of Food, Drink, and Tobacco as Per Cent of Total Imports
	(Rs. million)	(per cent)	(Rs. million)	(per cent)
1936–38	273	95.6	231	44.9
1948–52	1,337	95.1	1,290	48.3
1952–56	1,629	94.6	1,559	45.9
1957	1,588	95.5	1,804	40.8
1958	1,651	96.0	1,717	41.7
1959	1,692	96.1	2,005	40.5

* Source: *Ceylon Customs Returns (Series)*.

the only major source of productive activity. Tea, rubber, and coconut occupy nearly two-thirds of the total cultivated area and account for one quarter of the gainfully employed population. About a third of the national income is derived from the plantation crops, with tea alone being responsible for more than 20 per cent. Peasant agriculture, which is primarily concerned with paddy production, contributes about 7 per cent and 13 per cent respectively to income and employment while industry accounts for another 8 per cent and 9 per cent respectively. To an export-import economy that is dependent on its exports to finance the imports of nearly half its requirements of food and most of its requirements of textiles and other manufactured goods, what is perhaps more significant is that tea, rubber, and coconut account for more than 95 per cent of the total export earnings. (See Table 10.3.)

Since World War II, plantation agriculture has shown substantial increases in productivity. Per acre yields of tea and rubber have risen by about 70 per cent and 50 per cent respectively during the twenty-year period 1938–58.[11] Comparable figures are not available for coconut because of the preponderance of smallholdings. Nor are accurate figures available to make an assessment of the productivity of labour. However, the labour population on the estates as a whole has remained substantially the same. The total labour employed on plantations increased by only 5 per cent during the period 1942–44 to 1956–58.[12]

The existence of an export industry of major dimensions and high levels of productivity in the plantation sector is of considerable significance. It has enabled Ceylon to earn a large volume of foreign

[11] *Statistical Abstract of Ceylon* (Series) 1938–1958. Dept. of Census and Statistics, Govt. Publications Bureau, Colombo.
[12] *Statistical Abstract of Ceylon, 1959, op. cit.*

exchange and this explains in a large measure Ceylon's favourable economic position today. Thus, Ceylon with a per capita income of about Rs. 492 comes next to Malaya and the Philippines in the southeast Asian region.[13] Such relatively high levels of living have been sustained by the imports of large quantities of food, textiles and other manufactured products. During the period 1946–56 annual imports of consumption goods have accounted for an average of nearly 75 per cent of the earnings of foreign exchange.[14] But what is more significant to a predominantly agricultural economy is that more than 40 per cent of the foreign exchange earnings are utilized on the imports of food, as shown in Table 10.3. This is a direct consequence of the inability of the peasant sector to increase its levels of productivity.

The peasant or subsistence sector of the economy has primarily concerned itself with the production of food crops. In Ceylon this has meant a concentration on paddy to the almost total exclusion of other subsidiary food products. Under foreign rule the attentions of the government were mainly directed towards the revenue-earning export crops. Thus the peasant sector was in a virtual state of stagnation and neglect resulting in a growing dependence on imports to meet the country's requirements of paddy and the other foodstuffs.

The peasant sector today is characterized by small and uneconomic holdings, heavy rural indebtedness, primitive methods of production, and low levels of productivity. The Report on the Survey of Landlessness, 1952, estimated that 26 per cent of the agricultural population have no land and that 42 per cent have less than half an acre. The Survey of Rural Indebtedness, 1957, revealed an incidence of indebtedness among 54 per cent of the population. The low levels of income, estimated by the Economic Survey of Rural Ceylon, 1950–51, at an average of Rs. 97 per family per month explains the high incidence of indebtedness.

The relative poverty of the peasant sector has attracted attention for a long time. Even the colonial governments attempted a policy of land settlement by restoring some of the ancient irrigation tanks in the relatively unpopulated dry zone. But land settlement as a means of relieving the poverty of the peasants did not make much headway till after 1931 when a measure of self-government was attained under the Donoughmore Constitution.[15] With the granting of independence in 1948, the development of the peasant sector received urgent consideration at the hands of the government. An accelerated programme of land development and peasant settlement cost the government an average of nearly Rs. 45 millions a year during the period 1956–59.[16] The scheme of producer subsidy on paddy involved the government

---

[13] Ceylon National Planning Council, *The Ten Year Plan*. Ceylon Government Press, 1959, p. 5.
[14] *Ibid.*, p. 37.
[15] See: B. H. Farmer, *Pioneer Peasant Colonization in Ceylon*. Oxford University Press, 1957, pp. 116–60.
[16], [17] Based on statistics from *The Ten Year Plan, op. cit.*

in an average expenditure of nearly Rs. 100 millions a year in the
same period.[17] In addition, the government has introduced measures
to encourage the development of co-operatives, provide credit and
marketing facilities, and regulate tenancy relationships. In recent
years, balance-of-payments difficulties and a greater awareness of the
role of agriculture in economic development have invested the programme of rural development with a much greater sense of urgency.

Despite vigorous attempts to develop the peasant sector, levels of
productivity still remain very low. While there have been some
significant increases in the per acre yields of paddy, Ceylon still has
one of the lowest yields among paddy-producing countries.[18] In fact,
agricultural production as a whole recorded an increase of only 2.5
per cent per annum during the periods 1952–53, 1954–55 to 1957–58,
and 1959–60.[19] Population, on the other hand, continues to increase
at the very high rate of 2.7 per cent per annum. Thanks to modern
science, Ceylon in the space of a couple of decades has reduced death
rates from about 37 per thousand to less than 10 per thousand. Birth
rates have remained stable at over 35 per thousand, giving Ceylon one
of the highest rates of population increase.

Peasant agriculture thus presents a picture that is in marked contrast to that of the plantation sector and does not seem to have benefited in any way from the progress that has been achieved there. Despite more than a century of capitalist development in the plantation
sector, accompanied by large-scale development of roads, railways,
ports, post and telegraph, banking and commercial facilities, Ceylon
presents all the characteristics of an under-developed economy.

The emergence of a highly productive commercial agriculture
operated on capitalist lines and existing side by side with a subsistence
sector of low productivity presents a good example of a dual economy.
Development in such economies, in Professor Lewis's view, is a process
of cumulative expansion of the capitalist sector leading to the absorption of surplus labour from the subsistence sector.[20] The cumulative expansion, made possible by the re-investment of profits, continues until the surplus labour in the peasant sector is completely absorbed. Thereafter expansion is made possible only by an increase in
the real wage level in the capitalist sector. The peasant sector therefore stands to benefit by an expansion in the capitalist sector to the
extent that the capitalist expansion reduces the surplus labour available in the peasant sector. In the case of Ceylon, however, no benefits
accrued to the peasant sector though the plantation sector has continued to expand. This is because the subsistence sector did not provide
the surplus labour. The existence of an unlimited reservoir of cheap

---

[18] *Economic Survey of Asia and the Far East, 1961*, p. 14.
[19] *Ibid.*, pp. 11–13.
[20] W. A. Lewis, "Economic Development with Unlimited Supplies of Labour,"
Manchester School of Economic and Social Studies, Vol. XXII, No. 2, May 1954.

labour in south India prevented the participation of local labour and maintained a subsistence wage level. It was only in 1939 that the importation of foreign labour was banned, but since that time the labour requirements of the plantations have not shown any appreciable increases.

The presence of a labour population of over a million in the plantation sector could have been expected to benefit the subsistence sector indirectly through the greatly increased demand for food. But an increase in the price of food would only have led to a reduction in the level of profits, and this was not in the interests of the plantation sector. Large-scale imports of rice helped feed the plantation workers and were also instrumental in lowering prices to the paddy producers. It was only after the attainment of independence that the government regulated the imports of rice and introduced a system of guaranteed prices for paddy with the object of increasing prices to the producers.

If the plantation labour had participated in the progress of industry, such benefits would have made themselves felt on the rest of the economy through increased demand for a wide variety of commodities. Higher incomes for plantation labour could have provided a basis for a rising demand for manufactured goods on which a programme of industrialization could have been based. But the plantation labour itself does not seem to have benefited in any way from the rapid expansion and rising levels of productivity of the plantation sector. Though it has enjoyed medical and educational facilities which were not always available to the indigenous population, its levels of living are below those of the rural population. Thus the Survey of Consumer Finances carried out by the Central Bank of Ceylon in 1954 revealed that the average income per head of the population in the estate sector was only Rs. 58.5 as against a figure of Rs. 121.8 for the non-estate sector. Profits from plantations, on the other hand, reached very high levels. It has been estimated, for instance, that most of the foreign tea companies in Ceylon paid out more than 100 per cent of their issued capital in dividends over the ten-year period 1948–57 alone.[21]

Another factor of importance is that not all the profits derived from the plantation sector were re-invested within the country. The fact that it owed its development to foreign capital and imported labour meant that a substantial part of the earnings of the plantation sector accrued to the foreigners and was sent out of the country. It is difficult to find any accurate figures of the outflow of capital in the pre-war period. During the period 1950–59, however, an average of Rs. 215 millions was sent out of the country annually.[22] This represents nearly 15 per cent of the average annual export earnings.

---

[21] *Agricultural Plan*, Ministry of Agriculture and Food, 1958, p. 173.
[22] Based on statistics from the *Annual Reports of the Central Bank of Ceylon*.

While the expansion of plantation agriculture has contributed substantially towards the economic development of the Island and made possible, in a large measure, standards of living higher than for most under-developed countries, it does not seem to have had any beneficial effects on the peasant sector. As Professor Lewis points out, large-scale importation of labour and export of capital only served to keep down the level of wages.[23] It also cut off the channel by which the plantation sector could have directly benefited peasant agriculture. Since an increase in the productivity of the peasant sector may have led to an increase in real wages to the plantation sector, which was not in its interests, it meant the comparative neglect of peasant agriculture by a government which was bent on safeguarding the interests of the planters. Additionally, in the early years, the development of the plantation sector led to the appropriation of land to which peasants had a traditional claim. It has thereby contributed largely to the problems of landlessness and uneconomic holdings which beset peasant agriculture in Ceylon. These factors help to explain the relative poverty and stagnation of the peasant sector, when the plantation sector itself was showing rapid expansion and high levels of productivity.

---

[23] W. A. Lewis, *op. cit.*

11

The Agricultural Economist
and the Welfare of Farm People

SHERMAN E. JOHNSON

Economic Research Service, U.S. Department of Agriculture,
Washington, D.C., U.S.A.

WELFARE CONSIDERATIONS IN
AGRICULTURAL ECONOMICS

AGRICULTURAL ECONOMISTS have considered the welfare problems of
farm people largely in the context of maximizing incomes to farm
firms and to farmers as a group. They frequently discuss the welfare
of farm people in terms of departures from the goal of equality of
economic opportunity. Achievement of this goal in any country would
require that farm people have an opportunity to earn *real incomes*
equal to those available in other occupations for the same effort, skill,
and managerial ability. It would also require freedom and ability of
farm people to transfer to other occupations if they believe that they
are likely to find the best outlet for their talents in non-farm employment.

In considering this goal we are reminded usually of the difficulties involved in measurement and comparison of real incomes in
different occupations.[1] Aside from income measurement, however,
consideration of economic opportunity provides no comparison of
the mental and spiritual attributes of different occupations. But although economic equality is not all-inclusive, its fulfilment would
include many things that are not apparent on first consideration. For
example, opportunity to earn comparable incomes either in agriculture or other occupations has one meaning for the present generation
of farm workers who may have limited skills and capacity because

---

[1] See especially: "Labor Mobility and Agricultural Adjustment," by D. Gale
Johnson, in *Agricultural Adjustment Problems in a Growing Economy.* Iowa State
Univ. Press, Ames, 1958, Chapter 10, pp. 163–72. Also: J. R. Bellerby *et al., Agri-
culture and Industry: Relative Income.* Macmillan & Co., Ltd., London, 1956.

they lack education and other adaptations necessary for income improvement. It could have an entirely different meaning for a generation growing up in a rural environment with health, education, and other cultural facilities equal to those in urban areas. In other words, even though farm workers received incomes which reflected their marginal value product, they would still be disadvantaged in comparison with those who had more adequate training.

Another question is whether we have in mind equality of income opportunity for *all farm people*—the hired workers, the sharecroppers, and subsistence farmers, as well as the families of operators of commercial farms. If the goal includes all farm people, it means an opportunity for *all children* on farms to grow up in an environment conducive to development of the full potentialities of each individual.

Realization of such an inclusive goal requires discovery of the reasons for disadvantaged classes within agriculture as well as stratification between agriculture and other groups. We shall come back to these questions later but, first, let us examine how agricultural economists have approached welfare problems in agriculture.

Early Welfare Considerations

Although agricultural economists as a group have been concerned with some welfare problems of farm people, they have not always considered the welfare of *all farm people*. The hired workers, the sharecroppers, and other low-income groups have been relatively neglected. This point will be emphasized as we trace the early development of the field, largely from experience in the United States.

The pioneers of the agricultural economics profession in the United States had an environmental bias which favoured the agricultural industry.[2] First, they grew up on farms, and second, they were employed either in land-grant colleges and universities or in the United States Department of Agriculture. Their assignments involved improvement of incomes of farmers, which then was conceived as the central core of the welfare problem of farm people.

The early studies in agricultural economics were concerned largely with efficient use of agricultural resources and with efficiency measured in terms of net money income to farm operators. In accordance with prevailing economic orthodoxy, it was implicitly assumed that if individual farmers made more money, the increase in farm prosperity also would benefit farmers as a group, and society as a whole. This would come about through the competitive functioning of the economic system. At that time little attention was given to income distribution either among different groups of farm people or between farmers and other groups in the economy.

---

[2] The statement refers to workers who were active from 1900 to 1920, notably, H. C. Taylor, George F. Warren, W. J. Spillman, and Andrew Boss. See: Henry C. and Anne Dewees Taylor, *The Story of Agricultural Economics*, Iowa State Univ. Press, 1952.

The pioneer studies were made in the northern states. This was an environment of family farm agriculture which had grown up from the struggle of settlers for the right to acquire government land at little or no initial cost. Settlement on free or nearly free land had resulted in fairly wide distribution of economic opportunity. Although agriculture was largely commercial even in the early 1900's, it still had a strong subsistence base, and most of the farm work was done by the farmer and members of his family. The occasional hired help consisted largely of the sons of neighbouring farmers who aspired eventually to become independent operators.

Out of the recognition that many hired farm workers were graduating to farm tenants and later to owner-operators, there evolved a concept of the "agricultural ladder," with the hired worker on the lower rung, and the owner-operator of a family farm on the upper. This was an idealized conception of the land tenure process even for the years preceding World War I, but its formulation indicated that many ambitious young men did acquire ownership of family farms.[3]

As farm economic research spread into the southern part of the United States, the northern-trained farm economists were faced with a quite different structure of agriculture. The concept of the ladder did not apply because sharecroppers and tenants had little opportunity to graduate into owner-operatorships. They competed for their living in a different group from the owner-operators. The conditions were similar to those which had been described in a much earlier period by Cairnes as non-competing groups.[4] Cairnes, with the British agrarian structure as background, classified agricultural labour with other unskilled labour at the bottom of the scale of his non-competing groups. He developed his classification of non-competing groups at a time when early attempts were being made to form unions of agricultural workers in Britain. These attempts were vigorously opposed by farm operators.[5]

Because the southern states were largely agricultural at the time the early economic studies were made, there was little opportunity for wage workers, sharecroppers, and share tenants to shift even into unskilled non-farm employment. Consequently, the avenues of escape were limited, except for individuals of unusual ability, or those who obtained outside assistance. The situation was somewhat comparable to present conditions in some of the less developed countries.

---

[3] See Carl C. Taylor, Louis J. Ducoff, and Margaret Jarman Hagood. "Trends in the Tenure Status of Farm Workers in the United States Since 1880," a processed report. Bureau of Agricultural Economics, U.S. Department of Agriculture, July 1948.

[4] J. E. Cairnes, *Some Leading Principles of Political Economy*, Harper & Row, New York, 1874, pp. 65–67. The Cairnes classification of non-competing groups of workers represented considerable modification and improvement of the wage theories formulated by the earlier classical economists. It is somewhat analogous to the more recent formulations of imperfect competition among business firms.

[5] Reg Groves, *Sharpen the Sickle! The History of the Farm Workers' Union*, The Porcupine Press, London, 1948, pp. 39–92.

Previous to World War I the farm economic studies in the South largely evaded the problem of non-competing groups by considering improvement of income for the farm or plantation as an operating unit. The sharecropper and tenant shares of the output were regarded as expenses of production without consideration of the equitableness of division of returns from the enterprise.

Thus, the early record of agricultural economics in the United States can be summarized in the statement that it was concerned for the most part with maximizing the net income of commercial farm operators. Improvement of farm incomes also meant increase in the welfare of people on commercial family farms. But on the larger farms and plantations, wherever hired workers or sharecroppers were employed, there was little consideration of the welfare of these groups of farm people. Although some research in tenure relations was undertaken, most of the studies were concerned with improvements which were designed to benefit farm operators. Much of the early agricultural economics literature from other countries reflects a similar approach.

Welfare Formulations in the Inter-war Years

Agricultural economists in the United States found themselves in a new environment during the depression following World War I. They became concerned with parity of income between agriculture and other sectors of the economy. Farm prices had dropped much more sharply than prices of industrial products, and they recovered only slowly in the 1920's. The parity index was developed to measure the disparity between the prices of farm products and the prices paid by farmers for production and family living. Although many other lines of research were pursued during the 1920's, much effort was devoted to analysis and measurement of incomes of farmers as compared with non-farm groups. This was an aggregative approach, and little attention was given to the welfare of different groups either within agriculture or within the different non-farm groups.

The disparity between incomes in agriculture and in other occupations which concerned so many agricultural economists in the 1920's was, in a sense, a recognition of the existence of non-competing groups in American economic society. To be sure, farm people were not completely excluded from the non-farm labour market in the 1920's. The transfer out was large, especially in the years of industrial prosperity, but the migration stream was not rapid enough to offset the disparity in incomes. And because of lack of education and special skills, most of the migrants from farms could only grasp the lower rungs of the non-farm employment ladder. This again is in accord with the Cairnes classification.

The migrants had a very insecure hold on even the lower rung of the non-farm employment ladder, and they were pushed off early in the deepening of the depression which began in 1929. Many had to go back to their old farm communities, there to eke out a living in subsistence farming. Looking back, it seems strange that economists who were so concerned with the disparity between farm and non-farm incomes did not give more attention to the forces which were impeding mobility of farm people—their lack of knowledge of employment opportunities, the education, training, and other background of the migrants, and the limited employment open to them because of restrictions on entry into other occupations.

Although some of the pioneers in agricultural economics had studied and travelled in Europe, there was relatively little contact between American and European agricultural economists before the first International Conference of Agricultural Economists in 1929. Leonard Elmhirst, the sponsor of that conference, became a graduate student in agricultural economics at Cornell University in 1919. He had served in India during the war and had worked for Sam Higginbottom, the agricultural missionary, at Allahabad Institute in India during a period of convalescence. There he had developed a sense of mission for the improvement of agriculture which prompted his studies at Cornell University. On completion of his graduate programme at Cornell he returned to India to work with Rabindranath Tagore on a pilot project of village rehabilitation in India. This was a pioneer attempt to apply to an eastern village environment the discipline of agricultural economics which had been developed in a western culture.[6] In his work in India, Elmhirst was interested in the improvement of all village people regardless of class or caste, and he became well acquainted with the rigidity of the Indian caste system which carries the concept of non-competing groups to its ultimate extreme. The Elmhirst agricultural projects at Dartington Hall (in Devon, England) are, in a sense, a case study in rehabilitation of British agriculture, with concern for the welfare of all farm people.

As the president of the International Conference of Agricultural Economists from its founding in 1929 at Dartington Hall through the Tenth Conference at Mysore, India, in 1958, Elmhirst has always given priority to the welfare of farm people. His broad approach to welfare is evident in his successive presidential addresses, but the rank and file of agricultural economists in most countries have pursued a much narrower path.

The world-wide depression of the 1930's was a soul-searching experience for agricultural economists in all countries. Because of their specialization in economic problems of agriculture, they did not feel adequately prepared to suggest measures to promote general economic recovery. Many, however, were reluctant even to advance

---

[6] *Rabindranath Tagore—Pioneer in Education.* Essays and exchanges between Rabindranath Tagore and L. K. Elmhirst, distributed by John Murray, 50 Albemarle Street, London, 1961.

measures for alleviating agricultural distress. And the remedies which were suggested dealt largely with increasing incomes on commercial farms, although in several countries small holdings were promoted for those on the fringes of commercial agriculture.

Agricultural economists in the United States centred primary attention on the financial survival of farm-operator families. Fairly soon, however, it became evident that large groups of farm families were not sharing in the early agricultural recovery. They were the wage workers, the sharecroppers, the Great Plains drought victims, and many farm-operator families who were living in the chronic low-income farming areas of the mountains and the cut-over regions. The dire poverty of these groups compelled consideration of the disadvantaged classes in agriculture.

Rural relief and rehabilitation programmes to aid these groups were organized by the Federal Government. After considerable modification these programmes eventually were consolidated into the ongoing work of the United States Department of Agriculture, as supervised credit and farm ownership programmes.

The rural sociologists and the professional social workers provided most of the background studies for the programmes designed for relief of disadvantaged rural families.[7] A few agricultural economists joined forces with them, but many were very critical of the relief programmes which were developed. They would have been much happier if farm programmes had been confined to the commercial farm-operator group. Admittedly, some of the leaders of rural relief programmes made many inept approaches but the conservative view held that the people who did not share in farm income recovery were shiftless and not worthy of assistance.

The disadvantaged classes had little or no farm organization support. But poverty was so prevalent that it claimed the attention of the Federal Government and gradually agricultural economists began to recognize the existence of non-competing groups within agriculture, although this term was not used to describe the prevailing situation.[8] Some of the studies conducted during World War II gave special attention to wage workers in agriculture.[9]

CONCERN FOR THE WELFARE OF ALL FARM PEOPLE

At the end of World War II the need for immediate food relief and, later, the rehabilitation of agriculture in war-torn countries, overshadowed any domestic farm problems in the United States. In

---

[7] For a listing of a number of studies of rural poverty see: Carl C. Taylor, Helen W. Wheeler, and E. L. Kirkpatrick, *Disadvantaged Classes in American Agriculture*. Social Research Rept. No. VIII, Farm Security Administration and Bureau of Agricultural Economics, co-operating, 1938.

[8] See: M. L. Wilson, "Problem of Poverty in Agriculture," *Journal of Farm Economics*, Proceedings Number, Vol. XXII, No. 1, Feb. 1940, pp. 10–33.

[9] See: Louis J. Ducoff, "Wages of Agricultural Labor in the United States." U.S. Department of Agriculture, Tech. Bul. No. 895, 1945.

the 1950's, however, many of the pre-war domestic problems returned to plague farmers and to command the attention of agricultural economists. Nevertheless, considerable effort has been focused on the potential contribution of agricultural economics to improvement of agriculture in the less developed countries.

Trained agricultural economists from both the United States and Europe have followed Elmhirst's footsteps in a desire to help rehabilitate agriculture in the less developed countries. Many citizens of the countries seeking aid in development have attended universities in Europe and the United States to obtain training for more effective work in their home countries. The present generation of agricultural economists are concerned over the welfare of farm people, as evidenced by their choice of occupation and their dedication to work in this field. As a basis for more effective attacks on problems in both the more and the less developed countries, there seems to be need for a reorientation of welfare considerations in their work.

Most of the current research and teaching centres on allocative efficiency in the firm and the industry. Little emphasis is placed on equitable distribution of the resulting income. This despite the experience in most developed countries that more equitable distribution of opportunities to earn higher incomes eventually results in income improvement for the entire group. Income increases in many less developed countries are likely to be dissipated in conspicuous consumption unless they are widely shared. Consumption expenditures by the élite do not promote accelerated economic development.

Sometimes an implicit assumption is made that income disparities would disappear if adjustments were made that would result in a greater tendency toward equality of marginal productivity in the use of production factors. But such assumptions ignore the effect on a worker's productivity of lack of opportunity for development of potential capacity. These handicaps, as well as the many barriers to mobility, result in persistence of non-competing groups—in agriculture as compared with other occupations, and perhaps even more importantly, among groups within agriculture. Neglect of the latter results in little attention being given to the most disadvantaged groups in agriculture. This is true in the more developed as well as in the less developed countries.

If we are seriously interested in the welfare of *all farm people*, perhaps we need to begin with the recognition that in all nations the most precious resource is the people, with the technical and managerial skills which they possess. The greatest scarcity in the less developed countries is trained manpower, despite their high levels of unemployment and under-employment. There is a dearth of people with requisite technical and managerial skills who can assume leadership to carry forward a development programme. Unfortunately, the superabundance of illiterate and unskilled labour cannot find productive employment because neither trained manpower nor capital is available to take advantage of improved technology that would provide employment. Both capital and trained manpower are essential for accelerated development, but more adequate recognition has been given to capital needs than either to education and training in technical and management skills or to the required institutional reforms.

The greatest need in the less developed countries, therefore, is education and training programmes *for all people*—not just the élite. Inauguration of programmes pointing in this direction requires acceptance of the scientific findings of geneticists, anthropologists, and psychologists that the bundles of aptitudes which constitute innate abilities are about equally distributed among all groups of people.[10] Acceptance of this statement does not imply that we are all born with equal endowment of aptitudes for either book learning or physical skills. There is a wide dispersion of aptitudes among all groups in a population. But it follows that a favourable environment will facilitate development of the innate capacities of each individual.

If these scientific findings are accepted, it is of crucial importance for every country to provide opportunities for each individual to develop his latent abilities in so far as this is possible within available national resources. Some countries have very limited natural resources in relation to population. Under these conditions, trained manpower becomes doubly important. Parental and home responsibility are involved in human development, but society as a whole has a large role to play. It can do much to overcome handicaps existent in the parental and home environment. A basic minimum of physical needs— food, housing, clothing, and health services of minimum adequacy— must be available to growing children if they are to avoid acquiring lifetime handicaps.

With such basic needs provided, proper education and training will discover and develop the combination of aptitudes that will enable each individual to make his greatest contribution to the society of which he is a member. If each individual in a society is given opportunity for training and for guidance on the choice of occupation in which he can make his greatest contribution, and if he is free to enter that occupation, the sum of maximum contributions from all individuals will result in the greatest total contribution to growth, progress, and satisfaction for the entire social group.

Because there are wide differences in aptitudes and abilities, training opportunities should be available for the development of innate capacities, and employment gates must be open to qualified entrants into the labour force in all different lines.[11] This is the only effective method of removing the barriers to mobility that otherwise would perpetuate the existence of non-competing groups.

The goals which individuals within a given social group wish to

---

[10] For a recent statement see: Theodosius Dobzhansky, "Genetics and Equality," *Science*, Vol. 137, No. 3524, July 13, 1962.

[11] See: William E. Hendrix, "Income Improvement Prospects in Low-Income Areas," *Journal of Farm Economics*, Vol. XLI, No. 5, Dec. 1959.

achieve vary with the cultural environment. Perhaps individual choices in western cultures give higher valuations to goods and services that make up the material content of living than will those who are primarily influenced by eastern backgrounds. Economic conditions also affect the choices which are made. But all individuals, somewhat regardless of the cultural and economic environment, seem to be motivated by the same basic urges—status, purpose, and security—SPS.

All individuals seem to have a basic longing for favourable status in the group to which they belong. They want to be recognized as important among their fellow men. Each person feels the need of a purpose in life, such as making a significant contribution to the welfare of his family, his village or community, or to the nation. The urge for fulfilling a purpose is the basis for national patriotism. All individuals strive to achieve basic security—for themselves, their families, and the larger group. It is only when one has become resigned to the hopelessness of greater achievement that the striving for security may be reduced to the barest existence.[12]

In some societies the basic urges (SPS) have been suppressed for so long in the lower income groups that they exist only under the surface, and it may appear to outsiders that they are non-existent. They are discovered only when individuals within such groups are provided with opportunities to satisfy their basic longings, because "where there is no hope, there is little endeavor."[13] Hope of betterment can kindle sparks of ambition and aspiration (at least in younger people), but they will not burst into full flame without reasonable expectation of reward for effort.

ACHIEVEMENT OF IMPROVEMENT LEVELS FOR ALL FARM PEOPLE

Is it possible to achieve a goal which includes improvement of welfare for all farm people? If so, what should be the role of the agricultural economist in this endeavour?

Although recent scientific developments indicate the technical feasibility of producing adequate supplies of food and other necessities, achievement of the physical potentialities would require adoption of improved technology in the areas where traditional methods are still being used. And the income problem of farm people remains unsolved even in the areas of plentiful production. The questions then arise how these two obstacles can be surmounted, and the benefits of science adapted to serve all farm people—in the less developed countries as well as in those which have achieved higher levels

---

[12] See: Kusum Nair, *Blossoms in the Dust.* Gerald Duckworth & Co., Ltd., London, 1961; especially Chap. IV, pp. 46–51.
[13] Quotation from Arthur F. Raper's review of Kusum Nair's *Blossoms in the Dust,* in *AID Digest,* July 1962. Raper originally used the expression with reference to Georgia sharecroppers in the 1930's. His book *Tenants of the Almighty,* Macmillan Co., 1943, reports the progress of sharecropper families when better opportunities became available.

of development. Economic and social institutions are needed that will assure not only adoption of improved technology but also the equitable distribution of benefits.

There is work to do to achieve this goal even in the more developed countries. Farm income problems are receiving much attention, but pockets of persistent poverty are found in many areas. The causes for such poverty must be ascertained and eliminated in so far as possible. The migrant farm workers seem to be at the bottom of the opportunity scale in most countries. Perhaps the largest welfare task involves providing better opportunities for all groups of rural youth. This requires facilities for education, training, health programmes, and other activities that are necessary for the development of potential aptitudes.

In many countries, regardless of stage of development, there is need for elimination of the cleavage between hired labour and supervisory management. In some areas and in certain types of farming, perhaps larger commercial farms with good management bring forth a larger product than family operation. But the question then arises as to division of benefits from the more efficient operations. If the larger farms, operating with hired labour, actually are more efficient, ways need to be devised to obtain for hired workers their marginal productivity wage when viewed over the longer term. The current marginal productivity may be very low because the workers are ignorant and unskilled, and perhaps suffering from malnutrition or other illness. The history of the labour movement in agriculture as well as in industry indicates that increased productivity usually results from higher wages, shorter hours, and opportunity for advancement.

The question of developing equality of bargaining power between hired workers and their employers, therefore, becomes important on large commercial farms. A similar bargaining problem arises between tenants and landlords in high-tenancy areas. One of the advantages of commercial family farming is the virtual elimination of the cleavage between labour and management, since most of the work is performed by the operator and members of his family.

Achievement of an improvement level for all farm people is much more difficult in the less developed countries than in those which have reached a fairly high stage of development. A beginning must be made, however, and this will require courageous leadership. The first essential is provision for education, training, health, and other services for children and youth.[14] These essentials should be provided with a sense of mission concerning the need for improvement; a firm resolution that the *status quo* cannot be tolerated. Teachers with a sense of mission are much more important than expensive buildings, although a necessary minimum of shelter and of equipment must be provided.

---

[14] See: T. W. Schultz, "Investment in Human Capital," *The American Economic Review*, Vol. LI, No. 1, March 1961.

Operators of both large and small farms will need technical assistance in adopting the improved practices which are essential for increased output and higher incomes. Operators of the smaller farms, especially, will require a bundle of assistance which can only be provided by establishment of rural institutions to provide equitable tenure arrangements, and to make credit, production supplies, storage facilities, and technical and other assistance available to farm operators.[15]

Perhaps the knottiest problem of all is to find productive employment for landless rural people who are now unemployed or under-employed. Even though the long-term solution is found in non-farm employment, the rural unemployed will need to be supported in rural areas over a considerable period. If a more favourable agricultural environment is developed, perhaps some of the unemployed can find work on the larger farms, but supplementary employment on public improvement programmes is likely to be necessary. Such programmes can be developed to result in fairly rapid increase in agricultural output, but they do require funds from a public budget that may be stretched almost to capacity because of the need for investment in other lines of endeavour.

If agricultural economists are to play an important role in achievement of an improvement level for all farm people, they must view their work in terms of seeking alternative ways of improving income and living for all the rural people in the community or the nation of which they are members. Although analyses designed to maximize income to farm firms as well as to the agricultural industry are important, achievements of these aims may not result in better living for *all farm people*. Agricultural economists also must be concerned with income and living problems of all farm families; with education, health, housing, and security for all groups of farm people; and with ways of paying for these amenities whether from private or public funds. Hired labour is then viewed not only as one of the expenses of farm production; the hired workers become farm people with aspirations for better living and opportunities for their children similar to those found in operator families.

These concerns involve equitable distribution of the available income from agriculture and development of a rural society that provides opportunities for rural youth to develop their potential capacities. In this setting, agricultural economists will be engaged in discovering major obstacles to achieving equality of economic opportunity for all farm people, and with outlining alternative ways of removing them. This may involve suggesting new rural institutions, or improving those now in existence. In such additional activities, agricultural economists will satisfy their own urges for status and purpose by contributing to social betterment.

[15] See: Douglas Ensminger, "Overcoming Obstacles to Farm Economic Development in the Less Developed Countries," *Journal of Farm Economics*, Proceedings issue, Vol. XLIV, No. 5, Dec. 1962; especially his discussion of the "Package Program," pp. 1377 ff.

12

The Collective Farms (Kolkhozes) of the U.S.S.R.

I. S. KUVSHINOV

Timiriazev Agricultural Academy, Moscow, U.S.S.R.

THE SOVIET UNION has created a huge industry and a completely developed and highly productive agriculture. The great October socialist revolution in Russia in 1917 and the new socialist regime carried out the greatest change in all branches of the national economy. The reorganization of agriculture began immediately.

The first law, adopted by the Second All-Russia Congress of Soviets in 1917, was about the land. It decreed that landlord ownership of land was immediately abolished without payment. All land became national property to be used by all the workers. Under this law the nationalization of all land was carried out with the confiscation of the landlords' land. This reform is the basis for the development of the new social relations in the village.

V. I. Lenin, who studied deeply the economic, social and political processes in the village, created theoretical and practical programmes for the peasantry, and developed the means and tools for the reorganization of the peasants' economy and the life of the village on a socialist basis. This meant the transfer of the ownership of the peasants to the united farming and collective farms. The nationalization of land created a ". . . land regime, the most flexible for transition to socialism . . . gave the greatest possibilities for the proletarian state to carry out the socialist transformation of agriculture." [1] The peasants received more than 150 million hectares of former landlords' land,

---

[1] *V. I. Lenin,* Complete edition, 4th ed., Vol. 32, p. 193.

and lands belonging to the tsar family and the tsarist estate and 50 million hectares of other lands.

Before the revolution 10.5 million peasant households had 75 million hectares, but at the same time 75 thousand landlords possessed 70 million hectares. Annually, the peasants paid 700 million gold rubles to landlords as rent. The peasants were tremendously in debt to the peasants' bank—1,300 million rubles. On receiving land and some implements without charge, and being liberated from indebtedness to banks, the poor and average peasantry increased their capacity for agricultural production. The co-operative plan was accepted by them. The nature of the plan is that the peasantry with the help of the state and on a voluntary basis gradually unite and carry out co-operative farming.

From the first, the Soviet State took serious measures to assist the co-operative societies in the collective cultivation of land; it appropriated funds to give credits to peasant households; and it united them in collective farms, as completely voluntary unions of peasants for the development of agricultural production. In the first period these unions were rather small. They had some difficulty in obtaining the new complicated machines, sufficient quantities of fertilizers, the necessary amount of credits, implements, and tools, and in acquiring the requisite manual skills.

In order to obtain all these it was necessary to create larger agricultural collective enterprises, and it was then possible to possess the latest machines—tractors, combines, and other implements, which improved the work of the peasants and sharply increased the productivity of labour. But ". . . it is impossible to create immediately large enterprises from a lot of small households."[2] For the transition of small peasant enterprises to a socialist basis it was necessary to carry out some intermediate measures. The Soviet Government undertook these so as to create conditions for the voluntary transition of small peasant farms to large co-operative enterprises. More than a million peasant households received state credit in 1925, and 77 per cent of all the loans was used for productive purposes—the purchase of working animals, agricultural machines and implements, seeds, and mineral fertilizers; these contributed to the expansion and improvement of agricultural production in all the peasant households, and especially in the collective enterprises. Agricultural co-operatives in 1925 purchased and produced for the State supply 80 per cent of sugar beet, 76 per cent of cotton, 25 per cent of flax, 92 per cent of butter, and 42 per cent of starch products.

Great financial aid was given by the Soviet State directly to collective farms and particularly to the machine and tractor stations. Machine and tractor stations played a significant role at a certain stage of agricultural development. They were a form of socialist enterprise in

---

[2] *V. I. Lenin*, Complete edition, Vol. 28, p. 152.

which there was co-operation between state leadership and the productive effort of collective farms in the development of the social
economy.

In the process of this development of co-operation in the peasants'
enterprises the main form of collectivization (the collective farms) was
strengthened.

In 1940 the co-operatives included 18.7 million peasant households. There were more than 400 thousand tractors in the machine
and tractor stations which could cultivate 94 per cent of all the arable
land. There has been a continuous process of building farm imple-
ment plants in industry. New models of modern agricultural machines
have been introduced—tractors, combines, trucks, and engines of indigenous production. Mechanization has played a major role in production.

This has been a ". . . most difficult problem—the transition of
small agricultural households on the basis of socialist co-operation. . . .
The transition of the Soviet village to large agricultural enterprises
means a great revolution in economic relations, in the whole way of
life of the peasantry. Collectivization put an end forever to the exploitation of the peasants by large farmers (kulaks), class fragmentation, and poverty. The peasant problem has been really settled on the
basis of the Lenin co-operative plan." [3]

By November 1961 the collective farms of the U.S.S.R. had 529.2
million hectares of land, including 261.4 million hectares of cultivated
land, of which 123.4 million hectares were arable land. By January
1962, the number of collective farms was about 41.3 thousand with an
average sown area of 3 thousand hectares per farm. The total area
of sown land in collective farms was 110.6 million hectares, and the
area of peasant households in the collective farms 4.3 million hectares.

The number of cattle in collective farms amounted to 36.8 million (including 12.8 million cows); hogs, 30.1 million; sheep, 67.1 million; goats, 0.9 million. The improvement in breeding qualities of
livestock and their better feeding and management enable the most
progressive collective farms to obtain high yields of milk, butter, meat,
and other livestock products. The high energy supply in the collective
farms (4.1 horsepower per worker) makes for easier conditions of work
for the peasantry in mechanized agricultural and livestock production,
thus increasing sharply the labour productivity. The collective farms
have in 1962 large numbers of farm machines and implements: 596
thousand tractors, 231 thousand grain combines, 432 thousand trucks,
and many other kinds of machines. The indivisible funds of collective
farms in 1961 amounted to 27 billion rubles, and their incomes increased 28 times in comparison with 1932. The large collective farms—
by strengthening and developing their collective enterprises, by intro-

---

[3] The XXII Congress of the Communist Party of the Soviet Union, *Proceedings*,
p. 328.

ducing scientific achievements, and by progressive practical experience in production—continuously increase their labour productivity, improve their techniques of farm management, and increase the amount of gross and marketable product of agriculture and animal husbandry.

Of the total agricultural production of the U.S.S.R. the share of collective farms in the production of major products in 1961 was: grain, 60 per cent; cotton, 83 per cent; sugar beet, 92 per cent; potatoes, 25 per cent; vegetables, 26 per cent; meat, 30 per cent; milk, 35 per cent; wool, 47 per cent; and eggs, 11 per cent. The share of collective farms in marketable production (state purchase) was somewhat higher. The growth of marketable production on the collective farms, and the increase of sales to the state, has enabled the state to abolish the obligatory procurement of products grown on the peasants' household plots. The Soviet peasantry have participated in collective farming for many years and they are convinced of its stability, progressiveness, and profitability.

The greatest role in the strengthening of the collective farm system has been played by the supply of land without charge. The system corresponds completely to the modern productive forces of the village, permits the use of new machines and scientific advances, and effective use of labour.

There is complete agreement between the private interests of the peasants and the collective and national interests in the results of production. The system opens wide possibilities to increased incomes and improved welfare of the peasants as labour productivity grows.

The collective farm is a type of social enterprise both on account of its organization and democratic basis, which will be more and more developed, and on account of the management, in which the peasants have wide participation and develop their own creative abilities.

A collective farm is an independent agricultural enterprise, created as a result of the voluntary union of peasants. The most important and decisive force of the farm is the farming, which is conducted on a completely commercial basis on land belonging to the state with the main means of production belonging to the collective farm. The products also belong to the collective farms. The working and productive animals, the agricultural buildings, the farm machines and implements, the repair shops, the orchards, and other goods are included in the indivisible funds of the farms.

On the farms all the main works are carried out by the peasant members. They themselves determine the minimum number of labour days each member of the farm is obliged to work. The general order and norms of work are determined by the general meetings of the members. All the production is owned by the collective which can allocate it on the basis of the laws of the socialist state and the decisions of the chapter of the collective farm. Part of the product is used to meet the costs of production incurred by the farm and the state, part is appropriated to the state as the collective farm's contribution to all state expenses, and a considerable part goes to increase the collective funds of the farm and as payment for the labour of its members. The members of the farm do not receive wages. Their labour is rewarded by the distribution of part of the farm income between the members who have participated in the collective production. The highest executive body of the collective farm is a general meeting of all the members. The general meeting manages all the business activity of the farm, and the chairman and the executive council are responsible to the meeting.

Besides the collective production, each peasant household as may be decided by the chapter of the farm has its private small enterprise on a small plot of land: dwelling house, productive livestock, poultry, and small farm implements to supply those needs of the household not completely satisfied by the collective farming. These decisions depend upon the co-operative character of the farm. The chapter has the duty to reconcile the collective and private interests of its members, and to decide when the collective interests should dominate.

With the development of collective farm production, the supply of modern farm implements, and the growth of skill of the workers, the demands of the members will be satisfied more and more by the collective production, and their private enterprise will diminish in importance. The progressive collective farms in all zones of the country already satisfy the needs and demands of their members by means of the collective income.

There are houses of culture, secondary schools and special schools, kindergartens, hospitals, libraries, shops, and moto-clubs in the collective farms. The children of the members study in higher and special secondary schools at the expense of the state. The members have improved dwelling houses and communal services. They have guaranteed pension rights in case of old age and incapacity, payable from the collective farm income. The members have a month's vacation each year and have reduced travelling rates, when going to sanatoriums and houses of rest. They are paid on the basis of labour days of eight hours.

Showing its growing enthusiasm for the fulfilment of production plans, the Soviet collective farm peasantry under the conditions of the socialist production system develops its potential and increases its labour productivity. The workers receive bonus payments for good work and for the best results in agricultural production.

Lenin's co-operative plan set the pattern of the socialist transition of agriculture—the creation of large collective farms. Co-operation played an extremely important role in the ". . . transition to new conditions by the simplest, easiest means, which are the most common to the peasantry." [4]

The development of productive co-operation in most countries of peoples' democracies has been carried out by adapting the U.S.S.R. experience to the peculiarities of each country. The proportion of socialist sectors in the total agricultural land of all the socialist countries is more than 90 per cent.[5] The collective agriculture of the Soviet Union conducts its farming on the basis of socialist production, of science, technical improvement, and progressive practical experience. This increases the cultural level of farming, the amount of production, and the quality of products, and creates all of the conditions necessary for the improvement of the well-being of the collective farm peasantry.

---

[4] V. I. Lenin, Complete edition, 4th ed., p. 428.
[5] Report of N. Kruchev, the XXII Congress of the Communist Party of the Soviet Union, *Proceedings*, p. 8.

13

Kibbutz and Moshav in Israel: An Economic Study

YEHUDA LOWE

Ministry of Agriculture, Israel

THE DEVELOPMENT OF KIBBUTZ AND MOSHAV

CO-OPERATIVE FARMING forms the bulk of the agricultural economy of Israel. Of 808 villages (May 1961) no less than 594 were either co-operative or collective settlements. Forty or fifty years ago there developed two distinct new forms of agricultural settlement: The Kibbutz (plural: Kibbutzim) and the Moshav (plural: Moshavim). The Kibbutz is a collective settlement the members of which form a large-scale enterprise based upon common ownership of resources and upon the pooling of labour, income, and expenditure. The Moshav is a co-operative smallholders' settlement in which there are 60 to 150 individual farmsteads, all belonging to one village co-operative through which they sell their produce and buy their supplies, and which is largely responsible for the management of the village as a whole.

Both types were founded on land belonging to the Jewish National Fund which is given to the settlers in hereditary leasehold against a nominal rent. The settlers usually had no means of their own and started by obtaining long-term, low-interest loans from the Foundation Fund for the initial capital investments. Jews from all over the world made voluntary contributions to the Funds.

The relative importance of Kibbutz and Moshav has changed over the years. For a long period they have kept each other in balance. During the last few years preceding the foundation of the State of Israel (in 1948) the Kibbutzim gained the upper hand to such an extent that they comprised almost one half of the Jewish rural popula-

[*126*]

tion, as against one quarter living in Moshavim, and another quarter belonging to other forms of settlements. With the start of mass immigration after the foundation of the State, the Moshavim expanded much faster and in 1963 comprised 40 per cent of the Jewish rural population, whereas the share of the Kibbutzim has receded to 26 per cent with another 34 per cent living in other forms of settlements.

The population of the 228 Kibbutzim is around 77,000, and that of the 347 Moshavim is around 120,000. Of the collective and co-operative settlements founded before 1948, two-thirds of the population belonged to Kibbutzim and only one-third to Moshavim, while the share of the Kibbutz population in settlements founded after the declaration of the State amounts to less than 16 per cent.

This change-over can be explained by the fact that to become a member of a Kibbutz presupposes a renouncement of individualistic inclinations for the common benefit of the closely knit society (a feature characteristic of many pioneer settlers in earlier periods), whereas the farmer in a Moshav lives and works in the circle of his own family. The choice of joining one form or the other was always free and there was never any coercion exerted either by the settling agency or by the Government. Yet the Kibbutz organizations used to recruit their members at an early age and train them in youth groups, often before their immigration to Palestine. Most of their members were avowed socialists who saw in the collective way of life the realization of their ideal to form a new society, and in farming, the long desired "return to nature." These motives hardly persisted into the post-State period, when people came to Israel in waves of mass immigration, mostly from under-developed countries, and a certain proportion of them chose farming as their vocation. The co-operative form of settlement—the Moshav—was their only choice, because they did not have the means of setting up private farms and they had no desire to venture into the collective way of life of a Kibbutz.

It should be stressed that a purely economic approach to the advantages and disadvantages of either form of settlement misses the point. Modern economic theory occasionally tends to overstress the importance of the profit motive in farming. It can be shown easily by the example of Kibbutz and Moshav in Israel that there are other no less decisive factors for making a choice. Suffice it to mention that the Kibbutz economy allows its members to restrict the working hours to 8 or 9 hours a day and gives each member a 1 or 2 weeks' holiday a year, facilities which are almost out of reach on the ordinary individual farm. This kind of regulation can hardly be measured in money terms. It would be unjust, however, to compare the net profit of either form of enterprise with the other without taking it into consideration. Obviously, Kibbutzim cannot disregard their profitability, existing as they do in the midst of a highly developed capitalistic society; but they do not regard maximization of net profit as the only measure of success. They place no less value on human relationships and on the happiness of their members.

It is much the same in an individual farm of a Moshav. Quite often one encounters a farmer who foregoes maximum profit for a little more comfort or an alleviation of his manual work by making more use of machinery than would be necessary from a purely economic point of view. The decision to join a Kibbutz or a Moshav definitely does not depend on economic motives only; in fact, it is hardly dependent on them at all. Foremost in such a choice is the preference for one way of life over another, influenced by the personal, social, and psychological circumstances of the individual.

If in spite of this an attempt is made to compare both forms of settlement from an economic point of view, the author is aware of the limitations of such an approach. Yet it may be of some interest for the student of the economics of various forms of co-operation in agriculture.

MAIN FEATURES OF THE KIBBUTZ ECONOMY

Kibbutzim are large-scale enterprises comprising from less than 200 to more than 600 adult members with their dependents. On the average 63 per cent of the occupied population are engaged in farming, 17 per cent in industrial enterprises of many different kinds, and the rest in work outside the settlement as wage-earners, some of whom are also employed in new investments, such as the erection of new buildings, water installations, etc. on their own farms. These percentages vary widely from one Kibbutz to another. All income is pooled regardless of its derivation. The Kibbutz provides all its members with all the necessaries of life according to its economic capability. It determines the annual household budget in advance for each item of expenditure, starting from costs of living and ending with all kinds of cultural activities, including housing, clothing, care and education of the children, etc. Meals are prepared in large, highly mechanized kitchens and served in a common dining hall. Laundering and mending are done in special workshops. Often there are beautiful recreation facilities, including libraries, well-tended parks, swimming pools, etc. The children usually live in their own quarters, divided according to age groups, where they are also taught. Apart from all these services, the Kibbutz has to provide from among its own members the labour force for its administration and for municipal duties. These include not only management of all farming and other activities, budgeting and financial transactions, purchasing farm supplies and consumer goods, disposing of farm and other produce through sales and home consumption, but also the various civil service duties of a village and, last but not least, security measures.

The Kibbutz is guided by the principle "everyone according to his ability—to everyone according to his needs." There is a growing

TABLE 13.1

TIME DISPOSITION OF A FAMILY UNIT (2 ADULTS) IN A KIBBUTZ
(Schematic example)

	No. of Days	Days:	Percentage of Total
Calendar Days Per Year.......................730		730 =	100
Total Off-days.............................202		202 =	28
of which:			
Sabbath and holidays.........116			
Sick leave...................32			
Off-days for leave, training			
childbearing, etc...........54			
202			
Total Work Days............................528		528 =	72
of which:			
Total services......................220		220 =	30
of which:			
Services for 2 adults.......120			
Services for an average of			
1.4 children per family...100*			
220			
Total Administration................... 50		50 =	7
of which:			
Management............... 35 (5%)			
Municipal affairs........... 15 (2%)			
50			
Total Services and Administration.............270		270 =	37
Balance: Work Days in Production...............258		258 =	35
			72

* After deducting work done by the children, converted into man-days.

tendency of differentiation in well-established settlements in giving members more liberty to decide on preferences in spending over and above their daily needs, such as books or records, but no one is allowed to make private savings.

The Kibbutz is managed by elected committees among whom the one responsible for labour distribution plays an important role. The proportion of the number of earners to the total available labour force forms one of the main keys for explaining the Kibbutz economy—a fact which is quite often misinterpreted when comparing different forms of settlement. Taking two adult members as a *family unit* (although there may be more men than women or *vice versa* in a specific Kibbutz) we arrive at the typical picture of time disposition in an old, established settlement as shown in Table 13.1.

At first it may appear that the proportion of work in purely remunerative occupations is very low, but it will be shown later that this is a fallacy. In effect, other forms of settlement hardly reach a higher share although the individual farmer's family spends many more days in gainful work.

No further explanation is needed to show that the relationship between non-work, services, and remunerative work is the same in all kinds of enterprises within the Kibbutz. The services being given to all members simultaneously, they cannot be determined separately for a man working in agriculture or one working in a factory. All members have the same rights for leave. Sickness days per family unit are calculated by dividing their total number by the average number of units, etc. If, for instance, a Kibbutz numbers 300 adult members, or 150 family units, it may be assumed that 35 per cent, or 105 members, are engaged in all kinds of enterprises. They form the *earners* of the Kibbutz. If we further assume that the farm employs 60 per cent, industrial workshops 20 per cent, and outside work and investments another 20 per cent, we arrive at the conclusion that there are 63 agricultural earners, or that 60 per cent of the 150 family units, or 90 families, depend for their living on farming, 30 on industrial enterprises and another 30 on other occupations.

In relating the agricultural resources to the agricultural population (those living on non-agricultural enterprises have naturally to be excluded), we arrive on the average of all Kibbutzim at the figures shown in Table 13.2.

There is wide variation in the scope and composition of the agricultural enterprises among the different Kibbutzim and the table gives only a rough picture. Usually every Kibbutz comprises around 8–10 different farm enterprises, the relative importance of which vary with the natural conditions. In some districts a single enterprise, such as banana, apple, or carp growing, makes up 30–40 per cent of the total income from farming; in many districts dairy and poultry together account for around 50 per cent in varying proportions, supplemented by a number of other small enterprises.

TABLE 13.2

AVERAGE RESOURCES PER AGRICULTURAL FAMILY UNIT
(2 ADULTS) IN A KIBBUTZ, 1958–59

	(hectares)
Total Cultivated Area	10.8
of which:	
Unirrigated field crops	8.3
Irrigated field crops	1.3
Orchards	0.8
Fish-ponds	0.3
Woodland	0.1
Livestock:	*(numbers)*
Milch-cows	1.0
Young stock	1.1
Beef cattle	1.6
Sheep and goats	3.1
Laying hens	135.0

TABLE 13.3

TYPICAL CAPITAL INVESTMENTS AT RENEWAL VALUE IN A FULLY ESTABLISHED KIBBUTZ,
GIVEN IN I£ (Israel Pounds) PER FAMILY UNIT

Per Family Unit	Production Assets	Consumers' Assets	Total Assets
In agriculture...............	30,000	10,000	40,000
In workshops................	20,000	10,000	30,000
In outside work..............	......	10,000	10,000

Generally, the Kibbutzim fulfil in Israel the role which in other countries is played by large-scale farms. They concentrate especially on enterprises which lend themselves to mechanization, such as grain crops, quite often cultivating up to a thousand hectares. They keep herds of 120–200 cows and more than 10,000 layers, specializing in the production of broilers and practically monopolizing the growing of carp in artificial ponds, the growing of bananas and the keeping of herds of beef cattle on natural pasture.

The renewal value of capital assets per family unit in a fully established Kibbutz at present prices may be estimated as shown in Table 13.3. (I£3 = $1.)

In a Kibbutz composed of, say, 60 per cent earners in agriculture, 20 per cent earners in industrial enterprises and 20 per cent earners in outside work or new investments, the weighted average of production assets amounts to I£22,000 and that of consumer assets to I£10,000, totaling I£32,000 per family unit.

The investment rate in production assets per earner in agriculture varies widely among the different enterprises. In the dairy and poultry enterprises it amounts to around I£40,000; in fruit orchards, sheep or carp breeding to I£15 to 30,000, and in unirrigated field crops, vegetable growing, or industrial crops (sugar beet, cotton, or peanuts) to I£6 to 11,000, so that the average total investment per earner may also vary considerably according to the proportions of the respective enterprises in each district. Similarly the workshops and industrial enterprises also show very large differences in investment rates per worker. Workers engaged in outside work are not equipped with productive capital assets, by definition, so that they share in only the consumers' assets of the Kibbutz which may amount to I£8 to 12,000 per family unit depending on the size and type of dwelling houses, dining halls, recreation rooms, etc.

The liabilities of a typical Kibbutz consist of long-, medium-, and short-term loans and open credits. Owing to inflation, most old, established settlements paid off their initial foundation loans and acquired a substantial part of their assets as equities. On the average older settlement, loan capital forms around 50 per cent of the present renewal value of the assets. A rapid expansion during the last decade has led to a considerable worsening of the financial structure as most of the additional investments were made with medium- or even short-term loans at relatively high interest rates, averaging 10 per cent and more per annum.

All Kibbutzim keep very extensive records which are published in an abridged form by an audit union as annual balance sheets. These publications, however, are outdated and suffer from a number of shortcomings. They do not contain quantitative but only money data. The incomes from different sources and enterprises appear separately but the expenditures are lumped together according to items for all enterprises. Purchased and farm-produced supplies, such as feed for livestock, appear in one figure. Costs of living of the member units are regarded as wages and are not separated from costs of production, so that the final result appears in the form of net profit or net loss instead of net income before deducting costs of living. This makes it difficult to distinguish between the influence of business activities and standards of living on the final result. A high profit may be due either to very efficient production or to a lower standard of living, and a net loss either to higher costs of living or inefficient production. Only special surveys can reveal the true nature of affairs and serve as a basis for economic analysis. Such surveys have rarely been undertaken and there is little factual material from which to draw conclusions on the over-all profitability of Kibbutzim during recent years. There are ample examples, however, of the profitability of certain main branches, such as dairy and poultry, which are representative of the variations in economic results. These enterprise analyses were carried out by the Division of Farm Management of the Joint Extension Authority and we shall base this discussion mainly on these findings when comparing Kibbutz and Moshav economies in this study.

MAIN FEATURES OF THE MOSHAV ECONOMY

The Moshav consists of two parts: the co-operative of the village as a whole and the individual farms.

Every farmer in a Moshav is *eo ipso* a member of the village co-operative which is managed by elected members. The co-operative acts as the agent for selling all farm produce and buying farm supplies, food, and household goods for the farmers. It owns and operates the water plant and mains installation, storehouses and cold storage rooms, milk-delivery station, incubators, heavy machinery and repair shops, a general store, etc. It runs the educational institutions (kindergarten, schools, youth centres, adult education and cultural activities). It fulfils the obligations of municipal and administrative services, contracts loans for the farmers, and makes investments for the development of the village. It keeps records of all its transactions on behalf of every farmer and the village as a whole. Quite often some of the fields, especially unirrigated grain crops, are mechanically cultivated by the co-operative, and the yields divided among the farmers. All these tasks serve one purpose: to relieve the farmers of as many obligations and burdens as possible and to set them free for operating and managing their individual farms, according to their own plans and abilities.

These services, carried out by hired workers, are costly and the costs have to be borne by the farmers. The co-operative covers its costs in three ways: by deducting a certain percentage from the price of produce sold, by adding a percentage to the price of supplies bought, and by levying direct taxes. The costs vary widely from place to place according to the scope of services rendered and, on the average of old, established Moshavim, amounted in 1960–61 to around I£2,000 p.a. per farmstead. Of this sum I£1,500 were derived from levies on sales and purchases, representing 13 per cent of the value of sales of farm produce through the co-operative, and another I£500 from direct taxes for municipal services. It is interesting to note that the higher the absolute expenditure for services, the lower is their percentage in relation to the value of turn-over. In other words, a very efficient Moshav can afford expensive services, as these tend to increase the productive capacity of the farmer-members. In a less efficient Moshav even the smaller expenses for less extensive services may form a heavy burden. The costs and functioning of services are determined by the strict adherence of all farmer-members to the principles of co-operative marketing. Members who, for instance, exploit the credit facilities of a co-operative without selling all their produce through it, are undermining the economic existence of a Moshav. Co-operation is a two-way road.

This division of work between the farming and the service population, whereby the farmers pay for services instead of doing them themselves, distinguishes the Moshav from the Kibbutz where all such tasks are carried out by the members themselves. For this reason there can be no direct comparison between the annual work schedule of a farmer in a Moshav and in a Kibbutz. An economic appraisal has to take this difference into account and try to bring both types of settlement to a common denominator in this respect. In otherwise equal circumstances, it can be assumed that the proportion of earning to total population is of decisive influence on the economic result. In this respect a Moshav is not very different from a Kibbutz. On the average old, established Moshavim there are 80 farmsteads. These are served by 23 workers, 3 of whom work in the store and in municipal services, on the payroll of the co-operative. Relying on survey data, we may assume that the 80 farmsteads contain around 240 adults whom we may define as 120 family units. Adding the 23 families of service workers, such a Moshav consists of 143 family units, of whom 84 per cent are farmers and 16 per cent non-farm population. On each farmstead around 500 days a year, equalling 330 days per family unit,

TABLE 13.4

WORK SCHEDULE IN A TYPICAL MOSHAV

| | | | Time Spent in Productive Activities | | | |
| | | | By the group | | Related to the Moshav | |
Group	Number	Per Cent	Days	Per cent of calendar days	Days	Per cent of calendar days
Farmers' families.......	120	84	330	45	277	37.8
Co-op workers in productive services......	20	14	290	40	41	5.6
Co-op workers in consumer services.......	3	2	...	..	...	....
Weighted Average..318						43.4

are spent in production and management on the farm. The service workers' families spend around 290 days each in earning activities. By pro-rating these work schedules we arrive at calculations of time spent in productive work in the Moshav as a whole, as shown in Table 13.4.

These 318 days (or 43.4 per cent of the calendar days) per family unit may be compared with those on the Kibbutz. There we found 258 days in production to which another 35 days for management have to be added, so that one arrives at 293 days as a comparable figure. There remains a difference of 25 days per year per family unit in favour of the Moshav. All other conditions being equal, one could conclude that the average family unit in a Moshav has an earning capacity exceeding that of the Kibbutz by 8.5 per cent.

The farmsteads of a Moshav are all of the same size and get the same equipment at the time of establishment. Yet, over the years, they develop in very different ways and become more and more unequal. As every farmer is free to operate and manage his farm according to his own wishes, there are those who succeed in expanding their enterprises and others who do not. The former occasionally rent additional land from the latter, but the main differences lie in the extent of the livestock enterprises. To give a typical example of an old, established Moshav: the number of milch-cows varies from 1 to 10, with an average of 4.4, the number of laying hens from 0 to 800, with an average of 350, the total value of farm assets (dwelling houses excluded) at renewal value from I£20,000 to I£72,000, with an average of I£45,000. Accordingly, there are great differences in the value of the annual output which varies between less than I£8,000 and more than I£50,000, averaging I£25,000, and in net incomes which vary

TABLE 13.5

AVERAGE RESOURCES PER FARM IN MOSHAVIM, 1958–59

	Old, Established Moshavim	Younger Moshavim	Young Moshavim	All Moshavim
	(hectares)	(hectares)	(hectares)	(hectares)
Cultivated Area.............	5.2	3.7	3.4	3.8
of which:				
Unirrigated field crops.....	3.0	1.6	1.7	2.0
Irrigated field crops.......	1.4	1.6	1.1	1.2
Orchards...............	0.8	0.5	0.6	0.6
	(number)	(number)	(number)	(number)
Livestock:				
Milch-cows..............	2.3	2.9	1.2	1.7
Young stock.............	2.6	2.4	1.1	1.6
Beef cattle..............	1.4	1.4	0.4	0.8
Sheep and goats..........	0.4	0.8	2.4	1.7
Laying hens	300	100	50	100

from less than I£1,500 to more than I£20,000 per farm. Similar are the differences in the labour input of the families which varies between less than 200 and more than 650 labour days per farm, depending on the size of the family and the work opportunities on the farm.

In view of the large degree of variability it does not make sense to compare the Moshav as a whole with a Kibbutz and even the average farm of a specific Moshav does not reveal the huge differences between one farm and another.

For comparison's sake we give in Table 13.5 a few data on the over-all picture of the average resources and the farm structure in Moshavim for the year 1958–59, relating to the average farm.

Comparing the average resources per farm in Moshavim with those per agricultural family unit in Kibbutzim (see Table 13.2) we see that the cultivated area in the former is far smaller. This is mainly due to the difference in unirrigated field crops, whereas irrigated field crops and orchards are almost the same. (In old, established Moshavim they even exceed the area of the Kibbutz.) Farms in Moshavim are more heavily stocked with livestock, especially dairy animals and, in old, established Moshavim, also with poultry. The numbers of beef cattle, sheep, and goats, on the other hand, are much smaller. (Fish-ponds are the exclusive domain of Kibbutzim.)

There are striking differences with regard to mechanical equipment. We find in Table 13.6 the relation between the number of tractors and other heavy machinery to the number of Kibbutzim and Moshavim respectively.

Even the old, established Moshavim, not to speak of the average Moshav, possess much less machinery than the average Kibbutz. This is largely a result of the different farm structures. The large-scale farm

TABLE 13.6
EQUIPMENT WITH HEAVY MACHINERY

	Per Kibbutz	Per Average Moshav	Per Old, Established Moshav
Number of crawler tractors.............	4.2	1.3	2.4
Number of wheel tractors................	8.1	4.1	9.8
Number of combine-harvesters...........	2.7	0.6	1.3
Number of hay-balers...................	1.9	0.6	1.5
Number of trucks......................	2.1	1.3	2.0

TABLE 13.7
CAPITAL ASSETS IN I£ AT RENEWAL VALUE IN TYPICAL FARMS OF OLD, ESTABLISHED MOSHAVIM

	Average	Highest*	Lowest*
Cow shed with equipment............	10,500	15,000	6,000
Poultry houses with equipment........	8,700	17,000	4,000
Irrigation network...................	1,600	2,200	600
Machinery and tools................	3,200	9,000	400
Orchards.........................	6,000	8,000	4,000
Dairy herd........................	14,000	18,000	10,000
Poultry...........................	3,000	4,000	1,000
TOTAL PRODUCTION ASSETS On the farm......................	47,000	71,000	36,000
Share in production assets of the co-operative....................	6,500	12,000	3,000
TOTAL PRODUCTION ASSETS..	53,500	80,000*	40,000*
Dwelling house....................	25,000	40,000	6,000
Share in consumers' assets of the co-operative....................	2,500	5,000	1,000
TOTAL CONSUMERS' ASSETS...	27,500	44,000*	7,500*
TOTAL ASSETS................	81,000	115,000*	47,500*

* It is self-evident that highest and lowest data do not occur on the same farm for all items.

TABLE 13.8
TYPICAL CAPITAL INVESTMENTS IN I£ PER FAMILY UNIT IN A MOSHAV AND A KIBBUTZ

	Moshav	Kibbutz
Production assets..............	36,000	30,000
Consumers' assets.............	18,000	10,000
TOTAL ASSETS.............	54,000	40,000

of a Kibbutz concentrates more on enterprises which lend themselves to mechanization (grain crops) or which can be handled more easily by group work (growing of bananas and alfalfa, maintaining fishponds for carp breeding, etc.). It places relatively less importance on the development of enterprises involving much hand labour, such as vegetable growing, or those requiring much individual care, such as dairying and poultry keeping. Within the livestock enterprises the Kibbutzim prefer beef cattle and broiler production to the keeping of dairy cows and laying hens.

We have touched already upon the question of capital invested in farm assets in a Moshav and have shown the large variation between one farm and another. When speaking of capital investments one has to take into account also those assets belonging to the co-operative which form part and parcel of the Moshav as a whole. Relating these figures to the number of farmsteads we arrive at the calculation shown in Table 13.7. In a well-developed Moshav the renewal value of the productive assets of the co-operative amounts to around I£6,500 and of consumers' assets (general store, recreation hall, school, etc.) to around I£2,500.

Table 13.7 contains a summary of the capital assets which may be regarded as typical for old, established Moshav farms.

The average well-developed farm in a Moshav represents a renewal value of approximately I£80,000. We may not be wrong in assuming that these farms acquired 70 to 90 per cent of their assets over the years as equity and owe no more than 10 to 30 per cent in the form of medium- and short-term loans. They show in this respect a very different picture from the Kibbutzim which are much more indebted. The reason is partly to be found in the fact that most of the older Moshavim entered the period of heavy inflation with better equipped farms so that they were able to exploit the receding value of the pound by repaying loans at nominal value. Kibbutzim, on the other hand, contracted more and more loans to expand their activities and to acquire capital assets, with the result that they now possess better production facilities but are also settled with large debts.

Just as with the work schedule one cannot directly compare the assets of a farmstead in a Moshav with those of a family unit in a Kibbutz. There are—according to the same definition—on average at least 1.5 family units in each farmstead, as mentioned above. By applying this key, we may roughly compare the assets per agricultural unit of a Kibbutz (as there are no non-agricultural units in a Moshav) to those of a family unit in a Moshav, as shown in Table 13.8.

The average family unit in a Moshav disposes of around 20 per cent more production assets than in a Kibbutz, but its investments in dwelling and other consumer assets are far higher. It is one of the characteristics of Kibbutzim that they are very modest in their individual housing standards, although they occasionally spend large sums for dining halls and cultural centres which, however, do not represent a very big investment per family unit. There can be no doubt that the difference between a Kibbutz and a Moshav with regard to capital investments is much larger than that between their *earning capacities,* as shown above. Although this is a very rough measurement, it has nevertheless a certain degree of validity. In order to compete in terms of profitability of capital invested, the farmer in a Moshav cannot rely upon his slightly larger working capacity but has to earn much more per day. If he does not, he has to be content either with a lower standard of living or with a lower profit on capital, or both. In effect, many Moshav farmers earn lower profits on capital than do Kibbutzim and can afford to because most of their investments are equity capital. That they do not judge capital according to opportunity costs bears witness to the fact that they do not look upon farming from a purely economic point of view but primarily as a way of living.

COMPARATIVE PROFITABILITY OF KIBBUTZ AND MOSHAV

There is no easy way of comparing the profitability of the two types of settlement, and this for a number of reasons. The Kibbutz economy is only partly based on farming and to a considerable degree on industry, handicraft, and labour outside the settlement, whereas the settler in a Moshav derives all his income from farming only. The farm structure itself is so different that no direct comparison can be drawn. It could be argued, for instance, that the profitability of agriculture in Kibbutzim depends on the preponderance of enterprises with very high profits, such as apples, fish-ponds, bananas, and grain crops, which are mainly concentrated in their hands and are hardly to be found at all, or play a very minor role, in Moshavim. In these cases the differences in profitability ought to be ascribed to the farm structure as such and not to the characteristics of the type of settlement which are discussed here. Yet, two main branches of Israel's agriculture—poultry and dairy—which together comprise no less than 44 per cent of the total value of output (in Jewish farming even 52 per cent) may safely serve as a basis of direct comparison since both types of settlement are engaged in them and they can be brought to a common denominator. Such investigations have been carried out in recent years in 70 Kibbutzim and in 58 individual farms of the Moshav type for poultry farming, and in 43 Kibbutzim and 63 individual farms for dairy farming.

To exclude the influence of scale of operation, the relative profitability of poultry farming was expressed in net profit "per ton of feed," and in dairy farming "per thousand feed units" used in the respective enterprises on each farm. The net profit is calculated as the profit or loss remaining after total expenses (including labour of the family, interest, and depreciation) have been deducted from the

TABLE 13.9
RELATIVE PROFITABILITY OF POULTRY FARMING
NET PROFIT IN I£ PER TON OF FEED, IN 1960

	In Kibbutzim	In Moshavim
Group A..............	+37	+54
Group B..............	− 3	− 2
Group C..............	−44	−63

TABLE 13.10
RELATIVE PROFITABILITY OF DAIRY FARMING
NET PROFIT IN I£ |PER THOUSAND FEED UNITS, IN 1960

	In Kibbutzim	In Moshavim
Group A..............	+51	+88
Group B..............	+23	+28
Group C..............	− 8	−17

value of output. In Kibbutzim the costs of labour are calculated according to the actual costs of living of all members and their dependents, pro-rated to the number of days spent in production. In Moshavim a careful calculation of the number of days required for every job was made and costs per day charged according to the same wage level as in Kibbutzim.

The farms of both types were divided into three groups: Group A containing the first 25 per cent, Group B the following 50 per cent, and Group C the last 25 per cent of the farms, arranged in decreasing order of profit. The results are seen in Tables 13.9 and 13.10.

The first conclusion to be drawn from these tables is the enormous variability of profits in each type of settlement. There are good, medium, and bad farms in both types and these differ within the same type much more than from one type to the other. This means that there is no significance in the *average* profitability of either the Kibbutz or the Moshav.

Without going into details about the absolute profitability of both enterprises (which naturally changes from year to year owing to price influences as well as changes in efficiency), there is one remarkable fact standing out clearly: farms in the Moshavim show a considerably larger variance than in the Kibbutzim. There is no doubt that an efficient individual farmer does reach higher profits than an efficient Kibbutz farm. On the other hand, an inefficient individual farmer also suffers greater losses than even an inefficient Kibbutz farm. This phenomenon, which repeats itself year after year and in every enterprise which can be compared, is obviously explained by the fact that in a Kibbutz the less efficient members need not be entrusted with the task of management. A man may be quite a good worker but not a good manager. In the collective farm he will then still be rather efficient as long as there are other members responsible for management. As an individual farmer who cannot divide his responsibilities but has to do his own work and to manage the farm as a whole he may not succeed at all.

For this reason the large-scale enterprise of a Kibbutz with its possibilities of division of work should be of special importance for a country in which a comparatively large percentage of farmers have taken up farming only recently, often without proper training, and have to adapt themselves to ever-changing conditions of prices and rapid developments in technique.

Apart from basing ourselves on exact calculations of profit in one branch or another we can also give an indirect proof of the fact that there is no definite advantage or disadvantage in the one type of settlement as against the other. Throughout the last thirty years, when both types of settlement existed side by side, there never was any special economic preference given to either. Both worked under the same conditions of price relations, subsidies, taxes, etc., and both had the same chances of success or failure. The fact that both continue to exist as going concerns proves that one is not inferior to the other *per se*. Given the same opportunities they can obtain similar results. It is not so much a question of type of settlement but rather of efficient management which proves decisive for their economic success. The independent farmer with managerial ability may be able to make better profits in a Moshav, but the average settler may feel more secure in a Kibbutz. Nevertheless, it has to be stressed again that the choice between the one type and the other never was, nor is, a question of economic considerations but rather one of individual inclination for a distinct way of life.

Both types have grown under the special conditions and in the specific social environment of Israel. No conclusions should be drawn from this experience for other countries without carefully investigating whether it is appropriate in other conditions.

14

Agricultural Planning in France

L. MALASSIS*

Central Directorate, Economic and Social Research,
(I.N.R.A.), France

DEPENDING ON THEIR TRADITIONS, their institutions, their political philosophies, and their levels of expansion, nations can think out several forms of social economic organization capable of promoting their social and economic development. These forms vary from capitalist free enterprise to integrated planning of the Soviet type. Countries of liberal traditions have a strong prejudice against planning but the necessity of economic forecasting is universally admitted. The United States of America have made remarkable progress towards this. Forecasting is necessary to planning but the latter goes further; it involves a series of well thought out and co-ordinated economic actions.

The degree and kind of intervention differentiate two categories of plans the imperative and the flexible [1, p. 34].† French planning is a prototype of the so-called flexible kind; it is actually a matter of great interest, as much in advanced countries as in those in course of development. We shall consider it in its technical aspects, its institutions, and its results. This chapter is called "Agricultural Planning in France," but we must emphasize that the planning of the agricultural sector is only one of the aspects of global planning, and that a study limited too exclusively to the agricultural sector would not show the originality of French planning.

As a first approach, this planning can be called "an hypothesis

---

* I wish to thank M. G. Brown (Maître de Conférences d'Économie Rurale à l'E.N.S.A.R.) for having kindly read this essay in the original French and in the translation.

† Numerals within brackets indicate references at end of chapter.

of chosen growth." It takes account of long-term structural changes (historical processes of growth, recent fundamental tendencies, disparity of sectors and zones, etc.) but depends also on short-term situations and events. The choice of a plan implies a series of preliminary projections towards "the horizon" and towards "the end of the plan" at various growth rates (e.g., for the preparation of the Fourth French Plan, projections were made for 1975 and 1965 at 6, 4.5, and 3 per cent growth rates). The plan is a pattern of practicable expansion taking account of past trends and desired goals.

The mean global annual growth rate is the product of the combined growth of the productive sectors. Analysis of the growth of the various sectors shows that they are generally of logistic form [2]. The production of a sector or an industry tends to reach a limit at the end of a certain length of time. Mathematically, the question of growth may be posed as follows [2]: "In what conditions does a quantity of production which conforms to logistic law obey exponential law?" It is perfectly possible to construct a system of logistic functions of which the sum is exponential, but the rates of growth, mathematically compatible, must be feasible. This involves amongst other things, intersectoral transfers so far as economically possible (introduction of constraints into the system) and socially acceptable, that is to say, not giving rise to intolerable social tensions. The chosen hypothesis must be acceptable both economically and socially. Consequently, it is necessary to indicate in outline the ways of elaborating the hypotheses and the process of choice.

In practice the starting point is the estimation of final demand in order to determine the necessary production and the corresponding growth rates. This estimate is made at constant prices, both in value and physical quantities, so as to determine the quantitative objectives by sectors. Household consumption is valued according to the structure of the population, its income elasticities, and the theoretical rate of growth adopted. Public consumption is estimated as a function of the costs of civil and military administration, of education and research costs, of external aid, etc. Thanks to the inter-industrial picture resulting from Leontief's research, the total production of each sector is linked with intermediate products, and these can be determined for each industry and sector. The structure of production must be compatible with fundamental equilibrium in relation to the external balance: consumption, saving and investment, employment, and currency. For the preparation of the Fourth French Plan this considerable work was done for the three annual growth rates already mentioned, and the economic scheme for the final year of the plan was constructed for twenty-eight sectors.

The Government finally assumed a mean annual global growth rate of 5 per cent. Although very desirable, the 6 per cent rate was rejected owing to lack of productive capacity and of qualified workers, a situation which would be liable to involve changes of wages and prices and to cause a deficit in the commercial balance.

The French Plan is global and sectoral because, within a global growth theory, the objectives are built up by sectors and by productive industries. These are imperative for the basic sectors (the mineral fuel industry, the electricity and gas industries, the Renault works, and the large credit institutions were nationalized immediately after the war) and indicative for the others. Objectives are realized sooner by stimulation than by compulsion and prohibition. The French economy is conducted, on the whole, as a decentralized economy. There is no systematic intervention. This characterizes a second aspect of French planning which can therefore be called flexible planning.

The choice of a global rate of growth and the determination of objectives of production of each sector and industry allow us to calculate, for each sector and industry, the *rate of growth aimed at*. These desirable rates differ more or less from spontaneous rates. The differences point to direction and intensity of intervention. Some sectors need stimulation, others slowing down, while for others intervention is not necessary [3]. The plan thus provides a framework for co-ordinated and justifiable political intervention in accordance with the assumed rate of growth chosen.

To encourage private undertakings to act in the way thought to be most favourable to the general interest, the public authorities can adopt several courses of action: subvention, credits, fiscal arrangements, public orders, intervention on the market, etc. The success of the plan depends also on adherence by the active parts of the nation. This point will be considered under institutions.

The programming of agriculture is included in the global plan of growth because of the part played by agriculture in it and of the proper distribution of its products. In advanced countries continuous industrialization is followed by a reduction in the contribution of agriculture to global revenue. Agricultural growth rate is weaker than that of other sectors. Agricultural workers tend to transfer to industry. Agriculture is increasingly modernized, and the productivity of agricultural work improves. In the advanced countries, the food per head of population has increased both in quantity and quality and there is less fluctuation. This is equally noticeable in socialist economies. In economies reaching the stage of *mass consumption* [4] the fundamental problem is to know how to give the agriculturist an income to compare with that of other social professional categories (parity). In the meantime production has to be adjusted to possible outlets whether profitable or not which tend to be less than the production potential (the sectoral economic objective), by improving productivity (the productivity objective) and by providing facilities for the necessary global economic growth transfers (the global economic objective).

All advanced countries have surplus problems, agricultural support, and methods for reducing disparity between town and country.

At the heart of the global plan it is the agricultural plan which raises the most difficulties and uncertainties because of the natural conditions of production, its extreme fragmentation, and its unfavourable economic circumstances, whilst the agriculturists' aspirations and expectations keep rising. Estimation of the home market is not very difficult as the economic laws concerning food consumption in relation to income variations are relatively well known. Estimation of foreign markets offers a wider degree of uncertainty.

The agricultural economy is characterized by an almost permanent state of disequilibrium because of the difficulties of adjustment of production to needs: disequilibrium of shortages in the east and surpluses in the west.

In view of the economy of abundance, the fixing of the level of production is a matter of political decision in which help given to agriculture is involved as is the encouragement of progress leading to expansion, the development of the non-agricultural sectors and the consequent growth of the agricultural population, and the evolution of international policies to help countries in the course of development. In the Fourth French Plan the existence of agricultural surpluses is explicitly admitted [5]. Evidently it is impossible to decide on and to carry out a rural development strategy involving economic growth within the limited framework of a plan. It will be many years, both in France and in most other European countries, before agriculture can be brought into global economy and agriculturists achieve *mass consumption*.

The choice and implementation of a global growth hypothesis, the determination of the sectors' objectives (and eventually of the zones), the definition and putting into action of the means of intervention involve methods of decision and action which, in Western society, must be compatible with the functioning of a democratic society. In the present stage of the French experiment, the institutions of planning are: the General Commission of the Plan, the Commissions of Modernization, the regional organizations, the Supreme Council of the Plan, and the Inter-ministerial Committee.

The General Commission of the Plan, established by the decree of 3 January 1946, is a permanent body with a limited establishment of 100 to 150 employees, very different from the enormous administration of the East. It is directed by a commissioner-general (the first was M. Jean Monnet), permanent delegate of the Prime Minister in all the ministerial departments for everything concerning the Plan. The Commission has one particular duty, the comparison and coordination of the Plans. It examines the proposals submitted and watches the execution of the Plan.

The Commissions of Modernization are the most original of the institutions of French planning. They are composed of members of the higher civil service and the ministries, leaders of industry, bankers, trade union leaders, experts, etc. These commissions are called vertical when they are concerned with the modernization of a single productive sector (agriculture, power, etc.), horizontal when they are concerned with problems common to several sectors (employment, investment, etc.). Each of these commissions forms the "working groups" (groupes de travail) which seem necessary. Within the groups, advice may be sought from experts who are not necessarily members of the commissions. This explains why 991 commission members and as many as 3,137 people (of whom 107 were agriculturists) have taken part in the preparation of the Fourth Plan. This system, founded by M. Jean Monnet, arose out of the *planned economy;* its aim is to make all the active forces of the nation take part in the building of the Plan, to make them conscious of the phenomena of growth, and to make it easier for them to comply with the working out of the Plan.

The regional organizations, which have been so much in mind these last few years have not found their final forms yet; their function is concerned with the planning of space. The excessive growth of Paris, the success of J. F. Gravier's work, *Paris et le desert francais* [6], increasing regional imbalance—together have caused the public authorities to pay more and more attention to the decentralization of Paris and to regional activity. During recent years many articles have been published. One need only mention that France has been divided into 21 areas of regional operation (*circonscriptions d'action régionale*) which in accordance with the General Commission of the Plan gradually become the effective organization for executive action which assures the regional nature of the national plan.

The Supreme Council of the Plan and the Inter-ministerial Committee have the task of supervision and co-ordination. The participation of social groups is provided for through the Economic and Social Council and the Fourth Plan has been examined and passed by Parliament. The trade unions, the political parties and general opinion have paid much attention lately to the democratization of the Plan. The debate has turned on the control of economic and social development and the distribution of the results of growth between monopolies, financial groups, and labour. This debate is important but cannot be brought into this discussion. The importance of planning within French institutions is made clear by the interest shown by the various social elements in its control.

Having mentioned the techniques of planning in the first section, and the institutions in the present one, it is now possible to point out the practical methods of working out the Plan and the special features of French planning.

The working out of the Plan comprises the following phases:

1. Ascertaining an hypothesis of growth at various rates (e.g. Fourth Plan scheme, at 6, 4, and 3 per cent rates).
2. The Government's choice of a rate of growth, taking account of its effect on fundamental economic balance and social tensions. The assumed growth rate (e.g., 5 per cent in 1960) is the basic point for the detailed elaboration of the Plan.
3. Within the assumed rate of growth selected (expressed in directives), the Commissions of Modernization are asked to state the conditions for expansion by sectors and industries (Commission reports).
4. The final synthesis aims at eliminating the worst inconsistencies resulting from the Commissions' proposals and at establishing a coherent and practicable total Plan.

The special features of French planning may be summarized as follows: Global (and sectoral), flexible (no systematic interference) proceeding from concerted economy (co-operation from different social and professional categories) combining in its fulfilment ". . . the force of authority and the spontaneous reactions of industries and individuals on the market to achieve the allotted collective goals or to get near them." (F. Perroux [3].)

Since the foundation of the General Commission in 1946, three Plans have been worked out and applied, the Fourth (1962–1965) is in process of execution. In this section we shall describe each of the plans in outline, mentioning the fundamental innovations in agricultural policy. (It is not possible here to proceed to a detailed study of objectives and investment [7].)

The design of the Plans aims at long-term perspectives, but is always more or less influenced by events as they proceed. In order that readers may see several important aspects of recent progress made by the agricultural economy of France three graphs are subjoined as Figures 14.1, 14.2, and 14.3.

The First Plan, also called the Monnet Plan (1946–1956), was designed with a view to the reconstruction and modernization of the French economy. It was particularly concerned with basic industries (coal, electricity, iron, cement, agricultural machinery, and transport) considered to have priority for economic expansion. Although agriculture was not classified as a basic activity, three modernization commissions were constituted. They proposed as a global objective for agriculture that it should exceed its pre-war level by 1950; a result achieved as shown in Figure 14.1. In the immediate post-war situation, individual and general interests coincided, the King effect (price depression) did not come into force, and incomes increased with production. Public and professional authorities agreed to act so as to increase production and the first agricultural Plan was essentially a collection

Index base 100—average 1934–1938

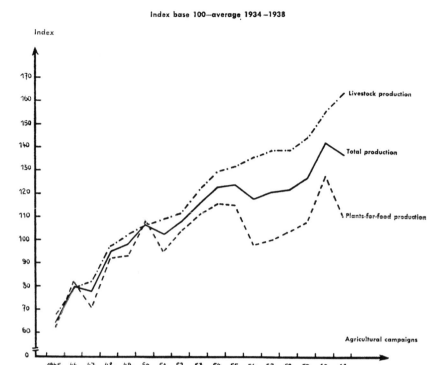

Fig. 14.1. Evolution of Agricultural Production, Final Net, 1945–62. (Source: Agricultural Statistics from Agricultural Department, 1961.)

of technical recommendations designed to increase agricultural production.

In 1948, the national economic situation was modified. The index of industrial prices reached and then exceeded the index of food products (Fig. 14.2). Agriculture which was the starting point of inflation then began to trail behind it.

On the international plane, General George C. Marshall gave a famous lecture at Harvard University which gave birth to concerted international policy and was followed by a revision of the Monnet Plan. The Plan which had been decided for 1946 was replaced by a four-year Plan on 1 January 1949 (1949–1952) the aim of which was to reach equilibrium in the balance of payments by 30 June 1952 (a condition for Marshall aid). On the agricultural side, the fundamental aspect of this revision was its swing towards the export of basic agricultural products (wheat, meat, and milk). This was prompted by

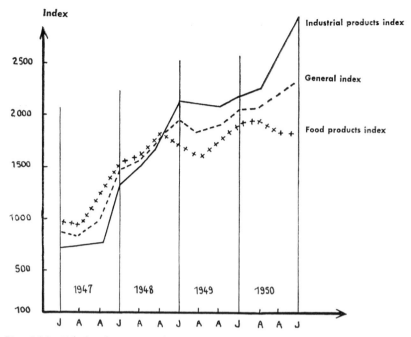

Base 100 in 1938

Fig. 14.2. Wholesale price index comparing rate of increase of food and industrial products with the general index, 1947–50. (Source: Monthly Bulletin for Statistics, I.N.S.E.E.)

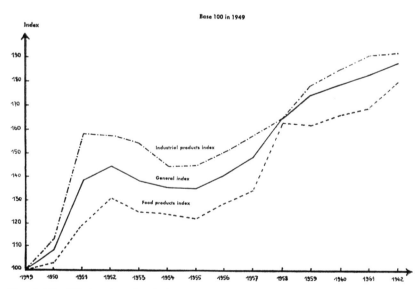

Base 100 in 1949

Fig. 14.3. Wholesale price index comparing rate of increase of food and industrial products with the general index, 1949–62. (Source: Monthly Bulletin for Statistics, I.N.S.E.E.)

several factors: the fall of agricultural prices in 1948 corresponding with the increase of production; the lack of foodstuffs and strong currencies in Europe; and the need to import raw material for industrial expansion—the contribution to the achievement of equilibrium in the balance of payments by 1952. Nevertheless, during this period the necessity to control food prices in order to stop inflation (Fig. 14.3) seems to have been decisive and agricultural policy was deceptive in its results.

The Second Plan (1952–1957) was designed in a situation in which surpluses were difficult to assimilate and in which there were inequalities of incomes and in standards of living, and when prices were becoming stabilized at levels too high for freedom of international exchange. This situation necessitated more serious investigations and, for the first time, thanks to improvements in national accounting, a scheme for global economic growth was established [1, p. 74]. The assumed rate of growth was increased by 25 per cent of the national product, involving a 20 per cent increase of agricultural production, 25 per cent of industry and 60 per cent of building.

When the General Commission of the Plan proposed a growth increase of 20 per cent to the agricultural commissions, professional people feared that production would break prices and interfere with modernization. When the public authorities encouraged production, professional people asked that the expansion should be organized. It was during the period of the Second Plan, that steps to support markets and to orientate agricultural production were taken (30 September 1953, decrees for market organization). At the same time a great effort was made in agricultural extension services. With regard to aid for regions in economic difficulties, the need for which was so often stressed during the Second Plan, it took shape essentially in the project for improving the region Bas Rhone-Lauguedoe.

When the Third Plan (1958–1961) was drawn up, the situation was characterized by a rather fast expansion together with inflation and imbalance between sectors and zones which became more and more worrying. Foreign balance was in deficit while France had to give greater help to countries which were reaching independence. In this situation, and with a global growth outlook, the Third Plan's main objectives were as follows: to increase home products by 27 per cent—of which 30 per cent would be industrial and 20 per cent agricultural; to restabilize the balance of payments; to make a special effort for housing and education; to limit development in the region of Paris; and to increase help to the countries in course of development.

So far as agriculture was concerned, the Third Plan was marked by two fundamental ideas: (a) The agricultural production rate should increase more rapidly than home consumption. The success of the agricultural expansion policy would depend entirely on the success of the export policy. (b) It became necessary to reorientate French agricultural production: beef, mutton, and pork production needed to be increased as well as milk and dairy products, eggs and poultry, fruit, and fresh vegetables—while wheat, potato, beet (industrial), and wine production should be decreased. This Plan took account of both the techniques and methods for changing the direction of agricultural production: extension services, price regulations, market organization and financial grants. The organization of a system of price targets (système de prix d'objectifs) forms the most original aspect of the agricultural policy of the Third Plan [8] because of its attempt to orientate agricultural production through prices.

In the historical process of economic growth France has reached the stage of mass consumption with the Fourth Plan (1962–1965). Care for social affairs is kept in mind more than it has been in previous Plans, and emphasis is laid on the need to help poor districts and the less favoured social classes (old people, paid workers, craftsmen, and low-income agriculturists), on the expansion of collective services and equipment, on help to developing countries. This Plan is appropriate to a society which is tending towards relative abundance and to the re-building of Europe and the reinforcement of help towards countries in course of development. Some points which characterize this orientation are: home production should be increased by 24 per cent (agriculture 19 per cent), economic investment by 28 per cent, and social investment, in the form of collective equipment, by 50 per cent—national education, scientific research, sports equipment, public health, cultural equipment, town and country equipment [9].

In the agricultural sector, planning comes at a time when there is a prospect of saturation, which may mean permanent surpluses. It is faced with the aspiration of agriculturists for economic well-being more and more clearly and emphatically expressed. In this situation, while continuing to favour a policy of exports and the reconstruction of Europe, the principle of surpluses is accepted and a special effort is made towards investment for agriculture and rural areas (credits being doubled compared with the Third Plan). Provisional estimates for agriculture show that, through quantities, prices, and transfers, an increase of revenue for agriculturists would result, analogous to that of other social and professional classes. This programme conforms with successive legislative provisions (the agricultural orientation law of 5 August 1960, and the complementary law of agricultural planning of 8 August 1962), which allows agriculturists to reach parity by altering the structural set-up (ways of making it easier to create holdings which are economically viable, to limit unsatisfactory collections of holdings, to found land-management societies, to legislate about groups of holdings for joint operation), by altering the system of distribution (producer groups, agricultural economic committees, adaptation of the market organization to a common agricultural policy), by facilitating the professional advancement of agriculturists (grants towards professional re-education), or geographic mobility (encouraging rural migration), and entry of young people into management (retirement pensions for elderly people). At the same time an unprecedented effort is put into agricultural education (law of 20 August 1960) for the teaching of agriculture as a profession, and (law of 23 July 1962) for establishing and expanding teaching schools for agriculture as a profession.

A real effort is undoubtedly being made for agriculturists' benefit. Nevertheless it would be too much to hope that parity for the rural sector can be realized in a short time.

Apart from short-term vicissitudes, the evolution of the French economy seems clear. After the period of post-war reconstruction which gave priority to basic industry, expansion set out to achieve the mass consumption stage which French people are now reaching. The mean annual growth rate of gross national global product at constant prices, for the 1950–60 period, was 4.3 per cent; this was lower than in Germany (7.6 per cent), Italy (5.9 per cent) and the Netherlands (4.9 per cent), but higher than in the north-western countries of Europe.

France has expanded its industrialization; the industrial rate of growth has been higher than that of agriculture, agriculture's contribution to global revenue has decreased, and part of the agricultural population has had to migrate to other sectors (there has been a 1.5 per cent yearly decrease of agricultural population during the last few years); this has been accompanied by a spread of technical advances in agriculture as well as by improvement in agricultural productivity which is higher than in industry, and by a rise of agriculturists' incomes, which are nevertheless lower than in other social and professional classes. The objective of productivity has been reached, but not parity. This is not only so in France—in advanced countries generally, the integration of agriculture into the national economy and the agriculturists' attainment to the benefits of industrial civilization are among the most important and most difficult problems. The analysis of the development of agriculture in global economic growth is the most fundamental task confronting rural economists.

Finally we must pose one more question: to what extent can French economic expansion be attributed to planning, and to what extent can it help us in further development by reducing and making tolerable the imbalance of sectors and zones?

Comparisons between the forecasts and the realizations of plans make one appreciate their realism. Some mistakes may have been made but, on the whole, the forecasts have been confirmed and full employment ensured; unemployment has been almost non-existent. Yet, comparisons with expansion rates in capitalist countries may show that higher expansion rates may be reached without planning; there are several factors in growth and, as always, it is difficult to distinguish exact causes correctly. In France, planning has become one of our most fundamental social institutions. No doubt it will change both in content and method because it is experimental rather than dogmatic and because it will become more and more the instrument of economic democracy, but it is inconceivable that it will be abandoned.

REFERENCES

1. Bauchet, Pierre, *La planification française (quinze ans d'expérience)*. Ed. du Seuil, Paris, 1962.
2. Cotta, A., "Un modèle intersectoriel de croissance." *Eco. Appliquée*, No. 1–2, 1962, pp. 199–227.
3. Perroux, F., "Le IV° plan français (1962–1965). En quoi consiste notre 'planification indicative.'" *Eco. Appliquée*, No. 1–2, 1962, pp. 5–65.
4. Rostow, W., *Les étapes de la croissance économique*. Ed. du Seuil, Paris, 1962.
5. Ripert, J., "Le plan agricole dans l'ensemble de la planification." *Eco. Ru.* (sous presse).
6. Gravier, F., *Paris et le désert français*. Flammarion, 1958.
7. Malassis, L., "La politique agricole de 1946 à 1958 (dans 'l'économie agricole française 1938–1958')." *Eco. Ru.* No. 39–40, Paris.
8. ——, "Politique agricole à long terme et prix d'objectifs." *Académie d' Agriculture de France*. Séance du 6 Nov., 1957.
9. IV° Plan, *La documentation française illustrée*. Paris, Oct.–Nov., 1962.

15

Pulverization and Fragmentation of Landed Property in Italy

GIUSEPPE MEDICI

National Institute of Agrarian Economics,
Rome, Italy

GENERAL CONSIDERATIONS

IN ALL COUNTRIES where private ownership of land has existed for centuries we find side by side with the large properties, which at times show the drawbacks particular to the latifundium, the small landed property. In the course of time these have become increasingly smaller and fractionalized, especially where laws gave the right of all heirs to a share of the inheritance. Thus the two fundamental pathological aspects of landed property asserted themselves: the latifundium on one hand and, on the other, the pulverized and fragmented property, the minifundium of Spanish authors.

For long periods two facts, the political importance of the latifundium and the peasants' clinging to the soil, relegated the problem of pulverized and dispersed landed property to a matter of minor importance, especially in Mediterranean countries. Whereas in several other European nations, such as the Scandinavian countries, western Germany, France and still others, where the industrial revolution had already offered profitable employment to great numbers of peasants, the serious impediments to agricultural development caused by pulverized and fragmented farm land gave rise to powerful movements of ideas and interests. These in turn gave approval to those special laws which led to a partially accomplished readjustment.

The figures in Table 15.1, published by the International Institute for Land Reclamation and Improvement in Wageningen, Holland, are a result of findings and estimates which are not always comparable. But they clearly show, together with others we have not

TABLE 15.1
LAND READJUSTMENT IN SEVERAL EUROPEAN COUNTRIES*
(All except Greece given in hectares)

	Already Accomplished	In Process	Still To Be Done
Finland...................	2,319,452	300,000	*Province of Vasa*
Germany..................	4,320,400	800,000	5,737,800
France...................	2,020,260	862,234	14,000,000
Austria..................	313,654	46,428	1,180,000
Greece...................	28 (farms)	6 (farms)	⅓ to ½ of the total
Spain....................	70,000	180,000	630,000

* Source: International Institute for Land Reclamation, Wageningen, Holland.

listed, that readjustment has been carried out to a considerable extent in central and northern European countries. It was limited to rather scanty areas in southern European countries, such as Greece, Spain, and Italy.

In countries where readjustment has been tackled methodically and where it concerned rather extensive areas, it led to a real and proper land reform. It did not consist in the expropriation of large properties, however, but rather in the readjustment of small ones. It aimed at resettling peasant titleholders on suitable units of land. Although this movement, when it led to the acquisition of land in order to consolidate and increase smaller properties, sometimes lacked spontaneous consent by the peasants, they began to realize its significance gradually and have now understood the advantage of working farms of a size and nature which are better adapted to modern exigencies of production.

But when the readjustment of fragmented property fails to bring about a radical agricultural revival, when it is just the result of topographical estimates, as it often has been, the main purpose of land readjustment, i.e. the creation of organic agricultural enterprises, is not attained. Assistance by co-operation becomes fully justified when, after the removal of juridical obstacles, the necessary conditions are created for the affirmation of a rational agriculture where, thanks to modern techniques, more is produced with less effort.

That the problem is of importance for Italy is demonstrated by her Constitution. As a matter of fact, Article 44 of the Italian Constitution states that, in order to obtain a rational exploitation of the soil and to establish equitable social relations, the Law imposes reclamation of land, transformation of the latifundium, and a *reconstruction of the productive unit.*

From another point of view, the problem concerns the safe-guarding of the agricultural unit of minimum size, a juridical institution which has given rise to polemics among experts and to preoccupation of both a political and a social nature. This may explain why the then minister for agriculture—when he submitted a bill in 1954 for the simple application of the Civil Code's stipulations to avoid further fragmentation of property and to maintain, at least, the so-called minimum agricultural unit (Art. 846 of the Code)—did not succeed in finding a majority for his moderate initiative. At the very moment, when the land reform laws were becoming operative however, this initiative spelled a warning—a warning that, apart from the question of fractionalizing the latifundium, there existed the problem of safe-guarding the old and the new agricultural properties; in other words, the problem of the minimum agricultural unit.

These considerations may lead to the following questions:

1. Have developments in Italy created situations analogous to those in central and northern European countries where energetic action for land readjustment has been undertaken?
2. Have the necessary premises for an intervention by legislators been created also in Italy?
3. Does the phenomenon also exist on a significant scale on Italian soil?

In the following pages I shall attempt to answer these questions.

PULVERIZATION AND FRAGMENTATION OF LAND IN ITALY

The phenomenon we are examining appears mostly in the form of a pulverization, meaning a tiny property not necessarily fragmented into several parts, but always insufficient to support an autonomous farm. Although such pulverization clearly shows pathological symptoms when the farm is the only source of work for a peasant family, it is fully justified from the economic viewpoint when the family can find work for some of its members outside the tiny landed property.

The so-called residential and part-time farms are often pulverized. On such farms the not-exclusively-rural family lives, devoting some of its free time for part of the year or of the day to farming, prevalently for home consumption. A rather particular case are those farm hands who own small pieces of land on which they grow grain and vegetables and raise poultry for family consumption while spending most of the day working on neighbouring farms. Although pulverized physically, such properties rarely have a pathological nature. This becomes evident in the Lombardy highlands between the rivers Ticino and Adda and, generally, in the pre-Alpine regions where intensive industrial activity finds work for the greater part of the working capacity of families who remain rural by force of habit and tradition. The property is pulverized—and often fragmented—but it provides useful occupation for part of the family as well as a house to live in. And it avoids the serious drawbacks of big industrial towns where living is less comfortable than it is in modernized farmhouses.

The fact that physical pulverization of property is not always evil confirms the concept that the pathological side of the phenomenon is conditioned not only by the size of the property, be it 10 or 5 hectares, but by numerous other circumstances. For this reason it seems advisable to stress that pulverized property is a pathological fact *when the peasant family living on it and doing only farm work owns insufficient land to run an autonomous agricultural enterprise.* (We use the terms physiological and pathological because they are now in common usage and it is not our task to look for substitutes. But they are on loan from biology and are not always appropriate.)

Pulverization, which is frequent in countries with dense rural populations like Italy, is often linked to fragmentation. The owner of a tiny property does not always own a connected parcel of land, but often many disconnected parcels. In some Italian regions at least, however, pulverization exists without fragmentation. In this connexion we may mention the pulverized olive grove properties in Liguria where there are many very small holdings consisting of single patches. This also applies to the pulverized properties prevalent in some wine and vegetable growing districts of Piedmont, Latium, Apulia, and Campania. Analogously, there are cases of fragmentation which do not involve pulverization but medium-sized properties such as those often found in central and northern Europe.

The fact that pulverization is frequently accompanied by fragmentation has led, at least in Italy, to facing the problem of readjustment by limiting it to properties that are both pulverized and fragmented. On the other hand, in several central and northern European countries readjustment is often concerned with fragmented, but not pulverized, properties. But it is inescapable that the consolidation of tiny properties which are too small to form organic units needs more land. Such land can be obtained either by reducing the number of farm properties or by acquiring and expropriating unfarmed land for distribution to peasant families who would then have to refrain from again dividing up the minimum agricultural unit that has been formed with such difficulty.

Partly influenced by a period in history when the active agrarian population showed no signs of decrease, Italian economic literature has not laid the necessary stress on the problem of consolidation. As a matter of fact it is only recently that it has become an up-to-date topic.

The abandoning of farm land by *mezzadri* (peasants operating under conditions of *metayage,* i.e. paying no fixed rent, but tilling the soil for the landowner and receiving some proportion of its produce) and even by independent farmers in the hill and low mountain zones of central Italy, recently followed by similar abandonment in fertile zones of the Po valley, demonstrates the bitter truth that the rural exodus starts when the peasant population can find better remuneration for their labour elsewhere. Even when psychological factors (real or presumed better living, social security, independence for the younger generation, etc.) become determining factors for the exodus, it certainly takes place mainly where the pay for a work unit in agriculture is significantly lower than what can be earned by the same work unit in other available sectors of economic activity. If in *metayage* or similar systems the lower earnings depend on the type of contract, those of independent farmers are frequently due to the size of the farm and to its pathological state of fragmentation. There exists, consequently, a rural exodus caused by the pulverization of property and, sometimes, by its dispersion. This is why the promotion of consolidation and readjustment will not only create agricultural enterprises adequate (or less inadequate) to the working capacity and income exigencies of the peasant family, but will also render less precipitate the abandoning of poor soil, the rational utilization of which will, in turn, become possible. These considerations lay further stress on the difference between the drawbacks of pulverized properties to be remedied by consolidation, and those of fragmentation which can be healed by readjustment.

In Italy, the phenomenon appears in various degrees of intensity. There are zones where properties obviously are seriously pulverized and dispersed, while in others it is still uncertain whether the pathological factor has appeared. Hence, it should be useful to recall that a pathological state is present whenever an autonomous, or at least a viable, farm can be created under given conditions of property distribution. This does not prevent a farm from being viable even when it is fragmented for technical reasons, such as those connected with agricultural production and livestock raising.

Several specific cases can be cited. For example, farms in mountain regions should have their meadows in the valley, their pastures, cultivated land, woods, and, sometimes, their vineyards on slopes. Unluckily, however, such farms generally no longer consist of the five original parts, but of twenty or thirty, owing to the splitting up of the initial five. This also applies to other types of farms in the Apennines or near the coast, which have a plurality of parts, with different kinds of cultivation according to the special conditions of their sites.

Readjustment and consolidation should therefore be based on the requirements of an autonomous farm. In other words, they should create a farm which would enable the peasant family working exclusively on it to make full use of its potential and to derive from it an income appropriate to their requirements. They should thus obtain a satisfactory income in equilibrium with one they could earn in other kinds of work. Such considerations should not induce us to conclude, however, that readjustment is useless if it cannot lead to the creation of an autonomous farm. And this for the simple reason that not all viable farms are necessarily autonomous. It has been clearly stated that when a peasant family has members working at other, non-agricultural jobs, even a non-self-sufficient farm may be viable.

It has been observed that pulverization and fragmentation may also concern rented land. In fact, they can occur in the complexity of medium or large-sized properties. In such cases the problem is solved by the readjustment of the farm land within the given property. Pulverization and fragmentation of rented land are often found in southern Italy where medium-sized and large properties frequently organize their agricultural production in small, pulverized, and fragmented farms generally worked by petty tenants or *metayers* of some kind. Exactly the contrary happens when a pulverized property attains self-sufficiency in farming by renting the land it needs or contracting some *metayage* on it. It is especially in zones where pulverized properties prevail that many landowner farmers without sufficient land, rent the plots they need or take them over by contracting some form of *metayage* or association, thereby creating mixed farms which frequently turn out to be of precarious viability.

Finally it should be noticed that estimates concerning the phenomenon are often rendered more difficult by the fact that in many hill and mountain zones pulverization and fragmentation are more frequent than the tax registers show. The number of unregistered or unrecorded transfers of property is surprisingly high. In such cases readjustment operations meet with unforeseen difficulties, the more so because owners have often emigrated to foreign countries.

To make it still clearer that even a property of moderate area can be viable, though not always autonomous, we recall that Italian agriculture shows situations of the following types, listed here as indications only:

1. 5,000 square metres of citrus plantation and 2 hectares sown land;
2. 5,000 square metres of well watered sown land for floriculture and 1.5 hectare sown land;
3. 1,000 square metres of hothouse with 5,000 square metres of watered market garden;
4. one hectare of watered market garden;
5. one hectare of vineyard with 1.5 sown land;
6. one hectare of orchard and 1.0 sown land;
7. 3 hectares of watered sown land.

Such properties are certainly very small but they are still capable of being viable farms which, if the families are not large, may even become autonomous.

The question may be raised: how can one ascertain the amount of land involved in this problem when conditions differ so greatly that a property of one hectare may either allow for intense and rational agricultural production or be practically useless?

My answer is that the difficulty of ascertaining the numerous causes of pulverization makes it practically impossible to establish the exact area afflicted by the evil. It cannot be compared with measuring the area of vineyards in a given zone, or with the number of inhabitants of a city, or with the average stature of a population. *The phenomenon is complex and its extent can be discovered only by means of a widely approximate estimate. Apart from the basic data concerning the extent of the property and the average composition of the peasant family, such an estimate would have to take into account the quality of performance, the rate of activity, the amount of invested capital and, finally, the gross marketable output obtainable.* Proceeding in this manner one can obtain a picture of the incidence of the phenomenon in the various agricultural zones on which to base the estimate in question. This gives a practical notion of sufficiently representative value which can be compared with data of other countries. When it is related to the areas in agriculture and forestry and the gross saleable production, it conveys an idea of the relative importance of the phenomenon.

LOCALIZATION OF THE PHENOMENON

In an accentuated form the phenomenon appears in nearly all the Alpine and pre-Alpine valleys from Piedmont to the Venetia Julia. With the exception of a few sporadic cases, it is insignificant in the great plain of the Po river and the bordering hill zones. But it is more common in Friuli and in the hilly plateau between Vicenza and Udine, as well as in the hill zones of Piedmont (especially in the Monferrato district and the Langhe). Apart from the well-known phenomena of the highlands and hills between the Ticino and Adda rivers which also occur in the whole pre-Alpine belt, Lombardy shows an intense pulverization and fragmentation of land beyond the river Po, near Pavia. The phenomenon is serious throughout Liguria, in Versilia, around Lucca, in Valdarno, and in many Apennine zones. In the extensive farm land zones of central Italy the phenomenon has the sporadic character already noted in those of northern Italy.

Farther to the south we meet it again in the mountainous Umbria (in the valleys between Foligno, Spoleto, Cascia and Terni), in the Ciociaria (Frosinone), and in the provinces of Teramo, Pescara, and Chieti. It begins to be really serious, however, on entering the typical South of Italy. In fact, we find pronounced instances of it in nearly all the arable mountain lands of the Abruzzi and Molise, as well as in Campania, both in the famous Sabato and Calore valleys and in the remarkable volcanic slopes leading down to Naples. Examples of similar intensity are found in Lucania, especially in the part gravitating to the Tyrrhenian (the Diano valley, middle of the Sele valley, etc.). Very frequent examples in Apulia are particularly evident in the central hills between Barletta and Brindisi, in the Salento, in the valleys opening towards the Lucania coast line between the Bradano and the Sinni, on the slopes of the Sila, of the Serre and of Aspromonte, along the coast between the plains of Sibari and Corace, along the Tyrrhenian coast between Sapri and Reggio, and between Squillace and Melito Porto Salco along the Ionian coast line.

The islands both large and small (e.g. Elba) show extensive zones of pulverization and dispersion. The phenomenon is still more serious in Sardinia where it has arisen through the history of landed property on that island. In Sicily, too, especially between Palermo and Castellamare del Golfo, between Agrigento and Enna, and in the land southeast of the Aetna, the phenomenon is so extensive that it calls for a careful investigation.

These are zones where pulverization and fragmentation appear with major intensity and are very prevalent. But just as in these zones there are places which are free from it, so in all other zones it exists to some extent without, however, being predominant. It constitutes a serious problem for readjustment only where, through its extent and concentration, it is of real and lasting importance, not where it appears occasionally and sporadically.

EXTENT OF THE PHENOMENON

The survey listed above may lead to the following estimate: Pulverization and fragmentation of landed property involves a total of about four million hectares which yield about sixteen per cent of the marketable gross national output, as shown in Table 15.2. Prevalently, this is sown land representing fifteen per cent of the agriculture and forest surface and nearly twenty per cent of the cultivated land.

It is clear that the phenomenon has a degree of density which cannot be neglected, especially in view of the present conditions of economic development which call for a more rational utilization of the soil. According to estimates, about one million of the four million hectares listed must be readjusted as an indispensable prelude to any economic development. The remaining area of pulverized and fragmented land—about three million hectares—is in the course of transformation from a type of intensive subsistence economy to new forms of utilization which are an outcome of great migratory movements which are in progress. It may be opportune to wait until these forces have begun to settle down before proceeding to overriding readjustments. By limiting it to about one million hectares, funds could be concentrated on places where intervention would guarantee higher productivity.

TABLE 15.2
SURFACE OF PULVERIZED AND FRAGMENTED LANDED PROPERTY
(Estimated)

	Hectares	Per Cent of Total	Per Cent of Agricultural Surface
Northern Italy.................	1,515,000	37.5	19.8
Mountain.................	725,000	17.9	30.8
Hill.....................	410,000	10.2	22.2
Plain.....................	380,000	9.4	11.1
Central Italy...................	555,000	13.8	14.7
Mountain.................	305,000	7.6	24.3
Hill.....................	210,000	5.2	9.6
Plain.....................	40,000	1.0	12.5
Southern Italy.................	1,300,000	32.2	23.4
Mountain.................	530,000	13.1	29.1
Hill.....................	630,000	15.6	22.4
Plain.....................	140,000	3.5	15.3
Italian Islands.................	665,000	16.5	16.3
Mountain.................	180,000	4.5	20.9
Hill.....................	380,000	9.4	15.0
Plain.....................	105,000	2.6	15.7
Italy.........................	4,035,000	100.0	19.2
Mountain.................	1,740,000	43.1	27.6
Hill.....................	1,630,000	40.4	17.3
Plain.....................	665,000	16.5	12.4

MEANS ADOPTED TO CHECK AGGRAVATION OF THE PHENOMENON

While tackling the problem of readjustment it would be reasonable also to stop the fragmentation of units worth being kept in their present condition and to stop the further fragmentation of properties already pulverized and fragmented. This does not mean that all suitable means should not be employed to avoid the spreading of the phenomenon to zones it has not yet affected, or its aggravation where it already exists. It simply means calling attention to the fact that one would commit a serious mistake by starting readjustment without at the same time stemming both the aggravation and the repetition of the phenomenon. In this connexion we should recall that the Italian law of 3 June 1940 (No. 1078) established norms to avoid the division of farm land units allotted to independent peasants. Article I of this law states that the farm land units formed as parts of reclamation districts by *colonization unions* or *reclamation consortia* and assigned to independent peasants cannot be divided following the death of the titleholder or by acts of transfer between living persons. Moreover, the Italian Civil Code contains a whole section (Articles 846 to 856) dealing with the matter of land readjustment.

CONCLUSIONS

Conservative estimates and reliable forecasting show that the increase of income derived from readjustment provides appropriate return for the necessary investment. But this is not the main justification or readjustment. The basic reason is to be seen in the transformation now taking place in the rural scene where there is increasing need to have farms which can make full use of modern agricultural techniques and can offer a consistent income to those who remain to till soil which is not always favoured by nature. The more a rural population can find profitable employment in other activities, the clearer it becomes that the low remuneration of agricultural labour is closely connected with a system of farm land distribution no longer in line with modern techniques for reducing effort and increasing productivity. Although residential and part-time farms which principally produce for family consumption may have their lasting justification, and if vegetable, flower, fruit, and partly grain-producing farms represent the centuries-old and enduring craftsmanship of the soil, no agricultural productive organization—from wheat to rice, from wine to oil, from sugar beets to maize—can yield great quantities at low cost except rationally organized medium- and large-sized farms.

These considerations go to explain why in a few years' time readjustment of farm land will become one of the major problems of Italian agriculture, when the 6.3 million agricultural workers have dwindled to 5 million. Moreover, readjustment will lead to the utilization of important areas of abandoned soil.

This is the real state of affairs. And it confirms, especially for certain sectors, the evident superiority of the family-run farm to capitalistic farming. The latter will never be able to play a greater part than it does now. For Italian agriculture comprises a series of productive activities necessitating the diligent, devoted, and patient toil of man, although technology may contribute significantly to reducing physical effort and increasing productivity.

To the typical case of vegetable and flower growing must be added the raising of livestock for milk, meat, or wool, and of poultry as well as a great number of minor enterprises. All this goes to show why agricultural production in communist countries has not been successful. The abolition of peasant farms tends to destroy the beneficial ties between man and the soil which are so important for by far the greater part of agricultural production in the western world.

The irrationality of small, fragmented farms imposed by the pitiless ratio between land and population should not serve as a pretext for justifying the alleged superiority of agrarian capitalism (both private and public), the success of which is difficult to forecast.

Finally we may state that Italian agriculture will be directed mainly towards two types of enterprise: that of the independent farmer with a holding adequate to the capacity of his family and of a size to allow profitable introduction of mechanized means and of rational management; and that of the capitalistic farm with wage earners, able to bear the weight of increasing wages thanks to the great increase of productivity to be obtained by the adoption of modern agricultural techniques.

16

Agricultural Credit in Western Europe

G. MINDERHOUD

Formerly of Landbouwhoogeschool,
Wageningen, The Netherlands

A FARMER, if he is to produce, must have land, capital and labour. In farming, the land is more important than it is in other branches of production. In order to obtain control of land the entrepreneur in agriculture has to acquire it in the same way as ordinary capital goods; and for that reason it is usual, in agricultural economics, to count land as capital. But it is a special kind of capital inasmuch as, unlike other capital goods, its productive capacity in normal use does not decline. It is therefore not necessary to apply depreciation to the capital invested in land.

On the other hand, depreciation must be applied to the farm buildings standing on the land. In the course of years they do decline in value. In general however their economic life is long so that their percentage rate of depreciation can be small.

On movable capital goods, that is to say on the live and dead stock, the rate of depreciation has to be a good deal higher.

Finally, the farmer needs capital in order to procure producer goods which he can use only once, such as seed, fertilizers, feeding-stuffs, pesticides, and veterinary preparations. On these the depreciation must amount to one hundred per cent per annum.

In view of this, we may classify the capital needed for agricultural production into that required for: (a) land and buildings, (b) live and dead stock, and (c) working funds.

In so far as the manpower of the farmer and his family is not enough to run the farm properly, he will have to take paid workers into his service. Their wages do not as a rule come back quickly in the form of saleable products. In determining the capital required for conducting a farm, therefore, it is necessary also to take account of a fairly long-term need for wages payable, as well as for payments to other people who render services to the farm.

The entrepreneur must either himself have the capital which he needs for production, or he must borrow it. In some countries, he can rent on a fairly large scale the required land and the buildings that go with it. In those countries land rent performs an important function in connexion with the supply of resources for financing agriculture. The reason is that a tenant farmer need have only the forms of working capital mentioned in b and c above.

In most countries farmers who own their land can obtain a part of the necessary capital, in the form of land and buildings, by granting a mortgage on their real properties. The degree to which the need for capital can be met in this way depends primarily on the amount of funds available in the capital market for investment, and on how good a guarantee the mortgage affords to the lender that he will be able to recover his money (plus any arrears of interest) out of the proceeds of selling the properties if the borrower does not meet his obligations.

The extent to which holders of capital are prepared to provide money by way of mortgage loans is of course not very great in countries where the land register is defective and where there is uncertainty about the rights actually possessed by people who claim to be owners of land. Other things being equal, the rate of interest demanded by lenders will be higher in these areas than in countries where rights to ownership of land are accurately recorded.

Since mortgage loans usually are given for lengthy periods, the lender runs the risk that, during the life of the loan, there may be an appreciable fall in the value of the currency unit in which the loan was granted. In countries where there is fear of inflation or where memories of past inflation are still vivid, some reluctance to grant mortgage loans is understandable, and in such countries the rate of interest which farmers have to pay for loans against their land will as a rule be high.

As a result of all this the extent to which farmers can borrow on land through the capital market varies greatly as between different European countries. It is thus easy to understand why many Governments have found themselves obliged to make money available in one way or another for loans against land, and/or to provide official subsidies so as to make such loans available to farmers at low interest rates.

The pressure to provide Government help in this form has not come from the farmers alone. During the last half-century most governments have made it their task more and more to increase and modernize their countries' agricultural production. One way to do this is to provide public funds to promote the lending of money against land. It is mostly in countries where the renting of agricultural land is unusual that one finds the authorities concerning themselves with land loans. There are in many cases further facilities available for the benefit of young farmers who are just starting.

In the course of the present century the need for working capital has become steadily greater. For a long time, in the greater part of western Europe, farming was mainly of the subsistence type and seldom exceeded the limits of a family enterprise. So long as that was the case the need for working funds was small, while the livestock and the modest amount of dead stock also called for relatively little capital. Nevertheless most farmers even then found it difficult to obtain the necessary working funds. For that purpose they largely relied on their families. In so far as their relatives could not or would not help them they depended on borrowing from outside lenders, a process frequently accompanied by abuses.

The banks which were established in the towns showed little or no interest in agricultural credit. The loans which the farmers wanted were taken in a large number of small amounts, and in most cases it took several months before the crops or the cattle could be turned into money and the loan repaid. Thus the loans were outstanding for quite long times, and most of them were wanted by small entrepreneurs who rarely or never could provide the securities which the commercial banks normally required. The result was that for these banks such loans were unattractive.

It is true that in many small provincial towns there were well established private bankers who were able in some measure to assess the pecuniary standing of the larger farmers in their neighbourhoods, but even these bankers were not interested in the smaller farmers. The great bulk of the farming community were therefore cut off from bank credit and had to make do, as best they could, with such advances as the buyers of their products would grant or with credit allowed by their suppliers. Many undesirable practices arose, while the rates of interest which had to be paid were often exorbitant.

In Germany during the second half of the 19th century, under the inspiring leadership of the rural mayor, F. W. Raiffeisen, very favourable experience was gained with mutual credit associations. On the one hand these served as savings banks for the village population; on the other they granted advances and loans out of the savings deposited with them, both to farmers and to small traders and craftsmen.

The members of these small Raiffeisen co-operative banks made themselves jointly and severally responsible for the savings entrusted to their institutions. At the same time some of the rural inhabitants who were better off, and who felt the urge of Christian neighbourly feeling or a sense of solidarity, became members of such co-operatives, so that these small banks won the confidence of all who were prepared to save.

The pattern in every case was the same. The bank would operate in a small area, so that all its members personally knew each other; it would be administered free of charge by a managing board elected from among the members; and all the profits earned would be allocated to reserve. The object was to give the bank, by degrees, some capital resources. The savings were backed by the members' unlimited liability for the bank's engagements.

From the outset Raiffeisen appreciated that, if these small co-operative banks were to stand on their own feet, they would not be able to achieve his intended object of providing proper credit for the rural areas. He therefore made the village banks combine in central institutions. One object of this action was to take the surplus monies, which some village banks had available, and to place them at the disposal of local banks short of resources. The idea was that these central institutions might serve *inter alia* as clearing houses, while the village banks remained independent.

Towards the end of the 19th century and at the beginning of the 20th a change took place in farming throughout western Europe, from producing for subsistence to producing for the market. This was accompanied by purchases of producer goods such as fertilizers, feeding-stuffs, and seed. Therefore the need for credit rapidly grew, and the German example was followed on a large scale and with great success in all the countries of central and western Europe. The greater prosperity which spread to the rural areas in the first half of the present century enabled many people to save more than before. The result was that the Raiffeisen co-operatives obtained more resources, and became important as institutions for financing both farmers and other country dwellers.

Outside Europe too, in fact throughout a large part of the world, the German example was followed. It was done with many variations, however, owing to the wide economic and political differences between countries.

In 1957 and 1958 the *International Journal of Agrarian Affairs* published, under the title "Capital and Credit in Agriculture," a number of articles dealing with the use of capital by farmers and with the provision of using it for agriculture in various countries. Additional data can be found, for instance, in a publication issued by the Organization for Economic Co-operation and Development (O.E.C.D.) in 1962, entitled *Improvement of Agricultural Credit Facilities.*

These publications show that Raiffeisen's example, as briefly described above, has been followed in a large number of countries other than the United Kingdom. But they also show that the general political, economic, and social conditions in the different countries have so greatly developed and altered that the resulting picture is a rather patchwork affair.

At the same time they indicate that on two points there is a large measure of concordance: (1) the provision of investment and working capital for agriculture has always entailed greater difficulties than the financing of industry; and (2) in order to reduce the difficulties the governments of nearly all countries have supported and supplemented the private supply of agricultural credit by making governmental funds available for the granting of such credit, and/or by providing subsidies to make such credit cheaper. The ways in which this official assistance is given in practice diverge widely in the different countries.

There is one country in western Europe where the Government has not entered this field, or has done so only by way of regional action in a few scattered cases; that country is the Netherlands. Despite this there is no country where the provision of credit for agriculture gives rise to so few complaints as in ours. An enquiry carried out among our farmers a few years back afforded clear evidence of this.

This example of self-help has attracted attention in many quarters abroad, and more particularly in countries which have become independent since World War II. In many of these, agriculture forms the chief basis of national prosperity, and the authorities are doing their best to raise it rapidly to a higher level. Many agronomists and politicians from these young countries have studied, on the spot, the system used for providing agricultural credit in the Netherlands. They mostly came in the hope that by following our country's example they could make their agriculture less dependent on help in the form of credit provided by their own or foreign Governments. So far as that hope is concerned they nearly all went home disappointed.

It is worth while looking into the question of how it was possible for sufficient credit always to be available in the Netherlands for the farmers on terms which, in many cases, were more favourable than those applicable to loans granted by commercial banks to trading and industrial enterprises.

The Netherlands have always been a comparatively prosperous country with few people who are either very rich or very poor. Even in the rural areas, and even during the years of crisis at the end of the last century, there were people who had a certain amount of capital. The feeling of solidarity among the agricultural population has always been strongly developed. There was a significant instance of this at a village in my neighbourhood when a few farmers decided to establish a local Raiffeisen bank. There was a landed proprietor in the neighbourhood whose wealth was undoubtedly greater than that of all the founders together; but nevertheless he was prepared to join the bank as a member and to serve as chairman of its Supervisory Board. By joining the new bank this man, like every other member, made himself liable without limit for its engagements. After that no villager was in the least worried about the safety of the savings which he deposited in the new institution. The landowner, by accepting the liability which membership entailed, had raised the bank's soundness above all doubt.

In general the people of the Netherlands are thrifty by nature, and accustomed to living sparingly. This is especially true of the rural population. The rapid industrializing of numerous villages and towns during the past quarter of a century has caused many of the younger people to find work in industry, although for the time being they continue to live in the country. There these new industrial workers form an important group of savers who deposit their funds in the Raiffeisen banks. These latter, incidentally, have understood the signs of the times and have conformed to industrial development. Some have done this by establishing branches at the new industrial centres; in other cases new and independent Raiffeisen banks have been set up.

The result is that in the course of years the character of many agricultural credit banks has changed quite considerably. In the early days the bank's office would be a single room in the house of the cashier, who nearly always performed that function as an addition to his normal work. But especially since World War II many Raiffeisen co-operatives have grown until they have become complete banks, with office buildings of their own, full-time cashiers, and frequently some office staff as well. In those cases both the members and the outside savers can obtain for all their banking business just as good service as the commercial banks can give their customers. The position in this respect differs considerably from that in central Europe, where most of the Raiffeisen banks are still much the same in general character as they were half a century ago.

In the Netherlands the will to save has been stimulated not only through the increase of prosperity but also by the fact that the purchasing power of the guilder has been better maintained than that of many other national currencies in western Europe.

It is true that savings can be deposited at every post office, even in the villages; it is also true that there are a great many municipal and private savings institutions. Despite these facts the savings deposits and current account balances held at all agricultural credit banks together in 1963 amounted to over 6,000 million guilders—that is, to nearly £600 million. With a population of just on 12 million this is equivalent to roughly 500 guilders or, say, £50 per head.

The Raiffeisen banks would not have achieved this result if they had not been combined in two central institutions. The reason why two institutions were established, and not one, lay in small differences of view among the promotors of co-operative agricultural credit. This absence of unity has had little effect on the growth of such credit. In many matters the two central institutions maintain contact with each other and they work well together.

The task of the central institutions has greatly changed in the course of this century. The orginal plan was that they were to act as clearing houses for the various local banks; but this part of their work has remained virtually a dead letter, because nearly all the village banks have more resources than the amount of credit sought by members within their own circles.

The local banks' surplus funds are deposited at the central institutions against payment of interest. The central institutions, in their turn, use the money by lending it to large agricultural co-operatives. There are a number of these, and they enjoy credit lines equivalent to some millions of pounds sterling at one or other of the two central institutions. The rest of the money deposited at these latter is employed by them on the money and capital markets, in which connexion the need for sufficient liquidity is kept in view. Besides administering the surpluses of the local banks the central institutions have an important task in auditing and supervising the administration of the latter. Also, a great deal of the publicity is conducted centrally.

The need for credit in agriculture is much affected by the fact that approximately one-half of all the cultivable land in Holland is rented by farmers and market gardeners who need no capital to cover the land and buildings which they use.

In cases where the farmers own their farms they can readily borrow up to two-thirds of the estimated value from private lenders, life assurance companies, pension funds, and other institutional investors. For both farmers and market gardeners the mortgage banks are as a rule too expensive. The proportion of agricultural credit provided by them is less than two per cent of the whole. The agricultural credit banks also provide capital on a modest scale for investment in land and buildings. But their real work is to provide both agriculture and horticulture with loans to finance the procurement of livestock, machines, and tools, as well as to cover annually recurrent operating expenditure.

For such agricultural operating credit in the narrower sense the farmers and market gardeners do not depend exclusively, nor even mainly, on the Raiffeisen banks. Parents, brothers, sisters, and other members of the family provide most of the funds which are needed, especially by the younger farmers and market gardeners, and frequently do so at very moderate rates of interest.

So far as the farmers' and market gardeners' relatives cannot or will not help them, the mutual agricultural credit banks have enough resources to provide the working credit required. In that connexion it is fortunate that agriculture in the Netherlands is highly varied in character.

The greater part of the farms are used purely for dairying, although in some districts there are purely arable farms; there are also a great many farms which have cultivable land, but do not market the produce grown on it. The farmers in this last group make their income by selling milk, cattle, pigs, chickens, and eggs. Horticulture too is an important form of agricultural production. Here again there are specialized producers. Large areas grow nothing but vegetables in greenhouses, others grow only bulbs, while others again produce solely or mainly fruit and the like.

For each group of producers there is one period in which falls the peak demand for credit. The result is that the total demand from agriculture for credit in current account is spread fairly evenly over the year.

Despite the still steadily rising credit requirements for the further modernizing, intensifying, and mechanizing of agriculture and horticulture all the experts take the view that co-operative agricultural credit will be able to meet those needs for the next five or ten years. The fact that the co-operative agricultural credit institutions have enough resources to meet the entire need for working credit does not mean that every farmer will be able to obtain as much credit as he wants. The co-operative banks, like any other banks, have to insist on adequate security to ensure payment of interest and redemption by the people who ask for loans.

The form of security most desired by the banks is the mortgage. Where the potential borrowers own real properties, those properties can serve as underlying security. In many cases they have to provide such security in order to procure sufficient credit for investment in land and buildings. Generally up to two-thirds of the estimated value of these is loaned. In certain cases the agricultural credit banks go further and lend up to 90 per cent of the estimated value. They do this only if the would-be borrower can prove, or credibly show by his accounts, that his operating results are such that he will be able to meet the interest and redemption out of his trading profit. In the case of such mortgage loans (up to an exceptionally high percentage of the estimated value of the security) the agricultural credit banks rely on the advice of credit specialists who are employed by both the central institutions. On any amount by which the loan exceeds two-thirds of the estimated value the borrower has to pay interest at a rate not more than one per cent above the normal rate for mortgage loans.

In the case of those applicants who can provide no adequate security in the form of real property, it has always been customary to require a guarantee by two persons regarded as having sufficient means. Since World War II, however, the relations between people in rural districts have become more business-like, and there has come to be a certain aversion to acting as guarantor for anybody. In fact guarantees nowadays are mainly confined to those given by relatives and friends. Nevertheless the guarantee, as a form of security, is still much used.

The law of the Netherlands, unlike that of various other

countries in western Europe, does not recognize the chattel mortgage. Strictly, therefore, livestock and machines cannot be accepted as security for proposed loans. But the agricultural credit banks have devised a method which can be used, in dealings with honest people, for granting credit against such security. A farmer who applies for credit on this basis has to sell his livestock or machines to the agricultural credit bank. The latter thereby becomes their owner, though they remain in use by the borrower as usual and there is nothing to show that the farmer has assigned them to the bank, since the sale is not recorded in any public register. This is the weak point in the arrangement. The bank, it is true, has become the owner of the livestock, but a farmer who is fraudulently minded can sell the same animals again to another lender. This leads to all sorts of legal difficulties. It is true of course that in the countryside everybody knows his fellow villagers and it is difficult to keep an illicit sale secret.

On livestock or machines thus transferred to them on trust the agricultural credit banks lend up to 50 per cent of the estimated value. For such loans they normally charge interest at a rate higher by $\frac{1}{2}$ per cent than that applied where there is fully sufficient security. Twenty years' experience has shown that the risks in this form of security are small.

In the Netherlands both the co-operative sale and the co-operative processing of agricultural and horticultural products are important. The members of any such co-operative are obliged to put their products at its disposal. Many co-operatives are prepared, at a member's request, to covenant with an agricultural credit bank to pay to the bank the amount of the claim which that member has or will have on them for products delivered, or to be delivered. To a farmer or market gardener who has assigned his claim in this way, the agricultural credit bank will grant credit up to between 50 and 60 per cent of that claim. Through such assignment of claims many agricultural producers are enabled to obtain additional credit for their operating requirements.

Young people who wish to start a farm or market garden often face great financial difficulties. With Marshall Aid monies the Government in 1951 formed a fund which can give agricultural credit banks a guarantee for capital development loans in cases where the would-be borrowers cannot themselves produce the required securities. This fund has made possible many capital projects which would otherwise have had to remain unexecuted. Until now the amount of losses which the fund has had to meet has been extremely limited.

Various provinces also give certain guarantees to market gardeners wishing to modernize their enterprises, to cover the payment of interest and redemption on advances granted by agricultural credit banks.

It would be fair to say that every farmer and market gardener who deserves confidence and who knows his job can obtain from his agricultural credit bank, in the form of an advance or loan, a considerable part of the working capital which he requires. That is why virtually all farmers and market gardeners are members of such a bank. Nevertheless, anybody wishing to start a farm or market garden must have some capital of his own. To conduct business without having any capital at all would not be justifiable.

Although the possibilities of obtaining credit are numerous, not all farmers and horticulturists make full use of them. Especially among the older ones there are many who carry out less capital development than they might, because they do not wish to assume the risk of heavy debt service. The general opinion is that these people are wrong to take that view, although nobody can say so with absolute certainty. One would have to be able to see into the future, since only then will it appear whether capital expenditure incurred in previous years has yielded a profit. Unfortunately people with such prophetic gifts are not found among those in the service of co-operative agricultural credit!

In the Netherlands it has been found possible, with a minimum of Government aid, to build up a system of mutual credit-granting for agriculture and horticulture which works well and about which few complaints are heard. Even though in most other countries it is not possible to follow this example unchanged, it may be an advantage to know about it.

17

The Role of Education in Agricultural Development

WILLIAM I. MYERS*

Formerly of Cornell University, Ithaca, N.Y., U.S.A.

GREATER URGENCY has been given to economic development by two factors that have become more important in recent years. One of these is the rapid increase in population in less developed countries owing to the maintenance of usual birth rates and the decline in mortality resulting from improved disease control. The other is the burning desire to improve levels of living with maximum speed that is especially strong in new nations which have emerged recently from colonial status. Under these pressures national leaders are unwilling to accept the relatively slow evolution of economic development that has characterized western Europe and North America during the past half-century. With a net population increase of two or three per cent a year it will be necessary to achieve a larger continuing gain in output if levels of living are to be raised. If these countries wish to speed up the rate of economic development, it will be essential to analyse the experience of older nations in order to determine principles and priorities which, if followed, will enable them to achieve economic growth at maximum continuing speed and sustainable cost.

One of the striking characteristics of economic development in the twentieth century has been the rapid growth of industrialization in western Europe, North America, and Japan as well as in Soviet

* The writer wishes to acknowledge his indebtedness for ideas, suggestions, and criticisms to Richard Bradfield, Professor of Soil Technology, Emeritus, and Professors G. W. Hedlund and John W. Mellor of the Department of Agricultural Economics, Cornell University.

[*174*]

Russia. Since the leading countries of the modern world are highly industrialized and relatively prosperous, there has been a strong tendency for under-developed countries to imitate the present economic organization of these leaders by emphasizing industrial growth and to neglect the development of their basic economic activity, agriculture. The most dramatic example of the disastrous results of such a programme is the failure of the "Great Leap Forward" of Communist China, but similar less serious mistakes have been made by other countries.

THE IMPORTANCE OF AGRICULTURE IN ECONOMIC DEVELOPMENT

In practically all low-income countries, agriculture is the dominant industry and frequently the only one of any real significance. In most cases from half to three-fourths of the total labour force is engaged in farm production and half or more of the national income is derived from this source. Although a major part of the national resources of labour as well as land is devoted to agriculture, it is being used at very low levels of productivity. It is obvious that agricultural improvement is essential to economic growth under these conditions.

The experience of other countries has shown that the most effective method of achieving significant gains in agricultural output and productivity is through the use of modern scientific methods of farm production. Unfortunately modern agricultural technology is not a commodity that can be imported and applied on farms as if it were a new, highly potent fertilizer. General principles of the use of irrigation, improved seeds, fertilizers, and pesticides can be obtained from research in more highly developed countries, but it is neither possible nor profitable to imitate such practices exactly, because of differences in soil, climatic, economic, and social conditions. To be practical and constructive, improved practices must be adapted to conditions on farms in each country.

Although overshadowed by mechanization, higher yields per acre and per animal have also been a major factor in increasing agricultural output and productivity in the United States. Since most low-income countries have abundant farm labour but limited capital, the achievements of Japan and Taiwan are better examples of increasing agricultural production by more effective use of traditional resources. According to Johnston and Mellor,[1] "Labor productivity in Japanese agriculture approximately doubled over a span of 30 years comparing farm output and labor inputs during the years 1881–90 with the decade 1911–20. The comparable increase in Taiwan appears to have been even larger—something like 130 to 160 per cent over the 30-year span between 1901–10 and 1931–40." In both cases

---

[1] Bruce F. Johnston and John W. Mellor, "The Role of Agriculture in Economic Development," *American Economics Review*, Sept. 1961, pp. 566–91.

the major factors in improvement were agricultural research to develop higher yielding varieties of crops, increased use of fertilizers
and irrigation, and educational programmes to encourage wide use
of more productive varieties and improved cultural methods.

CONTRIBUTIONS OF AGRICULTURE TO ECONOMIC DEVELOPMENT

Since countries differ widely in physical endowment and educational levels as well as in historical background, there is no generally
applicable formula of the exact role which agriculture should play in
a well-planned programme of economic development. However,
there is ample evidence from experience of the important contribution of increased agricultural output and productivity to economic
growth.

In the first place, economic development is accompanied by a
marked increase in the demand for food. Failure to expand farm
production to keep pace with demand would result in higher prices
and political discontent or the importation of food by the use of
scarce foreign exchange needed for economic development. In either
case the effect on economic progress would be unfavourable.

The expansion of exports of adapted agricultural products is
usually the best way of increasing foreign exchange earnings, especially in the early stages of economic development. Increased production of an adapted export crop can often be obtained with a modest
capital investment while local processing may provide needed employment as well as experience in simple industrial operations. In
view of the urgent need for greater foreign exchange earnings and
the lack of alternative opportunities, considerable expansion of agricultural production for export is often a desirable policy even though
the world supply-demand situation for the commodity may not be
favourable.

The most difficult problem of low-income countries which are
making strenuous efforts to achieve economic progress is the large
amount of capital required. These needs far exceed the supply of
available funds except in rare cases of countries with large earnings
from oil or mineral exports. Since it is possible to increase agricultural productivity with moderate capital outlays, agriculture can
make a net contribution to industrial development in addition to
some improvement in the levels of consumption of the farm population. Furthermore, in view of rural population growth and the
potential for increasing output per man, agriculture will also be
able to spare labour when needed for industrial expansion provided
vigorous and intelligent efforts are made to increase farm productivity.

Historical evidence indicates that in less fully developed countries
in which agriculture constitutes the major part of the national
economy, sustained economic growth cannot be achieved without a

significant net contribution to capital requirements from agriculture. Although grants and long-term "soft" loans can help, the major part of the capital requirements for industrial growth must be provided by the country concerned. Hence free countries must find politically acceptable ways of obtaining a reasonable part of the capital required from agriculture by taxation or otherwise.

Although agricultural improvement is a basic requisite for economic growth of less developed countries, careful attention should also be given to industry, transportation, utilities, and other essential services. The best solution is a balanced programme of agricultural and industrial development adapted to the resources and conditions of the country concerned. As increased farm productivity is achieved, the long-time welfare of farm people as well as of the nation requires: (1) a gradual change in the economic structure with a relative decline of agriculture; and (2) a net contribution of capital and labour from agriculture to the industrial sector of the economy. Insufficient movement of workers out of agriculture will tend to result in excessively small farms and serious under-employment of labour. Orderly reduction of the farm labour force by competition from industry and commerce is essential to keep wages of farm workers in a reasonable relation to wages in other sectors.

PROBLEMS IN INCREASING AGRICULTURAL PRODUCTION

The low productivity of agriculture and the resulting poverty of low-income countries are due largely to the use of traditional methods of production carried on for decades or even centuries without significant improvement. One of the easily recognized causes of low crop yields is lack of water at critical periods. As a result there is a widespread belief that if plenty of water were provided by irrigation, their problems would be solved. If in such cases additional water is supplied, a significant increase in yields is obtained at first, but after a few years the results are disappointing. The addition of water changed the effectiveness of other important cultural factors and calls for a new system of management.[2] The drought-resistant variety which was adapted to former conditions is incapable of making a satisfactory response to the increased water supply and a new variety is needed to give higher yields under these conditions. With plenty of water there will be need for changes in fertilization and in plant population as well as in pest and weed control. The optimum use of water will also need to be known since too much or too little will decrease net returns.

The spectacular increases in yields made possible by hybrid corn

---

[2] Richard Bradfield, "Opportunities for Soil Scientists in Freeing the World From Hunger." Presidential address at the 7th International Congress of Soil Science, Madison, Wis., 1960. Reprinted by New York State College of Agriculture, 1960, pp. 6–7.

have encouraged the belief that all that is needed to increase corn yields is to get some hybrid seed. Any programme based on this assumption is bound to lead to disappointment. Even after hybrid seed adapted to local soil and climatic conditions has been developed it will not realize its potential increase unless other cultural factors are favourable. A successful programme to increase corn yields will involve not only adapted hybrid seed, but also changes in the use of fertilizer and water, the number of plants per acre, pest control, and other cultural factors. It is unfortunate but true that there is no simple, easy, magic formula to increase agricultural productivity.

Another frequent cause of unsatisfactory results in developing countries of improved practices obtained by research is due to the failure to try out the new practices in different regions before they are recommended to farmers. A new practice may appear very promising under conditions prevailing in the experimental plots but fails or is less effective in other areas because of differences in soil and climatic conditions. No recommendation of an improved practice can safely be made until it has been thoroughly tested on farms in the principal environmental areas of the country concerned.

In order to make progress in agricultural development it is necessary for farmers to believe in the desirability of change and to see the possibility of personal gain from improved practices. In some countries, existing tenure systems discourage the use of improved methods of production because farmers do not share fairly in the increased output. In such cases improved tenure arrangements are essential for technological progress.

IMPORTANT FACTORS IN PLANNING AGRICULTURAL DEVELOPMENT

In agricultural development every country must start where it is and make progress from that point. Political leaders in low-income countries with inadequate resources and unlimited needs are extremely anxious to get quick results. With little knowledge of agriculture, it not surprising that these leaders often tend to choose a spectacular proposal, such as an irrigation project or a fertilizer factory, as the answer to the problems of low farm production. Such a project may be a satisfactory way to start agricultural improvement but, as previously explained, it cannot assure steadily rising yields over a period of years because of the interrelationships of all important cultural factors involved in production. It is impossible to achieve a significant continuing increase in farm output and productivity without a comprehensive programme of agricultural development with reasonable dependable financial support.

The objective of agricultural development is to achieve a steady improvement in methods of production. This requires careful scientific research to determine the most important factors limiting yields at the time, and the most effective and economical ways to correct them. To develop and carry out such a programme it will be necessary to train the men needed, to carry on research to obtain essential information, to test its applicability under varying local conditions, to get this information into the hands of farmers for use in increasing the output of their crops and animals, and to see that new materials and services required—such as adapted improved seeds, fertilizers, pesticides, and credit—are available for use when and where needed.

The wide gap between the crop yields of under-developed countries and those of countries using modern technology indicates the large potential gain from a sound programme of agricultural development, but this goal cannot be attained quickly or cheaply. Agricultural research is the basic indispensable requisite in making effective use of modern scientific technology already known and practised in more advanced countries and in working out a programme of agricultural improvement adapted to conditions in the country concerned. Agricultural research is not a quick-acting cure-all; it is slow and unspectacular and involves an enormous amount of painstaking work. An effective research programme is a long-time project whose success depends primarily on continuity of full-time service by qualified, dedicated scientists. Although valuable returns can be expected in a few years, the results of such research are cumulative and in time will pay high returns on the costs involved. Adequate, dependable financial support is a basic requisite for success.

Although deficiencies in other forms of capital often receive more publicity, the most serious handicap to economic growth is the shortage of trained men. In many less well-developed countries, this shortage, which is especially acute in agriculture, is retarding progress in carrying out desirable programmes of land reform as well as in agricultural research and education. It can be made up only in part, temporarily, by the employment of skilled workers from abroad, and will continue to limit agricultural progress until it is corrected.

Although well-trained agricultural scientists are very scare, there is no shortage of men to be trained. The critical need is for a nucleus of trained scientists to start and carry on agricultural research and teaching. Such a programme must start slowly but later can grow at an accelerating rate as the supply of trained men increases. In most cases, time can be saved by training promising young men at the postgraduate and, if necessary at first, at the undergraduate levels in other countries. However, in order to achieve continuing progress at reasonable cost, it will be necessary to provide an agricultural college to train the large numbers of skilled workers required, at least at the undergraduate level. A successful programme of agricultural development will require a steadily increasing number of trained men not only for agricultural research and education, but also for agricultural vocational schools, government organizations, private business firms, and farming.

Agricultural Research and Teaching

The most critical bottlenecks in initiating a programme of agricultural development are productive research and the training of skilled scientists. The experience of other countries has demonstrated that the most effective way of carrying on these closely related activities is through an agricultural college which combines both functions. If properly organized and administered, colleges are freer from political influences and can provide a more favourable environment for a long-range research and teaching programme. It is imperative that agricultural college teachers be familiar with methods and results of up-to-date research in their fields in order to train students for effective service in scientific agriculture. Research scientists also benefit from the stimulation of questioning students. An agricultural college combining college teaching and research can make more efficient use of scarce trained men and produce better results by the mutual stimulation of scientists working in both of these closely related functions.

The establishment and maintenance of a strong institution combining agricultural research and teaching is a long-term project requiring adequate, dependable financial support, but it is of critical importance in achieving significant continuing agricultural progress. The success of such a college will depend largely on the ability, training, and character of its professors. If the needs for trained men are to be met, competitive salaries must be paid in order to obtain and retain the full-time services of able, well-trained scientists and, in the longer run, to attract more promising students to seek careers in agriculture. In order to keep up to date in scientific development, salary scales should encourage post-graduate training, should recognize exceptional performance, and should be maintained in a fair relation to other professions in the country concerned. More and better scientific equipment and buildings and adequate operating funds will also be essential.

Extension Education

In order to speed up the adoption by farmers of proven improved methods of production, it also is necessary to carry on an extension-education programme. If properly organized this can make a very important contribution to agricultural progress not only by taking proven research recommendations to farmers promptly, but also by bringing information on important farm problems back to the research staff so as to keep the research in reasonable adjustment to farm needs.

Although the Land-Grant college system of extension education has made a great contribution to American agricultural progress, it is seldom wise to imitate this system precisely in under-developed countries which differ widely from the United States in literacy, income, means of communication, and social organization. In this case, as in others, it is better to develop an organization to perform the essential functions, which is adapted to the country concerned and can be carried on at sustainable cost. The major purpose is to provide prompt and effective two-way communication between farmers and research workers, to help farmers increase yields and thus to accelerate sound agricultural improvement.

Organization of Agricultural Research, Teaching, and Extension Education

The great gains in farm productivity obtained through agricultural research, teaching, and extension education in developed nations have stimulated low-income countries to establish organizations with similar names in the hope of obtaining equally favourable results. Although some publicly supported services with these titles are now in existence in many such countries, the results have often been disappointing. In some cases there is little hope that they will be able to develop and carry out constructive programmes of continuing agricultural improvement as now staffed, organized, and operated.

One of the more serious common handicaps to effective work is the complete physical and administrative separation of agricultural research and teaching which is due to the fact that these intimately related functions are usually administered by different government departments. Under these conditions, teaching is often largely abstract and academic and much of it is carried on by poorly paid, part-time instructors with little or no experience in agricultural research and who have other jobs in order to make a living. Naturally their students receive little if any training in modern scientific methods of increasing production and controlling pests. It is not surprising that such colleges attract inadequate numbers of students since they do not provide satisfactory training for effective service in government organizations or private business.

In many less developed countries a high proportion of the students in the colleges of agriculture have been reared in cities and have had little or no contact with practical agriculture. Many of the teachers in the colleges have the same handicap. This situation is aggravated because of the widespread, deep-seated prejudice of "educated" men against taking part in practical farm work. As a result graduates of these agricultural colleges are not qualified for most types of positions in modern scientific agriculture. A partial remedy for these serious deficiencies would be a *farm practice* requirement for graduation which could be satisfied by working on an approved farm long enough to become familiar with common farm operations. Some farm experience could also be provided by having students assist with field operations on a research farm.

The results of complete separation of extension from research are equally unfortunate. In many cases, because of their urban background and academic training, so-called extension workers are entirely unfamiliar with farm operation and hence are unable to advise farmers on production problems. Since such extension workers are not acquainted with results of current research, their recommendations are neither respected nor followed by farmers because they have not been demonstrated to be applicable and profitable on farms in the area. An equally unfortunate result of such separation is the fact that information on critical farm problems is not taken back to research workers to keep the research programmes in adjustment with farm needs. Efforts to improve agricultural production will be wasted until they result in better practices on farms.

In view of its basic importance to agricultural progress, strong efforts should be made to combine administrative control of agricultural college teaching and research in one organization and, if practicable, to include agricultural extension as well. However, even where the severe handicap of separate, administrative control cannot be corrected, it should be possible to attain reasonable co-operation among the staff members engaged in these interrelated functions. The co-operation and mutual stimulation of agricultural resarch, teaching, and extension are essential to rapid and sustained progress in agricultural development.

There is a natural desire in every region of every country to have a local college and experiment station whenever such a programme is being developed and financed by the national government. In a number of countries this political pressure has resulted in the establishment of too many agricultural colleges and experiment stations all of which are severely handicapped by inadequate support. Even with more efficient use of trained men, the cost of a strong institution combining agricultural research and teaching will be substantial. Since agricultural research requires highly trained men and expensive equipment, it should usually be concentrated at one or two colleges with a minimum number of branch stations to meet the needs of different climatic and soil conditions. In view of substantial and rising costs of maintaining this vital part of an agricultural development programme, it is cheaper and better to expand an existing college to meet increasing needs for trained men rather than to establish additional institutions which could not do effective work because of inadequate support.

Rural Elementary and Secondary Education

Agricultural research, teaching, and extension education are of critical importance in initiating agricultural improvement in less developed countries. However, it is extremely difficult if not impossible to achieve continuing agricultural development with illiterate farmers. More and better general education of rural people is necessary to remove the inhibitions of tradition and ignorance, to increase the acceptance of desirable changes, to facilitate communication, and to ensure continuing progress.

One of the more serious handicaps of most less developed countries is the inadequacy of educational facilities at the elementary and secondary levels that is especially serious in rural areas. There are too few elementary schools and these often provide only from two to four years of low-quality instruction. Secondary education is frequently available only at private schools located in urban centres and these are too expensive for most rural children. Under these conditions it is almost impossible for rural boys to obtain college training in agriculture or in other professions. This unfortunate situation results in having few leaders who are familiar with farm problems. It is also a major factor contributing to the inadequate enrollment in colleges of agriculture in the countries concerned.

In a well-planned programme of agricultural development and economic growth, serious attention should be given to providing more and better elementary and high schools for rural as well as urban people. This national system should also provide for vocational education in agriculture at the lower levels, so that boys who do not continue their education will be better qualified for modern farming and for the large numbers of semi-skilled positions needed in agricultural development. It is also very desirable to integrate these vocational secondary schools with colleges so that qualified rural boys can progress to college in order to prepare for careers in agriculture or in other professions.

The most abundant resource of low-income countries is their human capital. Fortunately there is no deficiency in natural intelligence even among citizens who are handicapped by illiteracy. The cost of an adequate system of elementary and secondary education will bring good returns in increased productivity throughout the economy and a better life for all citizens. While the results of education are less spectacular than modern buildings and impressive machines, they are more important in achieving economic growth and political stability. Lengthening the period of education would also have a favourable, if small, effect on population growth by postponing marriage.

The importance of elementary and even secondary education for rural citizens has been greatly increased by the development of scientific agriculture because it involves a fundamental change from self-sufficient to some degree of commercial farm production. In free countries, modern scientific methods of production involve the purchase and use of fertilizers, pesticides, and improved seeds as well as the sale of farm products to repay their cost. In addition to assisting in allocating workers among various occupations and in strengthening free government, education stimulates the desire of farmers to increase production by suggesting new wants to be met by this means. Literacy of rural people is essential in teaching farmers how to apply modern technology in farm operation in a continuing programme to increase farm productivity. Education is necessary to enable farmers to learn how to make wise choices between enterprises, how to choose the best methods of production for their farms, how to buy fertilizers and pesticides, how to sell farm products, and how to use credit profitably.

Even after the use of fertilizers, pesticides, and better seeds has been shown to be profitable, it will not be possible to adopt such improved practices unless these materials are available when and where needed and farmers are able to buy them. Experience has shown that in many cases, farmer co-operatives are the most effective institutions to obtain and distribute the specific types of commodities and services required for desirable innovations to increase farm production. Such local farmer co-operatives may also be needed for marketing the larger farm output and for providing credit for the purchase of farm supplies. Better educated farmers will be required to organize and operate successfully these co-operative business organizations.

A well-planned programme of extension education is the most effective method yet devised to minimize the time lag between the discovery of improved methods and their use on farms. However, technical assistance to farmers by such programmes does not reduce the need for improving the education of rural people. Reasonable progress can be made in teaching illiterate farmers how to improve present methods of production by well-planned demonstrations in spite of the tremendous difficulties and high costs of mass communication under these conditions. However, a continuing programme of agricultural development to meet the rising needs of a growing population at reasonable cost will require better educated farmers as an essential condition for success. The outstanding records of steadily increasing production made by the farmers of Japan and Formosa give clear evidence of the advantages of education in applying scientific methods to farm operation.

Medical science has made a great contribution to human welfare by reducing sickness and lengthening life. At the same time it has also increased the severity of population pressures by reducing mortality rates especially among children. In spite of abundant land and other favourable conditions, the best that the United States has been able to do over the past half-century is to increase the national output of goods and services about 3 per cent a year. Since population has been rising at a lower rate, less than 2 per cent a year, it has been possible to earn a modest increase in output per person and a rising level of living.

The high rate of population growth is a major threat to the achievement of a continuing increase in levels of living and per capita incomes of many low-income countries. In view of the number and complexity of the problems to be solved and the rate of progress in economic development to date, the prospects are not bright for achieving a rising level of living without population control. The importance of this problem to the welfare of heavily populated countries is beginning to be recognized, and a few halting steps are being taken towards a solution. Reducing the rate of population growth deserves equal consideration with agricultural improvement in well-planned programmes of economic development of low-income countries.

The application of modern scientific technology to farm production has revolutionized former ideas about maximum yields of crops and animals. Earlier record yields are surpassed year after year and no one now knows the maximum yield of wheat or rice or any other crop. It will not be easy or cheap to raise yields above present high levels of some advanced countries, but there is no doubt that it can be done. As successively higher yields are obtained, more intensive research will be necessary to discover and correct the important factors limiting production at each level, as well as more and better education to get the improved methods into prompt use by farmers.

18

The Changing Pattern of Rural Socio-economy in India

SIR MANILAL B. NANAVATI
Indian Society of Agricultural Economics,
Bombay, India

INDIA LIVES IN VILLAGES. Nearly five of every six Indians live in rural areas. If we take rural India by itself, four of every five self-supporting persons who live in it are agriculturists. Nearly one-half of the national income is contributed by agriculture. Among the non-agriculturists in rural areas are village artisans and craftsmen, money-lenders and traders, and public servants, teachers, etc. Thus it is obvious that the economic prosperity and planning for development in India must concentrate on improving the technical efficiency of agriculture and raising the standard of living of the rural masses.

Indian agriculture has gone through a long period of stagnation. Briefly, the diagnosis is that the Indian economy has not been able for decades past to generate sufficient savings to support an investment programme which could make it possible for the growing population to secure larger per capita incomes. In fact the entire socio-economic climate in the countryside was unsuited to high levels of improvement. Agricultural practices have continued for the most part along traditional lines which could not yield enough food and raw materials to support a more progressive or diversified economic structure in the country. The rural economy settled down to an under-developed equilibrium with low levels of productivity, poor techniques of production, a high degree of under-employment, and stagnation of incomes and living standards.

There has been a continuous growth in population, leading to heavy pressure on land and consequently to subdivision and fragmentation of holdings, resulting in the vicious circle of low yields, low

[186]

incomes, lack of savings and investment, and low productivity. This has resulted in a growing imbalance between the requirements of food and raw materials and the rate of growth of agricultural production. The average increase of 3 per cent per annum in agricultural production that has been achieved in recent years is quite inadequate to support the increasing population at higher levels of living. The fact is that the country's needs are expanding rapidly and the plans for further development will be seriously jeopardized if agricultural production does not rise rapidly, to meet both the growing food demand and the expanding raw material requirements of growing industries. The Indian rural problem is thus not merely a problem concerning the rural population, it is part of the problem of the further development of the entire economy. More and more the problem merges into that of all-round economic and social development. Changes have to proceed both within the rural economy and outside in order to achieve the best results.

While studying the Indian rural problem and the ways and means of tackling it, it is essential to bear in mind the complexity of the rural structure. This has evolved through the centuries and shows diversities from region to region. Yet one discerns behind this diversity a certain uniformity of pattern. Perhaps the most important characteristic of the Indian village is hierarchy, of which one can distinguish three types: one of ritual prestige, one of wealth, and one of power. These hierarchies do not coincide today, but there is a high correlation among them, which has serious implications for the nature of the Indian village and the functioning of the village economy.

The ritual hierarchy arose because of the caste system. Although the origin of this system may be traced to the classification of society into occupational groups—which was useful at a particular stage of development—in the course of centuries it developed some social structural rigidities and social factions. Each caste became an endogamous group. An individual had no choice of occupation, as this was determined for him by his birth, and it had a dampening effect on his initiative, aspirations, and creative abilities, resulting in social waste and stagnation. His social status and relationships were determined by the caste hierarchy, which perpetuated group isolations and created social tensions. Furthermore, a large section of the rural population—those on the lowest rung of the ladder, eking out their livelihood by the sale of their labour and/or by cultivating tiny plots of land—remained perpetually in a depressed condition, without any hope of economic or social amelioration.

The hierarchy of wealth resulted from the land tenure systems created by the British Government and also from the introduction of a money economy, the opening of the countryside by the development of transport and communications, the access to foreign markets for Indian agricultural commodities, the recurrence of famines, and the recognition of proprietorship in land on the lines of the English land laws in the nineteenth century. As a result there was a heavy concentration of land ownership in the hands of a small section of intermediaries, landlords, and moneylenders and traders. With the growing pressure of population on land, the evils of sub-infeudation, rack renting, and illegal exactions from tenants were accentuated. The recognition of proprietory rights in land, the introduction of a money economy, and the rise in land values provided a favourable atmosphere for the village moneylenders to play their game, to grab large areas of land and to get greater control over the rural economy. All this had a depressing effect on the rural economy, leading to poverty and stagnation.

Discussing the combination of these hierarchies and their effects on the rural economy, the Rural Credit Survey Report[1] stated:

> It is not only the urban-induced power of the private moneylender and the private trader that affects the success of co-operatives when it manifests itself either inside or outside the society. Affinity is not confined to these two; it extends to the leadership in the village, whether this is based on property or derived from connexion with the administration. The bigger landlord has ways which conform with those of the moneylender and, indeed, he often is the moneylender or trader himself. The village headman is also drawn from the same class, and it is usual for these to have connexions which link them not only to the sources of finance but to the seats of administrative power. Among the combinations of factors which thus operate against the interests of the bulk of those who reside in the village is the rigidity of caste feeling in conjunction with the power derived from money, land, leadership, and above all, the affiliation with the superior forces of the urban economy. The rigidity of caste loyalty remains, while the original division of caste functions no longer does. The result is that the landlord who may also be moneylender, the moneylender who may also be trader and the educated person who may also be a subordinate official, all these through their association with the outside urban world of finance and power wield an influence in the village which at many points is diverted from the good of the village to the benefit of the caste or even of a close circle of relatives.

Thus it became clear that the rural socio-economic structure needed an overhaul if the rural development of India were to progress. Changes in the social framework became a pre-condition for rural development. The establishment of a socialistic pattern of society calls for measures to enlarge the opportunities, to promote enterprise among the disadvantaged classes and to create a sense of partnership among all sections of the community. Measures were taken in these directions, therefore, after the attainment of independence. They are mentioned briefly below and their impact on socio-economic structure discussed.

---

[1] *All-India Rural Credit Survey, Report of the Committee of Direction,* Vol. II, *The General Report,* Reserve Bank of India, Bombay, 1954, p. 277.

The most important achievement of the national government was the integration of the princely states which, with very few noteworthy exceptions, were relics of a feudal age. Another most important achievement was the preparation of the Indian Constitution which envisaged fundamental changes in the social pattern. According to the preamble to the Constitution, social, economic, and political justice is to be secured to all the citizens of the country. The Constitution grants the right of equality to all citizens. The directive principles laid down specifically require the State to take measures so that (1) the ownership and control of the material resources of the community are so distributed as best to subserve the common good and (2) the operation of the economic system does not result in a concentration of wealth and the means of production to the common detriment. The directive principles which have a direct bearing on rural development are (a) special care is to be given to the educational and economic interests of the weaker sections and in particular of the scheduled castes and the scheduled tribes, (b) village panchayats (local self-government bodies) are to be organized and given such powers and authority as may be necessary to enable them to function as units of self-government, (c) cottage industries in rural areas are to be promoted, and (d) agriculture and animal husbandry are to be organized on modern scientific lines.

The Indian Constitution has prohibited the practice of untouchability in any form. Already a favourable atmosphere had been created by the Harijan Movement led by Mahatma Gandhi. The Untouchability Offenses Act of 1955 makes the enforcement of any disability against a scheduled caste illegal and punishable. Temples have been thrown open to Harijans; educational facilities have been extended to them; in selection for employment in Government administration they receive favourable treatment; and each State ministry and the Central Cabinet has Harijan members. For the economic and social uplifting of the scheduled castes and tribes, special efforts are made through the commissioner appointed for the purpose. But it has to be recognized that traditions and attitudes perpetuated over centuries cannot be wiped out by legislation in a day. It is a process of education and of economic and social betterment which depends on breaking up the social and economic hierarchy in the villages and the creation of institutions for the benefit of the weaker sections in the community.

Another major obstacle to rural development arose from the traditional structure of rural society and the resulting concentration of wealth and power on the one hand and poverty and economic and social backwardness on the other. Lack of incentive, lack of education, and lack of resources stand in the way of the uplift of the poorer sections of villages. Steps were taken in the First Five-Year Plan and the two subsequent Plans to remove these obstacles. A brief idea of these various measures is given below:

LAND REFORMS–REMOVAL OF EXPLOITATION OF TILLERS BY LANDLORDS

Productivity of land and the welfare of those who are actually engaged in agriculture depend on the institutional arrangements with regard to ownership and use of land. Mention was made above of the existence of intermediaries and a heavy concentration of land ownership resulting in rack renting, insecurity, etc. which led to stagnation in agriculture. Thus a bold land reform programme was undertaken with the attainment of independence. As India's Third Five-Year Plan puts it,[2]

. . . land reform programmes . . . have two specific objects. The first is to remove such impediments to increase in agricultural production as arise from the agrarian structure from the past. This should help to create conditions for evolving as speedily as possible an agricultural economy with high levels of efficiency and productivity. The second object, which is closely related to the first, is to eliminate all elements of exploitation and social injustice within the agrarian system, to provide security for the tiller of soil, and assure equality of status and opportunity to all sections of the rural population.

Prior to the recent land reform measures, nearly half the area in India was held under one or other type of intermediary tenure under which revenue was fixed permanently or for a long period. Such landlords were mere intermediaries between the Government and the actual tillers. They collected the dues and they could enhance rents and impose other levies on the tillers. As a result, the farmers remained poor and backward and had very little incentive to improve agriculture. Such tenures were obviously overdue for abolition. In the rest of the country, the system of peasant-proprietorship was prevalent; but it could not yield the good results expected of it because of the emergence of certain undesirable features such as absentee landlordism, concentration of land ownership, and rack renting. In the context of acute land hunger in the country, the establishment of direct relationship between the State and the actual cultivator had to be accorded the highest priority.

Land reform comprises four sets of measures: abolition of intermediary tenures, tenancy reform, ceilings on agricultural holdings, and conferment of rights of ownership on tenant cultivators. Once accomplished, these measures are intended to pave the way for the growth of a co-operative rural economy. At Independence, intermediary tenures accounted for about forty-five per cent of the total area of the country. Except for the payment of compensation—a proc-

---

[2] *Third Five-Year Plan,* Planning Commission, Government of India, New Delhi, 1961, p. 220.

ess spread over 20 to 40 years—this phase of land reform has been completed. Similarly, despite occasional problems arising from the attempts of owners to resume land for "personal cultivation," and with certain variations between States, the programme for tenancy reform has been also substantially carried out. Together, abolition of intermediary rights and tenancy reform involve considerable *de facto* redistribution of land. On the other hand, proposals for imposing ceilings on agricultural holdings have only slowly found their way into State legislation, and a high proportion of the "surplus" lands has escaped through "transfers," many of them being essentially evasive of land reform. In due course, large holdings will disappear in fact as in law but, for the time being, an important public purpose sought through land reform has not been achieved. Nevertheless, whatever the limitations of the legislation, it is essential that it should be implemented as early as possible.

Apart from the imposition of ceilings on individual ownership of land, the next major step in land reform is the grant of rights of ownership to the bulk of tenant cultivators, especially to those occupying "non-resumable" lands. The direction of policy is that this task should be accomplished before the end of the Third Plan. Some States have undertaken the necessary legislation and are giving effect to it, elsewhere the objective has not so far been given the priority due to it.

In theory land reform was urged and broadly accepted as part of the Plans. In its actual implementation, instead of being developed as a movement rooted in mass opinion, it has been treated generally as an isolated programme. In every area in which land reform is carried out, there is need (1) for an intensive agricultural drive and provision of supplies, credit, and other services; (2) for greater emphasis on the organization of co-operative activity; and (3) for supporting rural employment programmes. Without such measures, the positive gains from land reform cannot be fully realized.

For the agricultural economy to be placed on a sound basis, the problem of small and uneconomic holdings still remains to be faced. To some extent, extreme fragmentation of holdings is now avoided in most states by fixing floor limits below which the division of land will not be permitted, but the limits are necessarily very low. Consolidation of individual holdings has been undertaken on a notable scale only in three or four States, but the total area benefited will at any time be not much in excess of 50 or 60 million acres. There is good scope for consolidation in areas which are irrigated or are likely to come under irrigation. Co-operative farming, rural works programmes, land settlement schemes, and intensive development of rural industry are essential not only in themselves but as a means of securing efficient cultivation of the holdings and completing the reorganization of the agrarian structure. These elements have to be brought into the Five-Year Plans on a much larger scale than at present.

By now, almost all the intermediary tenures have been removed and ownership rights—minus the right to transfer—have been conferred on some of the *bona fide* cultivators. Generally, cultivation by tenants has been discouraged and ownership of land is being transferred to tenants if they cultivate it for a sufficiently long period. Rents have been reduced to reasonable levels and tenancy conditions have been regulated. Steps have been taken to fix a ceiling on land ownership.

The implementation of land reforms is a difficult task. First, administrative machinery was not adequate in all the States. Secondly, the required measures were not enforced at one stroke, but only gradually. This gradualness in the programme unfortunately proved a major handicap to its effective implementation. Not only was uncertainty with regard to ownership unnecessarily created but also, following this, the persons who were likely to be adversely affected by land reforms found time to transfer land and resort to such other steps as would defeat the main purpose of the reforms. Tenants, through lack of alternative employment opportunities could not insist about their rights vis-à-vis landlords. Basically, the effective implementation of land reforms is a question of reducing the pressure of population on land and setting up an efficient and impartial administrative machinery. With the association of village panchayat bodies in the implementation of land reforms, it is expected that the legislation will be enforced more effectively, leading to better terms of tenancy and the conferment of ownership on *bona fide* tillers.

REGULATION OF MONEYLENDING—REMOVAL OF EXPLOITATION OF AGRICULTURISTS BY MONEYLENDERS

Another direction in which efforts were made to overcome the handicaps of the poorer sections of the community was the legislation for the regulation of moneylending and the development of co-operative institutions. The heavy indebtedness, exorbitant rates of interest, malpractices, and transfers of land from the cultivators to moneylenders, all these are well known to the students of Indian agricultural economy. Measures have been taken, therefore, to regulate the operations of moneylenders through legislation.

At present, legislation to regulate moneylending is in force in all the States. The basic objective of the legislation is to bring about an improvement in the terms on which credit is made available and to put legal restrictions on the malpractices likely to be indulged in. Licensing of moneylenders, fixing of maximum rates of interest, and powers given to the Governments to arbitrate are the major provisions of the moneylending Acts.[3] It is difficult to enforce this legislation very effectively, because it is not possible to regulate properly the lending activities of landlords and traders who are not professional moneylenders but who provide about one-third of the borrowings of agriculturists. These agencies have become relatively more important sources of rural credit in recent years as revealed by the Rural Credit Follow-up Surveys conducted by the Reserve Bank of India.

Realizing that the only effective solution would be to provide the cultivator with institutional credit, steps were initiated to organize co-operative credit societies more than fifty years ago. But, as experience has shown, this task is not simple, and initially the co-operatives did not succeed, the main cause of failure being economic and social disparities. In the words of the Committee of Direction of the All-India Rural Credit Survey,[4] " . . . the failure of co-operative credit is explicable in terms of the total impracticability of any attempt to combine the very weak in competition with the very strong and expect them by themselves to create conditions, first, for their emancipation from the interests which oppose them and, secondly, for their social and economic development in the context of severe disadvantages historically imposed on them. . . . The problem is not so much one of reorganization of co-operative credit as of the creation of new conditions in which it can operate effectively and for the benefit of the weaker." After a chequered career, the co-operative movement may be said to have come now into its own though there are a number of defects in the system which require to be rectified. Lack of resources is being met by State partnership in co-operatives under the Integrated Scheme of Rural Credit. As against the meagre finance (about 3 per cent of the total borrowings of cultivators) provided by the co-operatives in 1950–51, they provided more than 15 per cent of the cultivators' borrowings in 1959–60. There are certain areas, as revealed by the Rural Credit Follow-up Surveys, where the Co-operatives have now become a major source of credit.

REGULATION OF AGRICULTURAL MARKETING— REMOVAL OF EXPLOITATION OF AGRICULTURISTS BY TRADERS

Along with the landlords and moneylenders, traders also exploited the agriculturists. By combining trading with moneylending, they had the opportunity not only to charge high rates of interest but also to make a number of deductions in the price payable to the cultivator besides under-grading and under-weighing his produce. Prominent among the handicaps which have hitherto stood in the

---

[3] *Agricultural Legislation in India* (Vol. I), *Regulation of Moneylending*, Ministry of Food and Agriculture, Government of India, Delhi, 1956, p. xvii.

[4] *General Report, op. cit.*, p. 279.

way of the cultivators in realizing a reasonable share in the value of their produce, were heavy indebtedness accompanied by hypothecation of crop to the trader in advance, ignorance about market trends, and lack of combination among the cultivators themselves.

Regulation of agricultural markets was suggested as early as 1928 by the Royal Commission on Indian Agriculture. Legislation for this purpose was initiated around 1930. At present, agricultural markets have been regulated in almost all the States.[5] Legislation generally covers all agricultural commodities, but in actual practice only important commodities in a particular market area have been covered. It has been pointed out that if all the farm commodities were brought within the purview of the market, it would be helpful in preventing the market functionaries from putting undue pressure on growers in respect of commodities which do not come under regulation.[6] But this might aggravate the difficulties in the administration of the legislation. In addition to these practical problems, the basic difficulty of regulation of agricultural markets in India has been how to regulate effectively the sales of numerous farmers who, having small quantities of produce to sell, generally sell it to itinerant traders at the village level. Information available through the follow-up surveys conducted by the Reserve Bank of India has revealed that village sales predominate in most of the States, accounting for more than 50 per cent, of the value of crops sold. Further, the full benefits of improvements in market organization cannot reach the mass of agricultural producers unless they are free from indebtedness to traders. Needless to say that if agricultural marketing were made co-operative, this alone would remove the major disadvantages from which the cultivator suffers in marketing his produce. The basic idea underlying the Integrated Scheme of Rural Credit recommended by the All-India Rural Credit Survey Committee was that the progress of agricultural credit, marketing and processing must go hand in hand.[7] The Second and Third Plans place greater emphasis on the development of co-operative marketing and processing.

MINIMUM WAGE LEGISLATION—REMOVAL OF EXPLOITATION OF AGRICULTURAL LABOUR BY LANDLORDS

Among the Indian rural problems, the problem of agricultural workers has been found the most difficult because there are too many of them competing for limited opportunities of employment. The 1951 Census indicated that about 21 per cent of the total agricultural population was dependent on farm work for its livelihood. The results of the two Agricultural Labour Enquiries have shown that in

---

[5] For salient features of the legislation, see: a note on Regulated Markets in India, *Reserve Bank of India Bulletin,* June 1962.

[6] *Report of the Mysore Regulated Markets Enquiry Committee,* 1956, p. 17.

[7] See: *General Report, op. cit.,* Chapters VIII and IX.

TABLE 18.1

COMPARISON OF AGRICULTURAL LABOUR CONDITIONS, 1950–51 AND 1956–57

	1950–51	1956–57
Proportion of agricultural labour households	*(per cent)*	*(per cent)*
With land...............................	50	43
Without land...........................	50	57
Casual.................................	90	73
Attached...............................	10	27
Extent of annual wage-paid employment of all male agricultural labourers		
Daily average wage.....................	*(naye Paise)*	*(naye Paise)*
Men....................................	109	96
Women.................................	68	59
Average annual income of agricultural labour households...............................	*(Rupees)* 447	*(Rupees)* 437

1956–57, the proportion of agricultural labour to total rural households stood at 24 per cent compared with 30 per cent in 1950–51. Conditions of agricultural labour are revealed in Table 18.1.

Though the data provided by the First Enquiry for 1950–51 and by the Second for 1956–57 are not wholly comparable on account of changes in definition of concepts and methodology, the point that there was no distinct improvement in the conditions of agricultural labour cannot be denied.[8] One would like to know, therefore, what efforts have been made hitherto to ameliorate the conditions and what are the main bottlenecks.

The Constitution of India has given protection against forced labour. Though details are lacking, the hardships to which attached labour—viz., the *Kamias* in Bihar, the *Pannaiyals* in Madras, the *Halis* in Gujerat—were subject hitherto can be said to have been removed. A Central Advisory Committee on Agricultural Labour has been set up. The various social reforms referred to earlier have attempted to remove the social handicaps on the agricultural labourers most of whom belong to backward classes. As regards employment opportunities, development activities in general are said to have increased employment available to them. Agricultural extension activities, the increase in the irrigated area, etc. have increased the availability of farm employment. Promotion of rural industries has provided opportunities for these people to supplement their limited

---

[8] "What both Enquiries bring out is the enormous size of the problem, the widespread under-employment that exists, and the fact that increase in population has borne harshly on this section of the population."—*Third Five-Year Plan, op. cit.,* p. 374.

incomes from farm labour. Land reforms in this respect are not expected to provide a solution to the problem of farm labourers, but wherever possible they have enabled backward-class labourers to get some land. The Bhoodan movement conducted by Shri Vinoba Bhave has also given a lead towards settling their problem, though the achievements are rather limited. Agricultural worker families have been given protection against ejectment from homesteads. The Minimum Wages Act, 1948, has been applied to employment in agriculture. In enforcing this measure, low-wage pockets have been given special attention. But enforcement of the legislation is difficult because of the limited employment opportunities and absence of labour unions.

Despite all these special efforts, the experience in the first two Plans has shown that they have only touched the fringe of the problem. The improvement does not stand out distinctly, mainly because (1) efforts, however big by themselves, fall short of the needs, (2) many agricultural labourers have not taken advantage of the available supplementary employment through rural industries, and (3) as a result of lack of mobility, scarcity of labour is felt in some areas—canal and wet-land areas—while unemployment exists in other areas.[9] Emphasis on owner-cultivation and physical labour has forced many absentee landlords to create a façade of personal cultivation, resulting to some extent in a decrease of employment for casual farm labourers. Prominent among the efforts proposed in the Third Plan are (1) about 7 lakhs of labour families are to be settled by reclaiming five million acres of cultivable waste land; (2) under the rural works programme, additional wage employment for about 100 days in the year is to be provided for about 2.5 million persons; and (3) Rs.5 crores have been allotted for the acquistion of land for allotment as housesites to agricultural labourers. It may be said that rapid and intensive development of the rural economy and industrialization of the rural areas can alone ensure substantial improvement in the life and living of rural labour. That this is being done needs no mention. But greater efforts in certain particular directions such as co-operative processing industries, as the report of the Study Group of Landless Agricultural Labourers in Maharashtra has pleaded, are likely to provide immediate alternative employment.

ORGANIZATIONAL FRAMEWORK FOR RURAL DEVELOPMENT

Since 1950–51, when India's First Five-Year Plan was launched, efforts have been going on to evolve a suitable organizational set-up

---

[9] Village studies have revealed that most of the landless labourers had no information about opportunities available outside the villages. They do not generally prefer to take employment outside the village. See: *Shahajapur, (West Bengal) Socio-economic Study of a Village,* J. P. Bhattacharjee and Associates, Santiniketan, 1958, p. 91.

to ensure direct participation by the people in the planning and implementation of the socio-economic development programme. In this way the progress achieved is not only substantial but also self-generating and enduring. The foregoing discussion has indicated that the various social reforms and economic development measures introduced have not been a complete success owing to some extent to the apathy of the masses in general and the weaker sections in particular, to the dominance of the richer cultivators and traders, to moneylenders, and to the lack of full co-ordination between the felt needs of the local people and the priorities of the Plan laid down by Government. The Community Development Programme was introduced, therefore, in 1952 with a view to actively associating local communities in designing and executing the Plan programme. Since the Programme reached some kind of a stalemate and became more or less Government sponsored, controlled, and directed, fresh endeavours have been made to devise the most suitable organizational pattern for the devolution of planning and executive responsibilities on the local elected leadership.

On the lines of the Study Team on Community Development and National Extension Service, 1957, the three-tier system of Panchayati Raj or local self-government—village panchayat at the base, panchayat samiti at the block/taluka level, and zilla parishad at the district level—has been introduced in almost all the States. This experiment in grass-root democracy holds out good promise, provided it does not encourage the emergence of caste and class conflicts, if a fight for power instead of competition for service unfortunately becomes the main feature of the panchayat bodies. With a view to preventing the emergence of such a trend, attempts are being made to hold the elections on a non-party basis. Further, though the Panchayati Raj institutions are empowered to draft the schemes, the responsibility for their execution rests with the administrative staff who are answerable to the heads of their respective departments for the technical aspects of their work.

Features of the Panchayati Raj system, which are significant from the point of view of rural uplift, are: (1) provisions exist for the co-optation of members for giving representation to backward-class people, minority groups, and women; (2) the village panchayat is answerable to *gaon sabha* (village general body) which meets once or twice a year; (3) certain functions such as sanitation have been made obligatory functions of the panchayats, while the developmental programme is to be taken up to the extent that funds at their disposal permit; (4) panchayat bodies can levy certain taxes and have been allotted the bulk of land revenue collected by the State Governments; (5) the village panchayat is to be associated in the implementation of agrarian reforms; (6) while the over-all responsibility for planning and development is placed on the panchayats, the village co-operatives attend to details of programming and operation in their respective fields; and (7) local officials are under the general supervision of these bodies.

Though the panchayat system may be sound in principle, its ability to deliver the goods depends on how it is actually formed and how it functions. Thus a programme of education and social and economic welfare is essential for its success.

RURAL HEALTH PROGRAMME

If the rural health programme in a country like India is to fulfil its purpose, it has to provide, to start with, for mass education on health and sanitation schemes to convince people of the dangers of insanitary conditions and epidemics and of the need for preventive measures. As the Third Plan puts it, ". . . health education is of course a most important aspect of the programme of rural sanitation."[10] Such education, if it is promptly accompanied by a concrete health programme, would take root in villages. The basic health problems in the rural parts are: (1) inadequacy of drinking water facilities; (2) absence of location of responsibility for sanitary measures; (3) inadequacy of arrangements for first aid; (4) poor communications making prompt medical help difficult; and (5) concentration of medical personnel in urban areas.[11]

During the First and Second Plans, about Rs.33 crores were spent on rural water supply schemes and 11,000 villages were provided with water supplies through pipes. Under different programmes, a provision of about Rs.67 crores has been made for rural water supply in the Third Plan. While the Government proposes to give up to Rs.10,000 per village, the public is generally expected to contribute 50 per cent of the cost.

As regards the setting up of primary health units, 2,800 such units were to come into being in the development blocks by the end of the Second Plan. Progress was affected mainly by shortage of health personnel, inadequate training facilities for the different categories of staff, and delays in the construction of buildings and quarters for the staff. The Third Plan aims at establishing 2,000 more hospitals and dispensaries, the number at the end of 1960–61 being 12,600. The Third-Plan programme for controlling communicable diseases entails a total outlay of about Rs.70 crores. Family planning clinics numbering 1,121 were established in the rural areas during the two Plan periods. During the Third-Plan period, about 6,100 family planning clinics are proposed to be established in the rural areas. The progress of the health programme can be seen by the fact that (1) the death rate declined from 27 in 1941–51 to 22 in 1956–61, (2)

[10] *Third Five-Year Plan, op. cit.,* pp. 652, 655.
[11] *Ibid.*

infant mortality rate of male and female children declined from 190 and 175 in 1941–51 to 142 and 128 in 1956–61, and (3) the annual incidence of malaria declined from 75 million cases in 1952–53 to about 10 million in 1960–61.

In 1961, only 19 per cent of the rural population was literate. The task of further promoting rural literacy and rural education in India is thus the most urgent. The Constitution has laid down that provision should be made for free universal and compulsory education up to the age of 14 years. As a first step towards this goal, all the children in the age group 6 to 11 are being provided with facilities for compulsory schooling. The principal problems in achieving even this limited objective are (1) the difficulty of persuading parents to send their daughters to schools,[12] and (2) the extreme backwardness of certain areas and certain sections of the people. Parents take children away from school as soon as they are able to add to the family income. The progress of the child from the lower class to the upper class is not taken seriously by the parents.

Among the steps proposed to be taken, in addition to compulsion, to make the primary education programme a success are: (1) the appointment of trained and qualified teachers, (2) greater understanding on the part of parents of the desirability of letting their children remain at school, and (3) the planning of school holidays so that they coincide with the harvesting and sowing seasons.

As to the actual achievements, the development of elementary education was allotted Rs.85 crores or 64 per cent of the total outlay on education in the First Plan, Rs.87 crores or 42 per cent of the total outlay in the Second Plan, and Rs.209 crores or 50 per cent in the Third Plan. In the age group 6 to 11 years about 61 per cent were estimated to have entered the schools in 1960–61 as against 53 per cent in 1955–56 and 43 per cent in 1950–51. The school enrolment of the children in the age group 11 to 14 years was about 23 per cent in 1960–61 as compared to 17 per cent in 1955–56 and 13 per cent in 1950–51. During the first two Plan periods, the number of primary schools increased by 63 per cent. Obviously, the gaps are as yet large. It is revealed by the All-India Educational Survey, 1957–59, that in 1957 about 29 per cent of rural habitations and about 17 per cent of rural population were not served by any school. There has been a rise in the number of trained teachers in the primary schools; their proportion was 65 per cent in 1960–61. It is proposed to raise this to 75 per cent by the end of the Third-Plan period.[13]

The active association of local people and the mobilization of local resources are very important for the progress of the programme of rural education. Items such as the organization of enrolment

[12] In 1960–61, about 81 per cent of the boys of age group 6 to 11 were in school as against 40 per cent of the girls.—*Third Five-Year Plan, op. cit.,* p. 578.
[13] *Third Five-Year Plan, op. cit.,* pp. 576–81.

drives, persuading parents to send girls to school, the construction of school buildings, mid-day meals and free clothing for the poorer children, can be effectively pursued only if Panchayati Raj institutions play a major role in the mobilization of local resources for these purposes.

The Indian rural problem is a sociological one and its solution depends upon systematic reforms under three main heads, namely, land reform, man reform, and administrative reform. Success under these heads will depend mainly upon the efficiency of administration on whom the main responsibility for their implementation rests. Our brief review of development since Independence under these heads shows that the social change, though slow, has been taking place in the desired direction. The main reasons for the slowness of the pace of progress are: (1) despite development of transport and communications, large areas still remain isolated for much of the year; (2) rural society has not yet fully emerged as a homogeneous entity on account of the continuation, though on a reduced scale, of economic and social disparities; (3) the progress of the programmes for rural health and education has not quite reached expectations; (4) efforts to evolve a suitable institutional framework have started yielding fruits only recently; and (5) the progress of rural electrification, and dispersal of industries in rural areas has yet to gather momentum. It is important to note that democratic decentralization involves the entire rural population, through representative bodies, in both the formulation and execution of rural development programmes. Individual domination and authoritarian approach have been gradually giving way to institutional leadership and guidance. In due course as the rural peoples' standards of living improve and economic disparities narrow down and as they gain experience in running such institutions, more and more rural people are bound to identify themselves with the Plan and to participate actively in its formulation and implementation. The process that has been set in motion in India with its built-in dynamism can be expected to ensure self-generated and sustained development in the near future.

19

Concurrent Growth of Agriculture With Industry: A Study of the Japanese Case

KAZUSHI OHKAWA*

Hitotsubashi University, Japan

AGRICULTURE'S ROLE, its contribution, its function—whatever we may call it—(no one would deny its importance) in economic development is the subject of this chapter.

We shall not describe the details of the historical development of Japanese agriculture;[1] rather we shall attempt first to discuss conceptual problems which, we believe, require clarification. Second, in terms of our specified concepts, some factors crucial in attaining the concurrent growth of agriculture with industry will be discussed. In so doing, the Japanese experience will be examined in terms of concise presentations as one of the typical cases of economically backward countries.

THE NOTION OF "PREREQUISITES"

We choose 1868, the year of the Meiji Restoration, as the point of departure for modern economic development in Japan. We do so, as

* I should like to acknowledge my great indebtedness to Professor Henry Rosovsky, University of California, Berkeley, my collaborator in a research project on Japan's modern economic growth. The basic idea of this chapter came from discussions we enjoyed together in the course of working on this project.

[1] See: Kazushi Ohkawa and Henry Rosovsky, "The Role of Agriculture in Modern Japanese Economic Development," *Economic Development and Cultural Change,* Vol. IX, No. 1, Part II, Oct. 1960.

Kazushi Ohkawa, "Significant Changes in Japanese Agriculture since 1945," *Journal of Farm Economics,* Dec. 1961 (Proceedings issue).

Bruce F. Johnston, "Agricultural Development and Economic Transformation: A Comparative Study of the Japanese Experience," *Food Research Institute Studies,* (Stanford University) Vol. III, No. 3, Nov. 1962.

it can be claimed that at this point modern economic development became a national objective. Japan's given conditions—the inherited conditions from which modern economic growth started—are characterized by a typical pre-modern economic level and structure of the Asian type. Though the available data are not reliable enough with regard to the current conditions, we can make the following points. Both productivity and income per capita were very close to the present average low level of most countries in south-east Asia (rice yield, about 60 bushels per hectare; per capita national product, about $60 at the present rate of exchange). The industrial and occupational structure was of the typical pre-modern type (agricultural population, 75–80 per cent). Production organization of agriculture was extremely small scale (one hectare of farm land per household). Nevertheless a high rate of surplus existed, based on the inherited pattern of feudal income distribution (rent in kind, more than 50 per cent of rice yields).

None of the above should give the impression that Japan's economic structure was completely static in the period before 1868. Actually, a number of factors are often cited by some economic historians as evidence of changes in the economic structure for the later part of the pre-modern period. Among them, growth of output and commercialization of agriculture in particular are relevant here. Based on these facts they tend to emphasize a noticeable development of agriculture before Japan's start in industrialization. But we think these were limited regional phenomena and accordingly disagree with this argument. We take the view that the industrial revolution in Japan was not preceded by nationwide agricultural development but that agricultural development started simultaneously with industrial development.

There is a historical line of thought which assumes that the order or sequence of industrial development in advanced countries must be repeated in a more or less similar way in backward countries. In Britain the industrial revolution was preceded by the agricultural revolution, so that the development of agriculture may be considered a historical *prerequisite* for industrial development. I am afraid that this may be a too simplified presentation. But any sophisticated version may not alter the core of its thought. We see its integrated concept in the notion of *necessary prerequisites*. According to this notion, there are a number of necessary prerequisites or preconditions for industrial growth, without which it could not begin. Rostow's thesis of stages of economic growth is an outstanding example.

So far as agriculture is concerned, this notion seems to be not applicable to the Japanese case. As noted above, industrial development in this country may have begun without the precondition of agricultural development. In its basic contents, we believe, there is no doubt of this. With respect to its detailed implications, however, further explanations may be needed. Among them the following two points are indispensable.

First, we have to make a distinction between the abolition of a pre-modern institutional framework and the existence of an increase in the productivity of agriculture, although actually these two are closely interrelated. In our earlier discussions, the development of agriculture meant simply the latter—an increase in the productivity of agriculture, irrespective of the patterns of accompanying institutional changes. But the discussion of prerequisites usually contains both the former and the latter. Immediately after the Restoration the new Meiji Government, quickly and on a national basis, denounced all feudal regulations controlling such things as planting crops, private ownership and sale of land, as well as changes of occupation and residence. These revisions were indispensable to the subsequent modern economic development. Therefore we do not object to the assertion that abolition of these pre-modern regulations was the necessary precondition for modern economic growth. There is no vagueness in this as far as the Japanese case is concerned, because the legal emancipation was a clear-cut phenomenon. However, for the countries whose pre-modern restraints on peasant farming have been maintained to some extent into later periods, our conceptual distinction cannot be applied so clearly. Industrialization could begin with some pre-modern restraints. Even in Japan's case some economic historians claim the actual remnants of feudal restraints after 1868. Nevertheless, in principle we are much inclined to made a distinction between the two and to disagree with the notion of preconditions in terms of productivity development.

Secondly, we have an impression that there has often been confusion between *pre*conditions and conditions, and that these two different concepts have sometimes been used interchangeably without distinction. For example, there is an argument that the increase in labour productivity of agriculture is a necessary condition for industrial development, because industry cannot draw the required labour force away from the land if agriculture does not raise its productivity. This is simple logic and no one would deny it to the extent that the agricultural surplus produced by its increased productivity is the source of development of the non-agricultural sectors. However, such an argument often has been erroneously used in association with the thesis of preconditions of agriculture for industrialization. Such a line of thought seems to be strengthened by a feeling that the present level of productivity of agriculture in most countries in Asia is too low to be the required precondition for industrial development, in association with a recognition of a conspicuous gap between the present low level of productivity in these countries and the European level at the eve of industrialization.

This is misleading. There was an agricultural surplus even in the pre-modern era of every country—without exception. As previously noted with respect to the given conditions in Japan at the time of embarking on modern economic development, there was a high rate of surplus produced in agriculture. We have noted that this was possible not because of a high or an increased productivity of agriculture but because of the inherited pattern of pre-modern income distribution. The actual surplus tends to be much more influenced by the distribution pattern than by technical productivity. It is therefore risky to insist on a certain level of productivity of agriculture as a necessary precondition for industrialization.

THE CONTRIBUTION OF AGRICULTURE AND THE PATTERN OF SECTORAL INTERDEPENDENCE

Throughout the entire subsequent period of economic growth in Japan, there has been a continuing growth of agriculture. Though it was faster in favourable conditions and slower when conditions were unfavourable, its average high rate of growth was pronounced. It is hazardous to expect the measurement of growth rates to allow for reliable international comparisons. However, consulting such data as are available, we believe that Japan's rate of growth of agricultural output was comparable at least to the most speedy rates realized in advanced Western countries. For example, in terms of real G.D.P. produced in agriculture, the annual rate of growth was 1.8 per cent in the pre-war period. The fastest rates in Europe hardly ever exceeded 1.5 to 2 per cent according to our estimates. The rate of industrial growth was much faster, of course, than that of agriculture, recording around 5 per cent by corresponding measurements, but the gap between them is not our point here. The point is that Japanese agriculture developed not before but side by side with the process of speedy industrialization—a *concurrent* growth of industry and agriculture. What kind of conceptual framework is desirable to analyse this process?

The conventional approach has been given mostly in terms of a notion of *contribution* and the like. We have often heard the following: agriculture contributed to economic development by supplying food for increased demand and the labour force required for industrial development; it contributed by expanding the domestic market for industrial goods; the increase of its output-exports contributed by making it possible to promote the necessary imports of capital goods; the outflow of a surplus created in agriculture and directed to the rest of the economy was a contribution to the making of necessary investments and public expenditure for modernization. If we confine our discussion to the initial phase of modern economic growth, 1868 to 1905, all these versions in themselves are valid. There is no reason to doubt these historical facts. What puzzles us, however, is the vagueness of the notion of the so-called contribution. In a network of a concurrent growth process, is it really possible without difficulty to identify one sector's contribution to the growth of other sectors or of the economy as a whole? If it is, in what sense is it possible?

Let us begin with a simple fact. No one would deny that in the course of Japanese economic growth, industrial development also contributed to the growth of agriculture, especially if we were asked to use the notion of contribution: it gave a stimulus to agriculture by increasing and diversifying the demand for agricultural outputs; it contributed to the development of agriculture by absorbing the increased labour force in agriculture, thus preventing aggravated over-population on the land; it contributed to the development of agriculture by increasing the supply of improved inputs (fertilizers, etc.); the progress of technology in industry could bring forth an induced progress of related technology in agriculture. Again all these facts we can recognize without hesitation.

It is evident, therefore, that the notion of sectoral contribution cannot be entirely independent; to a large extent it must be a reciprocal concept. We see a good example of sectoral interdependence in the case of the labour force outflow from agriculture to the rest of the economy. One can certainly recognize its sectoral contribution from either side: agriculture contributed to industry by supplying the labour force required by that sector, while industry contributed to agriculture by absorbing the increased labour force in that sector and preventing aggravated over-population on the land. One may still argue that the labour transferred from agriculture to the rest of the economy was produced in farm-households, so that from the viewpoint of the production costs of human elements, agriculture contributed to the non-agricultural sector and not the reverse. But, one can also point out that an over-supply of labour on the land would lead to a diminishing return of agricultural production and/or prevent the introduction of technological innovations. This negative effect was removed when the expansion of industry created jobs away from the land, so that industry contributed to agriculture.

In general, the process of economic growth contains, as one of its major characteristics, the interdependence between various sectors of the economy: the growth (or retardation) of a particular sector influences, and in turn is influenced by, the growth (or retardation) of the other sectors. We call this relationship "sectoral interdependence." Economic growth usually leads to an increasingly close sectoral interdependence of the economy. Agriculture and industry would follow this general trend, but with a variety of patterns from one country to another and from one phase to another within a single country.

Therefore our task is to re-examine one by one the individual factors of contribution previously noted with respect to Japanese agriculture in order to answer the two questions:

1. What factors can really be identified as making a genuine sectoral contribution?
2. What was the specific pattern of sectoral interdependence?

Let us begin by discussing the former question. We previously referred to a well-known fact that the outflow of a surplus created in agriculture and directed to the rest of the economy was a contribution by making necessary investment and public expenditure for modernization. In Japan this was done mainly through the land-tax system. Its features were as follows: First, it fixed the land-tax rate as high as 30 per cent of rice yields at the beginning, a rate inherited from the pre-modern system; and second, in the subsequent period of economic growth, because of its fixed cash amount per area, its proportion gradually decreased as both productivity and the price of rice increased. This was economically rational for two reasons: possible decreases in the land-tax proportion acted as an incentive for developing agriculture; and other taxes based on the subsequent development of the non-agricultural sector substituted for it in later years.

We want to discuss this problem in theory apart from its practical means of transferring surplus. In a country where a concurrent growth of agriculture and industry is required, the possibility of transferring the agricultural surplus to the other sectors of the economy must be a decisive factor. By its very nature this cannot effectively be carried out by free market mechanisms and therefore requires government intervention of one kind or other. Japan's case presented an orthodox action of government in this general context apart from its actual means of implementation. This was a process of *forced* income transfer, unlike the cases of demand-supply interdependence, which will be discussed in subsequent pages. The sectoral transfer of resources in this sense is the only case which we can really call the sectoral "contribution" without conceptual vagueness.

In answer to the second question, it is convenient to discuss two aspects separately.

The Labour Force

Let us begin with the specific pattern of the labour market during the initial phase of modern economic growth. The main facts were as follows: (1) The labour force engaged in agriculture was almost unchanged or even slightly decreased, so that its net increase was all absorbed by the non-agricultural sector. In European countries the labour force in agriculture increased until almost the 1920's, so that Japan's pattern is worth noticing. (2) The rate of increase in the total population in Japan was 0.7 to 1.0 per cent per annum during the initial phase of modern economic growth and reached its maximum rate, 1.5 per cent around 1930. This is similar to the British pattern of population growth and implies a moderate rate close to the norm in Europe. We can assume that this was more or less the same with regard to the labour force growth, though the data are less reliable. (3) There was a pronounced difference, however, in the initial condition of industrial distribution of the labour force. As noted previously, in Japan the labour force engaged in agriculture was overwhelmingly large in proportion, while in advanced countries in Europe on the eve of industrialization it was much less, though again exact data are scanty. It is clear that, other things being equal, industry in Japan had to grow fast enough to absorb much more labour from agriculture if the agricultural population were to be unchanged. Population pressure of this kind, not that of the natural increase of the total population, was crucial in Japan's case.

A combined consideration of the above three facts would lead us to a valid question: How could Japan succeed in avoiding a much more aggravated population pressure on the land? Another question has often been raised: Why could not Japan reduce the farm population? This ignores facts 2 and 3 above, as well as the exceedingly high rate of growth of Japanese industry. To answer the former question, we have to mention the specific pattern of growth of the non-agricultural sector in particular, which growth was characterized by an application of relatively labour-intensive technology of production. This was particularly pronounced during the initial phase of industrialization. The rate of increase in employment amounted to two-thirds of its rate of output growth. Although capital-intensive technology came into prominence later, small-scale enterprises based on labour-intensive technology did not lose their importance in the post-war industrial spurt.

What was the mechanism of these interrelated phenomena? In a broad sense, it was "a labour market with an unlimited supply of labour," in Arthur Lewis' terminology. The supply price of labour was basically determined by the level of subsistence of the people on the land. With real wage rates determined correspondingly by it, the enterprisers in the non-agricultural sector could employ their required labour force in an almost perfectly elastic manner. A salient feature of this mechanism, however, was the fact that both the labour productivity of agriculture and industrial real wage rates did increase *pari passu* at least until 1905–10 (annual rates, roughly 1.0 to 1.5 per cent). This is worth noticing, because of its difference from classical models (for instance A. Lewis's), where no increase in real wage rates is assumed in principle. We believe that the notion of an unlimited supply of labour can still be applied in this case on the assumption of a trend line of an increasing supply price of labour at a certain rate.

Output-Input Relationships and Commercialization

The supply of food and materials for industrial use, the production of goods for export, and the demand for industrial products—these previously noted functions of agriculture can all be discussed in an integrated form of the conventional input-output relationship between sectors of the economy. Despite a lack of systematized statistical tables except for recent years, we can point out verbally the features of the Japanese pattern as follows.

1. Despite some partial commercialization of agriculture towards the end of the pre-modern period, industrialization started with typical subsistence farming. Because of the subsequent rapid changes in the institutional and economic structure and of the fast growth of industry, agriculture was integrated very rapidly into a monetized economy. Hence, the rapid response of agriculture to this drastic change contrasts with the slow, moderate response in advanced countries.

2. Ironically enough, Japanese agriculture changed its output structure not drastically but rather moderately through the subsequent years of rapid economic growth. The heavy yield of rice has long been maintained, forming the backbone of the traditional farm economy; diversification (especially into livestock farming) started on a significant scale only after World War II; structural change occurred only in the field of cash crops; even there the major line was an expansion of traditional sericulture, which during the initial phase was substituted for other traditional cash crops, especially cotton.

3. The moderate changes in the structure of output supply had their counterparts on the demand side. The people's pattern of food consumption changed little throughout the pre-war period, centering on rice, fish and traditional vegetables. Agriculture (and fishery) succeeded in increasing the supplies of these traditional crops to meet their increases in demand at least until around the time of World War I. This is proved by the *pari passu* trend of prices of agricultural commodities with that of the general price movement. The situation of an unlimited supply of labour was made possible by this equilibrium growth process of food supply-demand.

4. Expansion of the supply of agricultural material for industrial use was focused on sericulture and tea cultivation, which made possible an expansion of the exports of silk and tea. It is to be noted, however, that these products, and especially silk, differed from most export-orientated primary products in presently developing countries. They were combined products of domestic agriculture and domestic manufacturing and had a fairly extensive domestic market. Silk manufacturing especially was far from being a satellite of agriculture, unlike traditional food-processing industries, but had a noticeable effect in inducing the development of sericulture.

5. The failure to expand the cotton supply for the cotton-spinning industry, another major export sector in Japan, needs a brief explanation. In terms of comparative advantage of raising income per unit area, cocoons became increasingly superior to cotton, mainly because of giving many more opportunities of increasing labour inputs. A very unfavourable man-land ratio, which was one of the given conditions at the start of Japan's economic modernization, was the basic factor for determining the direction of such a cash crop structure.

6. With respect to the function of expanding the domestic market for industrial products, there is only one point to which we would like to draw attention. Both the input of intermediate goods for farm production and the purchase of consumption goods for farm households increased very moderately throughout the pre-war period, although a post-war increase is noticeable. In terms of individual items, a drastic increase in the input of commercial fertilizer was the only exception. But on an average, the proportion of inputs of intermediate goods of industrial origin to gross outputs amounted to barely 20 per cent in the pre-war period. Despite this moderate share of inputs in agriculture, it brought forth a significant increase in the demand for industrial goods, both intermediate and final. This was because the relative share of agriculture in the economy had been exceedingly high (in 1903 to 1907 the share of income produced in the primary sector was still 45 per cent).

Through all these six patterns, we see the underlying salient feature that a growth process with balanced input-output relationships was more or less maintained despite the drastic structural changes and differential growth rates between agriculture and industry, and that this was made possible by the dominant place of agriculture based on a moderate change in the traditional output structure of the economy.

TYPE OF TECHNOLOGICAL PROGRESS AND ECONOMIC BACKWARDNESS

The functions of agriculture discussed above were all made possible basically by the rapid progress of technology in increasing labour productivity. We noted that the behaviour of real wage rates was characterized by a sustained increase in the labour productivity of agriculture. Supply of agricultural outputs with almost unchanged relative prices implies shifts of supply functions corresponding to the rest of the economy. Enlarging the market for industrial goods, outflow of savings of agriculture to the rest of the economy—both were continuously possible only by an increase in productivity. There is no doubt that technological progress in agriculture was the crucial factor in the sense that without it any one of its functions previously noted could not be realized.

What type of technological progress? Under a sustained condition of small-scale individual farming of an almost unchanged labour force and area of farm land in the aggregate, the output per worker increased at an annual rate close to 2 per cent on average in the pre-war and at 3 per cent in the post-war period. Mechanization is quite a recent phenomenon and private investment for fixed capital was moderate. These facts suggest that the technological progress of Japanese agriculture was characterized by the land- and labour-saving type with a moderate increase of capital per unit of output. This pattern is defined, of course, in terms of changes over time. In the process of concurrent growth with industry, agricultural technology required a certain rate of progress in labour saving in order to follow the technological progress of this type in industry. In addition, this required an accompanying progress of land-saving technology because of the severe limitation of an unchanged labour-land ratio. Furthermore, this twofold requirement could be met economically only with a moderate increase of capital. How to meet these severe triple requirements at the same time was a basic problem for the technological development of Japanese agriculture. And to a considerable extent they were met.

It has been widely recognized that within an interrelated system of agricultural technology, each component can make progress only in complementary relationships with other related components. We know the difficulty of squeezing certain key factors out of this interrelated system. Nevertheless, in the light of the unchanged production organization of Japanese agriculture over a long time, it would not be illegitimate to point out crucial factors. It was the progress of cultivating techniques in a broad sense, including seed improvement as a most important factor.

In this kind of technical progress by trial and error, we can see two distinct elements which made them possible: fuller utilization of indigenous techniques and borrowing foreign science and technology. In the initial stage the government tried to borrow Western methods of large-scale farming. Since this ended in near failures the government started to encourage fuller utilization of indigenous techniques, and in fact this was successful. At the same time, however, the government extended a programme of technical-assistance activities so as to borrow foreign technology in a more appropriate way. This facilitated the application of the then newly developed agricultural sciences and technology to Japanese techniques of cultivation. During the initial phase of economic growth, the indigenous element played an import role, but foreign elements nonetheless contributed by bringing cumulative rewards in later periods.

What significant features does technological progress in Japanese agriculture suggest? We shall discuss this in terms of the notion of economic backwardness. However difficult it may be to quantify the degree of economic backwardness, whatever definition one may give to its concept, no one would deny the fact that Japan started economic modernization as a very late comer. Externally, by the 1870's the major Western countries were already in a stage of severe competition of imperialistic expansion. Internally, Japan's conditions were typically pre-modern.

Following the discussion of various patterns of agricultural development in Japan under the concept of sectoral interdependence, we wish to associate these patterns with the type of technological progress in the light of the general notion of economic backwardness.

An exceedingly fast rate of industrial growth implies various important patterns which can be understood in terms of this factor of severe economic backwardness. Most relevant here is borrowing modern technology from advanced countries. No one will doubt the fact that this was one of the major factors which were responsible for a fast rate of industrial growth.

In the case of concurrent growth, was this also true of agriculture? The answer to this, a natural question, is, "the same was true in agriculture." Irrespective of different types and degrees of borrowing advanced technology, we believe it is important to recognize the common element between the two major sectors of the economy. This is particularly so because it is widely recognized that backward countries in general have possible advantages in borrowing a backlog of advanced technology. Why has this been agreed to only with regard to manufacture? How about agriculture? One often has an impression that it is much more difficult in agriculture. Why? Various factors such as natural endowments (climate, soil, etc.), scale and organization of farming, institutional set-ups—the differences of these factors between advanced and backward countries, one may argue, are decisive in preventing the utilization of this possible advantage. Furthermore one would say this is still more difficult because of being combined with the non-mechanical, biological nature of agricultural technology.

We would say, however, that most of these do not prevent, they only modify, the factors of borrowing advanced technology. Japan's experience suggests the direction and type of modifications which were required to fit into its pattern of agricultural growth. Unlike the situation in manufacture, it suggests that it is not possible to borrow ready-made technology of foreign origin. A certain time interval is required before foreign elements can be used effectively to establish a country's own system of technology. In contrast to this handicap, the flexible nature of agricultural production in terms of factor-proportions and divisibility can count as a favourable element in agriculture as compared with manufacture. In manufacture, technological requirements often operate as a decisive factor in changing the scale and organization of production, which sometimes is out of keeping with the economic situation of backward countries. But in the case of agriculture, inputs such as seeds, fertilizers, and insecticides are all highly divisible and they can be used with different farm scales. In fact the fast progress of technology in Japanese agriculture, centering on the improvement of techniques of cultivation as noted previously, is highly characterized by the intensive use of this feature of agricultural technology: input divisibility and scale neutrality.

By way of conclusion, out of the various patterns of Japanese experience noted here, we would like to have the following points specifically high-lighted:

1. The nature of the problem of how to regard the functions of agriculture in economic development tends to differ according to the degree of economic backwardness of the country at issue.
2. Therefore, it is more useful to discover patterns of concurrent growth of agriculture and industry rather than to rely upon the conventional, rigid concept.
3. However, for economically backward countries in general it may not be illegitimate to say, first, that the nature of the problem for each country can most systematically be ascertained by applying a conceptual framework of sectoral interdependence. Secondly, with respect to agriculture specifically, the problem can be answered most effectively by examining the possible speed at which advanced technology in this sector may be borrowed in comparison with the corresponding speed in the case of manufacture.

20

Research in Agricultural Economics in Under-developed Countries

RUY MILLER PAIVA
Department of Agriculture
São Paulo, Brazil

THE OBJECT of this chapter is not to formulate a formal programme of research for under-developed countries or even to discuss the procedure on the formulation of such a programme. The objective is more limited: to present some suggestions on how to make research in agricultural economics more efficient and useful for these countries.

It is not an easy task to execute a research project in an under-developed country. Several difficulties can be easily pointed out. The *lack of competent personnel* is one of them. There are not many agricultural economic specialists in the under-developed countries who are able to undertake the planning and execution of research. It is also difficult to find personnel capable of doing the routine work in a reliable and efficient way, that is, without having to have their work carefully checked for ever-present omissions and mistakes. It is not that the technicians of these countries lack intelligence and education. What is usually lacking is the scientific attitude which causes a worker always to test his own personal observations and to check the results of his own deductive reasoning. It is not easy to develop these characteristics in the people of countries which have no tradition of research and where the schools still follow a descriptive system of learning.

The *lack of reliable statistical data* is another difficulty which the agricultural economic researcher has to face in under-developed countries. Not only are insufficient and perhaps inaccurate figures being published currently on total production, prices, and income, but it

[*213*]

also is difficult to obtain figures on farm operations. For this reason, it is very treacherous for a research worker to try to state the economic characteristics of a region or to apply inductive reasoning solely on the basis of the mean value and dispersion given by the statistics. Additionally, he must make his own first-hand observations and evaluate these observations on the basis of generally accepted tools of economic theory.

In under-developed countries, *it also is difficult to find a favourable atmosphere for research work.* Although these countries widely recognize the importance of having scientific information in order to improve the general economic situation, they rarely show a real interest in research; and as a result the research worker has very little incentive to continue. Farmers and merchants, for instance, frequently have little interest in micro-economic analyses because they are usually not yet concerned with the rationalization and full use of labour, the economies of scale, or least-cost methods of combining available productive resources, as are the farmers and merchants of countries more economically advanced. In the under-developed countries, it still is necessary to "sell" the results of research, that is, to convince the farmer or the middleman that the results of the work will benefit him by providing increased earnings if he changes his routine procedures in accordance with the methods suggested by research. Even the governmental agencies, which are frequently responsible for important economic decisions, do not always value research findings sufficiently. Very often, instead of accepting the results, they prefer to be guided by personal information from close friends. There is, then, an insufficient demand for research findings, resulting in little incentive for pursuing this kind of work. While politicians sometimes show a strong interest in supporting and even sponsoring research workers, it is seldom of much value because the political leaders have little objective knowledge of the nature of research, of the results that can be achieved from it, and the limitations accompanying the results. They may think that research is a remedy for all evils, hence become quickly discouraged with the results that are offered to them, especially if the results fail to confirm their original opinions about the causes of the problem under study.

The fact that many economic decisions in the under-developed countries are based on personal opinions or observations, brings another source of difficulty *which is felt mainly in the field of economic forecasting.* More than in other countries, the research worker in under-developed countries is compelled to do some economic forecasting. The problems of economic development and government policy, which are very dear to these countries, induce the use of projections, tendencies, and predictions. Yet it is not easy to make forecasts in these economies. Apart from the natural hazards that make such predictions uncertain, one must also try to take into account the fact that the economies of these countries are subject to various forms of governmental control and interference which do not always follow a rational pattern. Many important decisions on economic problems—for instance, price control, subsidies, exchange rates, and so on—are made on the basis of personal opinions and observations which can never fully account for the real trend of the economic forces at work. The results of these events become, then, even more unpredictable. Therefore, even if he uses the best techniques in analysing the economic forces affecting a problem, the research worker's chances of making an accurate forecast are greatly prejudiced by the effects of unforeseeable political actions.

Even without such difficulties, he has plenty of his own. First, there is the great number of problems which demand attention, in view of the economic development needs of an under-developed country. Even worse, these problems are extremely complex, making their study and resolution very difficult, especially under constant pressures for quick answers. It is necessary therefore, to be very careful in the choice both of the problems studied and of the methods used if the available research resources are to be most efficiently employed. It is important also that the research projects be properly designed to produce answers to the right questions.

How, then, may research in the several major fields of agricultural economics be made more efficient? Let us look first at production.

PRODUCTION ECONOMICS

The improvement of the production techniques used in the agricultural sector is one important area in which research in agricultural economics can be very helpful to the under-developed countries. Although there do exist some well-organized farms, using modern practices and adopting rational working measures, most of the properties in these countries leave much to be desired. An important problem in these countries is still that of substituting modern agricultural practices for traditional ones. Farm management must assist with studies which show the economic advantages of such a change. Some of these studies should follow classical lines, such as: (a) studies of agricultural practices which compare the economic advantages of alternative practices and processes actually used (or available for use) by farmers; (b) studies of the economic effects of intensification of certain practices, such as the use of different quantities of fertilizer, methods of cultivation, or rates of animal feeding; and (c) studies to determine the best combinations of enterprises for the different types of farming regions of the country.

However, less elaborate studies may also make a significant contribution. They need not necessarily include the most advanced practices, nor need they require accurate and detailed measurement as in time-and-motion studies. Simple determination of the comparative economic advantages of different practices or processes—as for instance, two ploughings against one, or weeding by machine against weeding by hoe—can be very useful. Even if such studies result only in a scientific determination of what is already known through practice, they may be worth while because they can serve as a demonstration to less progressive farmers. Thus they may supply valuable material with which the extension agencies can more effectively convince farmers to change their old fashioned ways.

Among the research methods used for the determination of the best techniques in agricultural economics, special reference should be made to the *survey method* in which a representative group of farmers is examined and the financial results of their activities correlated with the different techniques they use. Such surveys have been widely used in the United States of America by farm management and marketing specialists to promote the use of better techniques. If these surveys are to be applied efficiently in the under-developed countries, it is desirable to distinguish two classes of country: (1) those so backward that there are neither any farms employing the more modern techniques nor local research institutes to supply scientific knowledge of them; and (2) those in which some farmers are already applying modern techniques and where the research institutes have already studied some problems scientifically.

For the first group of countries, the survey method is inappropriate since, there being no modern techniques in actual use, comparisons would be practically useless. If scientific knowledge about the best techniques for these countries is desired, one must wait until the local research institutes can supply this information by experimental methods or until a group of farmer-innovators introduce different techniques, thus providing a basis for an empirical determination through the survey method. However, considering that time is an important element, it may be wiser to use instead some less scientific approach. It is possible, for example, to obtain some useful information on modern techniques on the basis of personal observations in other countries. It is known that some techniques may be brought directly from elsewhere and used by the under-developed country with small risk. This is true of several practices such as the use of cultivating machinery, soil preparation, insect control, and so on.

However, agricultural economics can contribute to lessen the risks resulting from these new techniques with the help of a survey somewhat different from that described above. In this latter type, a team of agronomists and agricultural economists, with practical knowledge of modern agriculture in similar countries, visits a representative group of producers. The agronomist collects information on the characteristics of the soil and climate, the techniques used by the producer, and the conditions of growth and productivity of the different varieties of crops and livestock, including susceptibility to the pests and diseases in the region. The agricultural economist is concerned with determining wage and price conditions, with the measurement of investment in farm capital, and especially with estimating the inputs in the different processes used by the producers. On the basis of this information, both the agricultural economist and the agronomist can arrive at new techniques or new varieties of crops which can be introduced into the country with greater possibilities of economic success. These new techniques should be followed by additional surveys to test the results.

With the other less backward group of under-developed countries—where some scientific knowledge of the use of modern techniques is found in the research institutes and where some farmers are already trying new procedures—it is possible to apply the typical economic survey method successfully. Even in this case it is wise to have in mind the possibilities of applying other practices which, while not yet being used by the producers, would appear to be advisable.

Attention also needs to be given to the problem of production adjustments. At first glance, the problem of production in the under-developed countries may seem to be restricted to poor techniques and insufficiency of production. Nevertheless, a closer study of the economics of these countries shows that they frequently suffer from the problem of maladjustment of production. Sometimes this takes the form of a chronic surplus of production as, for instance, in the case of coffee in Brazil. More frequently it reflects not a surplus of production but a more self-sufficient life of the farmers. This happens whenever (as in much of Latin America) the country has a small internal consumer market and a large agricultural sector, plenty of land as well as labour, and primitive techniques. Under these conditions, the agricultural labour cannot be used fully because, if it were, the volume of production would far exceed domestic demand and the price would fall below the level at which farmers are willing to abandon the goal of self-sufficiency and a tranquil life in favour of production on a commercial basis.

This type of mal-allocation of factors is not easily corrected. The development of an export market would increase the demand for these products, keeping the prices from falling to a low level. But this would be possible only if an over-all improvement of the techniques also occurred, because usually the current prices in the world market already reflect the supply conditions of countries technically more developed and efficient, and would not constitute a price incentive for the farmers of the under-developed country to increase their production.

Internal industrial-urban development also could be another

means of enlarging the demand for these products, though urbanization and higher incomes bring changes in consumer habits. The increase in demand for the traditional products which can be produced
easily by farmers is very small—it is more for products like fruit,
vegetables, chickens, eggs, and milk which cannot be produced by the
farmers unless they change their techniques. That is why, in countries
like Brazil where there have been developments of this nature, there
is at the same time an insufficient supply of the new products demanded by the urban population and a large supply of the traditional
products as shown by the low prices.

Still another point related to the problem of production is the
slowness with which new techniques are adopted by the farmers in
the under-developed countries. The number of farmers who are reluctant to accept a new technique, even after it has been proved
feasible by the research institutes and adopted by the most progressive ones, is always large. Many factors cause this delay, such as insufficient knowledge, lack of capital, and traditionalism.

It would be useful to carry out a special survey to determine the
importance of each of these factors, to find out where further studies
should be given priority. If such a study showed that insufficient knowledge is an important factor, additional studies should be conducted
to determine the causes which delay the improvement of the extension services or educational facilities, and to recommend means of
improving these services. If insufficient capital is indicated as an important cause, studies should be made of the effects of the banking
system and credit facilities. If the cause is mainly institutional (the
tenure system, for example), then further studies should be developed
in this direction.

Sometimes there are farmers who, despite having the necessary
technical knowledge and financial resources for adopting new techniques, are not willing to do so. To adopt a modern technique is
the end result of a long mental process. First, the farmer has to know
that the new technique is, in principle, better than the one he is
using. This he discovers from his reading, from demonstrations provided by the extension service, or from visits and conversations with
other farmers. This learning process is slow for the farmer who, because of his more backward culture, is not used to logical reasoning
and scientific demonstration. After he has accepted the fact that the
new technique is better in principle, he has to think about how it
may be adopted on his farm, what changes in his practices must be
carried out, and sometimes what modifications in his customs and
personal way of life must be made. It is then a matter of balancing the
pros and *cons* of the new technique against the old. If the farmer's
culture is of a less progressive nature, with traditional family customs

and stratified social values, the adoption of a new technique is more difficult because the gain in income would not warrant the great change required in his set of values. The economic risk usually involved has to be considered also in this balancing process. The economic risks are due not only to the natural hazards of agriculture but also to two other important elements, namely: (a) the examples of previous failures among people of his acquaintance who have adopted new techniques, and (b) the fear of price instability in the market. Failure of adoption is very common in under-developed countries because the extension services frequently do not help the farmer to adopt modern techniques successfully. Price instability also is all too common in under-developed countries, as the farmers know from their own experience. Hence, farmers are likely to be especially careful to balance these risks against the advantages of modern techniques.

It follows that if the survey showed scepticism among a large number of farmers, the research worker would have to look for its causes—the relative importance of the farmer's low level of general culture, the poor efficiency of the extension service, or the absence of price stability—before he could suggest a more effective way of speeding up the use of modern methods.

MARKETING AND PRICES

Techniques in the marketing of farm products in the under-developed countries vary a great deal. For a few products and in certain regions, marketing is well organized with almost all the facilities which characterize rational marketing: standardized products, a compulsory system of classification, adequate warehouses, commodity exchanges, financing facilities, well-established norms for buying and selling, etc. For most products, however, marketing is at a less satisfactory stage: qualities are not standardized, the packing system is inadequate, the methods of processing and distribution archaic, freezing facilities are lacking, etc. This low standard of efficiency results in a very large marketing margin for the middleman, besides giving him a monopoly which permits speculation and submits prices to violent fluctuations.

As one gets further away from the more advanced centres, the process of marketing becomes more unreliable and even quite primitive as, for example, in the rubber area of the Amazon Valley, where the buyers of the agricultural products are the only suppliers of consumer goods as well as the only production financiers. Marketing by co-operatives has not been successfully developed in most under-developed countries. Failures of these organizations have been very common owing mainly to improper management. In such circumstances, some classical research projects in the field of marketing may be suggested.

1. Studies of the marketing processes of the principal products of each region are needed. These should include a description of the channels and processes used in the different phases of marketing; a determination of the costs and margins of profit of each process; and comparisons of the costs of the different processes.

2. Because of the importance of export trade to the under-developed countries, the marketing of export products needs to be studied. The difficulties which arise in the export sector from bureaucratic complexities are well known and it is necessary to make the whole process more rational and more easily workable.

3. Studies of the market structure are much needed. Here the objective should be to determine the volume of business, the costs and margins of profit of the different types of firm, and the policies followed in establishing buying and selling prices. It would also be necessary to examine any causes which make it difficult for other firms to enter into the market. It is known that the market structure of the under-developed countries is very faulty. With some products such as cotton, a few very large firms buy the product from the farmers, process it, prepare it for export, or sell it to the local textile industries. It is recognized that, in the less well-developed countries, there are certain advantages in having the market in the hands of a few large firms because, being large, they have sufficient capital and managerial ability to go ahead with rational marketing. However, there is always serious danger in such a concentration since the market could become subject to types of manipulation prejudicial to the interests of producers and consumers. For some other products, the market presents a completely different structure characterized by an excessive number of small firms. Under these conditions, market efficiency is usually very low because these small firms have insufficient material resources and inadequate installations and therefore, notwithstanding persistent competition among them, the marketing margins remain high. This is most frequently found in the retail market. It reflects the situation of a country with plentiful labour and low wages where it is always possible to find personnel who are willing to undertake very unproductive jobs for a low wage.

4. Studies of urban wholesale marketing facilities are needed. The situation of the central markets in the large cities of the under-developed countries is usually very precarious. With the rapid growth of the towns, the location and facilities of the central markets easily become out of date and inefficient. The wholesalers already installed there tend to enjoy a privileged position since the central market, being enclosed within the city and unable to expand, makes it difficult

or impossible for new firms to enter or a greater volume of merchandise to be marketed. A new market building must then be constructed on another site. This requires special studies to determine the size, facilities, norms of operation, and so on.

Prices constitute another research field of great importance. In general, prices in the under-developed countries are subject to great fluctuations in time and space, owing to faulty market structure (which not only allows unsuitable differentiation but also makes it easy to speculate) and to inadequate storage and transport facilities. In order to explain the causes of price fluctuations and to suggest measures for bringing about a satisfactory stabilization, there is a great need for research to determine (a) the factors responsible for price fluctuations and (b) the factors responsible for price differences of the same product in different markets. Sometimes it would be important to determine the price and income elasticities of demand for certain products. These elasticities are of particular interest in the case of products controlled by official organizations because they would furnish these agencies with better knowledge for establishing levels of production and prices for these products in the best interests both of producers and of the country as a whole.

THE SUPPLY OF MODERN FACTORS OF PRODUCTION

An important characteristic of modern research in agricultural economics is the fact that it has enlarged its field of work to include not only the production and marketing of agricultural products but also the production and marketing of the factors of production needed by the producers. As Professor Schultz has stressed, the modernization of a traditional agriculture depends a great deal on the conditions of supply of the modern factors of production. It is therefore necessary to improve the efficiency of the production and marketing of the goods and services—such as fertilizer, farm machinery, credit, new knowledge, etc.—without which there is no possibility of improvement. In the under-developed countries, the way in which these factors are supplied to the farmers is very unsatisfactory, particularly in terms of the concomitant knowledge of modern practices which accompanies them. Research in this field can show how to make the "production" and the "distribution" of this knowledge, as well as the physical products needed by the farmers, more efficient.

AGRICULTURAL POLICY

From the point of view of under-developed countries, agricultural policy may be the most important branch of agricultural economic research. The government has an important role in the economic life of these countries and it is necessary to have the objectives of governmental action and their implementation well defined and planned so as to have it done more efficiently. No further economic development of these countries can be expected if their agricultural policy is not adequately established and conducted.

In dealing with specific problems in the various fields of agricultural economics, the measures that should be taken towards their solution were always a subject of research. This was a first incursion into the field of agricultural policy. In formulating these measures, attention was given only to the problem then under discussion. No specific consideration was given to the importance of the problem to the national economy as a whole. However, if a more effective agricultural programme is desired, each problem must be well evaluated in terms of its importance to the general economy, and any suggestions made must take into account the over-all economic conditions of the country. If this is to be done it is necessary first to acquire a large quantity of basic information about (a) the over-all economic situation of the agricultural sector; (b) the importance of the agricultural sector to the over-all economy of the country; and (c) the objectives or goals which should be established for agricultural development in the interests of the nation at large. Without this knowledge it is difficult to formulate measures that serve the true interests of the country. An example of this can be found when one tries to generalize the results of economic production studies conducted by the survey method. If figures obtained from a survey show, for instance, that the use of a large tractor is very profitable economically, we cannot safely generalize and state that every farmer of the region should have a large tractor, even if the farms examined constitute a statistically sound sample and even if the size of farm, type of crops, and so on, are taken into account. Given the over-all economic situation of the country, such a suggestion may not be applicable because there may be an excess of agricultural labour, or there may be difficulties in the balance of payments. A large increase in the use of tractors would then bring serious difficulties in the form of still lower agricultural wages or more unfavourable exchange rates.

Information on the over-all economic situation, as well as on the objectives which are established for agricultural development, is valuable both as a guide in formulating policy and as a basis for developing further studies of the causes which may be preventing the agricultural sector from obtaining these objectives. Finally, the development and construction of economic indices are indispensable to studies of policy, and should be given a high priority by the underdeveloped countries. These indices will permit the determination of the existence of maladjustments in the various sectors and even make it possible, in some cases, to anticipate their appearance.

21

The Nature of Agricultural Economics as a Discipline and Science

K. U. PIHKALA

University of Helsinki, Finland

AGRICULTURAL ECONOMICS is a conglomerate of which some branches have long since formed special fields of study separated from the mother science, general economics. In continental Europe, and especially in countries where German literature has been available for students, three branches have been usually recognized: *Farm Management* (Betriebslehre), *Farm Appraisal* (Taxationslehre) and *Agricultural Policy* (Agrarpolitik). The first two were often united under one chair, and a fourth branch, *Agricultural Marketing*, earlier neglected, was associated later with *Agricultural Policy*. In Britain and the United States it seems as if agricultural economics are a solid whole, though it is divided into courses corresponding to these same branches. The French *Economie rurale* is to some extent similar.

Closely related to agricultural economics is *Rural Sociology*, a branch of study first introduced in the United States of America, which has grown considerably in importance during recent decades. The implications of this science to agricultural economics will be discussed later.

Since the birth of economic science—wherever it can be located—an enormous development and specialization has taken place in its scope. Nobody can have full command of it. On the other hand, the research worker in its various fields needs to know the most important principles of economics. As the time for study is limited, the question arises: how thorough should the training in general economics be in the various specialized fields—in this case the field of

[*223*]

agricultural economics and its branches? Further, should the studies in general economics be more extensive than now, possibly making it necessary to curtail the study of technological science or the practical training in agriculture?

Economic science to some extent has a dual character. This has not always been understood clearly and has sometimes caused confusion as, for example, in an article by A. N. Halter and H. H. Jack in the *Journal of Farm Economics*, Vol. 43, No. 2, 1961. This science, like others, endeavours to *explain*—in this case certain behaviour of men or the phenomena caused by such behaviour—but at the same time, or independently, it endeavours to *guide*, to give advice, to prescribe how to act if specified goals are aimed at. If explanation is the main aim, the practical purpose of study may be *prediction* and such prediction may help in the guiding too.[1] To fulfil either of these tasks, the science has to define it concepts, to form purposeful classifications, and to develop its methods. Well-developed and appropriate concepts are always necessary for proper understanding between scientists.

The concepts and terminology of agricultural economics so far has developed on lines which differ somewhat from those used in general economics. Attempts to make them uniform in all respects have failed, especially owing to the family enterprise character of agricultural undertakings. The pricing of family labour has not been satisfactorily solved with the result that there has been a tendency to treat the net return to the farmer as a whole, not divided into labour income and profits. This has not removed the difficulty of comparing land use, for example, where one undertaking has much greater requirements of labour than the other. Classification is scarcely a productive part of science, but it is necessary, especially where the observational material must be set out to give the most advantageous starting point for more analytical studies.

A substantial contribution of economic science may be in the developing of methods. We may include in methods not only those applied in scientific research itself, but also those which have been developed for immediate practical use. Thus, the development of a book-keeping system or a suitable form of linear programming should be regarded as scientific work.

There is also dualism in the methods of economic science. It is customary to distinguish between two essentially different methods of study, the *deductive* and the *inductive*. Deduction is sometimes described as applicable only to analytical sciences, such as mathematics or logic. This is not so, because deduction is used whenever hypotheses and theories are formed to explain causal relationships. But there are still some differing lines of economic studies: economic

---

[1] The guiding, prescriptive science is sometimes called *normative*, but we avoid this because normative has been also used in other senses, concerned mainly with ethical values.

analysis which works with theoretical models, and empirical study in various forms, often connected in some way with analysis.

It has been said that economics is unique among sciences as its statements "are not *a priori* tautologies (i.e. analytic statements) nor are they simple empirical or historical generalization, rather they are combinations of these." It has been said to fall in a category which Immanuel Kant believed to operate with "*a priori* synthetic statements." The existence of such a category was later denied, for example, by the Finnish philosopher E. Kaila, who says that Kant's error was based on his belief that mathematics could not be regarded as an analytical science. It seems to me that economic analysis could be put in the category of analytical science as well as mathematics.

Economic analysis, as a producer of theoretical models, does not as such give results that are applicable for practical use. It inevitably needs "empirical flesh," as has been said. This raises the question, what kind of flesh? It is not surprising that misunderstandings have arisen here. It is evident that the needs are different according to whether science has to help the entrepreneur, the farmer, the government, or the planner of an industry in their decisions concerning production in given conditions.

The first great personalities representing agricultural economics, Albrecht Thaer and Heinrich v. Thuenen, gave us good examples of how to work with deduction and empiricism. Both made careful observations in practical farming about the use of labour and other resources, about crop yields and animal production, about the costs of transport, and so on. The former used such data taking into account the prevailing prices for determining the income value of farms located on various soil types, while the latter developed his famous theory of the location of agricultural industries. The working tools were both empirical data and the economic model.

We may regard v. Thuenen's model only as an experiment of thought, as we well understand that the real conditions can differ from the theoretical, not only because the transport facilities and soil conditions can alter the picture, but also because people are not always aware of the optimal organization of production. But if the planner or individual decision maker uses this model and applies data suitable for his case it can have practical value.

The numerous models developed later within the theory of the firm can be used for practical purposes if the needed numerical data are obtainable. The application of the models has proceeded along various lines of study, using more or less refined mathematical methods. To mention the most important, e.g. gross marginal analysis, linear programming, model calculation, and production functions have at least to some extent been used for managerial decisions.

There is still much discussion about the usefulness of the various methods. Thus, for example, linear programming, a method which should help in the optimum allocation of resources between competing alternatives, has been criticised as less well adapted to the complexity of agricultural production. Instead of this, farm models computed and varied by means of a slide rule are recommended. The empirical basis of production functions is said to be rather scanty, as the experimental research work has not been directed towards providing it. There is no doubt that these methods in future will be more and more useful as *guides* to decisions. The economists in this field of study should have very close contacts with agricultural science and practical farming. They can use this kind of knowledge much more than wide scholastic attainments of economic theory.

There is little hope of success if we want *predictions* of future developments of farm production on the basis of prescriptions made by production economists. Farmers' managerial behaviour may or may not follow the lines marked out by calculations of optimum organization. In contrary relation, studies of such behaviour may be interesting and valuable for purposes of policy, but they cannot give reliable advice on how to proceed in order to obtain optimum results.[2]

The dual nature of economic science is clearly seen if we study problems facing agriculture as an industry; for example, problems of agricultural marketing. Marketing is one aspect of production; and marketing firms have fully corresponding functions in organizing this production. The optimum use of resources can be determined there as well as in any kind of production, if the technical coefficients and prices are known. But the other aspect of marketing, *viz.* exchange, introduces problems of another kind. We cannot determine and force optimum consumption. As men are free to choose what they will consume, we have only to watch consumers' *behaviour,* to find out their demand curves. We can make *predictions* of future demand curves, and estimate the influences of, for example, advertisement or quality of product on demand.

Such studies of consumer behaviour may be exceedingly valuable for the determination of prices in the cases of monopoly or oligopoly. If the empirical demand curves for various products were known, the most advantageous prices could be determined in accordance with the theory of monopoly prices. In some cases even, different prices for the same product sold at different markets could be determined, to obtain the maximum income. As marketing associations have no power to restrict production, the behaviour of producers may become actual; and estimations of the shape of the supply curve are possibly needed to complete the picture.

---

[2] The value of book-keeping studies has been often over-estimated, and their results even misused. An example of this is when material classified according to physical output has been used to prove the advantages of intensification, or material classified by inputs to prove the opposite.

In practice the possibility of finding out demand and supply curves is often very limited, especially if the price variations are smoothed out by price determination. Claims for more realism in price theory have been put forward, but what does this mean? It will only show that rule of thumb measures, such as fixed margin or overhead costs, are usual in pricing. Often such rules used in trade are unreasonable to the producer, and not less to the consumer; for example, if percentage margins are applied to products with low elasticities of demand and largely varying prices.

Agricultural marketing science involves various kinds of problems, including those of technology, business management, and consumer psychology. There are the questions of grades and pricing of various qualities of products, the attractiveness of packages, the services performed for consumers' convenience, etc. Experimental studies have been used in investigations of consumer behaviour, but in addition to that the interview method, rather alien to economic study, is introduced.

Probably two kinds of experts in agricultural marketing are most needed, and specialization in studies should be contrived to suit their different qualifications. We need people who understand the technological aspects of marketing, and also people who are competent to do research in the field of marketing economics and policy. Wide schooling in general economics is a necessity for this latter group.

The field of *Agricultural Policy* is sometimes assumed to be wide, to include all aspects of the social economy of agriculture, and sometimes to be more narrow and concerned only with public measures and their consequences. In its wide meaning, agricultural policy as a science is interested in the institutional framework of agricultural productions, about the factual organization of agriculture and its deviations from the optimum, about the income and welfare of the rural population, and about the means by which these can be increased. It cannot disregard the evolution of economic data and measures of economic policy outside its own sector. In fact, the economic policy of a country, whether intended or not, is an organic whole, all measures having more or less influence on all economic phenomena.

In its narrowest meaning, agricultural policy as a science is an analysis of the impact of public measures on agriculture. As the public agencies generally do not direct economic activity, but only create stimuli, it is important not only to judge the economic consequences of the aimed changes in the target variables, but also the effect of the stimuli used on the decisions of entrepreneurs. The first part of the analysis is economic, the other part is more sociological in character. To explain it more clearly: if the stimulus is purely economic, there is no guarantee that the behaviour of decision makers is fully rational and follows strictly economic calculations. And if the stimulus created appeals to other motives than purely economic, the prediction of consequences is still more difficult, as the behaviour of the people concerned is determined by attitudes which are understood perhaps by sociologists or social psychologists, but not by economists.

Thus, if the consequences of direct control of prices are to be evaluated, the economist can only predict the probable formation of a black market price level, but he (or she) cannot predict the difference between the legal and the black market prices, as the attitude of people toward price control is not known to him. It is also impossible to predict, at least accurately, the consequences of the collectivization of agriculture in a given country, as the attitudes of people may be decisive for the success or failure of such a fundamental change.

Sociology and *Social Psychology* may give some aid to the economist when questions of this kind are put to him. Sociology deals with the behaviour of man as a member of society and its various groups, while social psychology endeavours to explain it from the standpoint of motives. Sociological study has revealed many effects of group attitudes on the economic decisions of individuals. Rural sociology as an applied science is devoted especially to the problems of agriculture, and its ultimate aim is to develop practices which will promote rural welfare.

The collaboration of agricultural economics with rural sociology is still in search of more fruitful forms. Economics and sociology, though they are both sciences which study human behaviour, are inherently dissimilar in some respects. Economics is a science operating so far as it can with measurable quantities. Economic welfare, according to Pigou is ". . . that part of social welfare that can be brought directly or indirectly into relation with the measuring-rod of money." Sociology is certainly using more and more statistical methods, but its variables are inherently qualitative.[3] There are, for example, positive or negative attitudes toward an innovation or policy; possibly they can be classified by degree in categories, but their intensity cannot be measured; it is not even reflected in a measurable magnitude as economic valuations are reflected in prices. In addition, the sociological study must usually resort to interviews which reveal personal opinions, but not always potential behaviour in real situations. Up to the present, only a few attempts to apply experimental methods to sociological studies are known.

It has been stressed that the goals of the family farm are not the same as those of the firm. The family farm will maximize the welfare of the family; and the welfare is not only economic welfare—

---

[3] Use of various scoring methods does not alter the qualitative character of this measurement.

measured in profits and labour income—but also non-economic welfare, such as the amount of leisure, the agreeableness of work, and the friendly relationships between workers. We are still without methods for measuring the total welfare produced on a family farm. By combining economic and sociological studies we can form an opinion, but not perfect knowledge. Thus, rural sociology cannot give exact instructions how to modify the plans made by farm management specialists to achieve maximum welfare.

To the specialist of agricultural marketing the methods of sociology can give some help when he is studying consumer behaviour.

To the planner of agricultural policy, wide knowledge both of general economics and production and marketing economics is necessary, and rural sociology is no less important. Scientific studies in these fields can give him valuable aid, but their utilization in planning is not simple. It is easier to understand that, if we appreciate what is needed before a good plan can be given to the policy maker. First, we must know the probable development without a policy aim. Then we have to set the targets for policy, or at least to take a stand in regard to targets set by politicians. Further we have to choose purposeful measures by which the attitudes of producers and consumers can be ascertained. There is still the task of establishing adequate quantitative measures for obtaining the target. And lastly, it may be necessary to adjust the measures to other simultaneous measures, to avoid controversies which may annul the effects of the planned measures.

Thus, agricultural economics can function only partially as a guide in the practical problems of agricultural policy. Economic advisers on agricultural policy must have high and many-sided qualifications, especially good schooling in general economics, and a satisfactory knowledge of rural sociology, but they also need contacts with practical farming.

An average student of agricultural economics, unfortunately, has little idea of the achievements and present high level of economic theory. It is inaccessible to him, unfortunately, because of its presentation in mathematical and very intricate ways. He should be encouraged, however, to increase his efforts to conquer some of those valuable weapons which economic theory can give. And in any case he should have the right idea of the nature of economic science.

22

African Agriculture

JOHN R. RAEBURN*

Department of Agriculture
University of Aberdeen, Scotland

THE WORLD'S INTERESTS in Africa have grown fast since 1945 and seem likely to continue to do so. The earlier interests were in coastal and other explorations, in the spread of Mohammedanism, in the slave trade, in barter, in Christian missions, and in securing such "law and order" as was compatible with the ideas of various European States from about 1880 onwards. Africa was a dark continent to be "opened up," and to be "governed for its own good." Arabs and Europeans themselves settled and farmed only in certain limited areas with attractive climates, in the south, east, and central parts of Africa—we shall not be able to consider the position in Africa north of the Sahara. But now Africa is a continent of "emergent" and "newly independent" nations, of "under-developed economies." From much of it, although not all, now come forth not the slaves and servants of the Nineteenth Century but delegates to the conferences of the Twentieth: not missionary tales and exhibits, but various trainees including some post-graduate students. Yet tribal conflicts obviously continue in new forms. All this provides political excitement and change, and arouses an interest in Africa at least as great as that in the days of Wilberforce and Livingstone, Gordon and Rhodes. What happens in the Congo, in Ghana, in South Africa and elsewhere is clearly recognized as im-

* Much of the research on which this chapter is based was sponsored by the Colonial Economic Research Committee, London, to whom the author is greatly indebted for academic encouragement as well as finance. Responsibility for conclusions drawn, and for mistakes, rests solely on the author.

[230]

portant, not to these countries alone, but to all mankind. Social and political *ideas* are seen to matter, and especially in the maturing of new nations.

All this continuing growth of general interest in Africa has naturally induced new intellectual activity. The *Africana* accumulated between Portuguese times and World War II is being sorted over. That sound grain is found among the inevitable chaff is not surprising. Africa has long attracted and encouraged those combinations of curiosity and perception, energy, and thoughtfulness, that are the foundation of good field studies. The early explorers, missionaries, and naturalists left some excellent records. The administrators have not been without their Lord Hailey and Joyce Carey: nor the settlers without their Elspeth Huxley. The anthropologists had from the start a great, varied, and fertile field and their harvest from it is rich for us.

The post-1945 interest has added substantially to the pre-war *Africana* in the subject fields of anthropology, politics, geography, and natural history. And now the studies beginning to emerge from the young universities and university colleges are especially interesting to watch, although these institutions have substantial difficulties which greatly retard their research.

It is against all this background that studies in agricultural economics should be viewed. The administrators and their agriculturists had early to consider land tenure and size-of-farm problems, the development of transport, the choice of saleable products suited to different localities, and marketing. The prevalence of pests and diseases and the risks of unfavourable rains aggravated many of their problems. They had much to learn about social organization, and tropical soils, and many other subjects. Not all their work can now be read: fire and termites have removed much of what was written, and much was never written. But in many ways the outcome of the interaction between their decisions and natural and human conditions can be examined— some of it easily from statistics of international trade and capital flows; more of it, much less easily, in the field; all of it against the broad background of summaries such as Lord Hailey's *African Survey* (Revised 1956) and more detailed annual reports of departments of agriculture, animal industry, co-operative development, and so on, and commission reports such as that of the East Africa Royal Commission, 1953–55.

There are, moreover, a substantial number of competent specialist studies in agricultural economics that deserve to be more widely known—pioneer studies made under difficult conditions. The best bibliography containing these is that prepared by P. Ady for the Organization for European Economic Co-operation, and special mention should be made of the early works of Liversage, Beckett, Makings, Haswell, Morgan Rees, Martin, Galletti, Baldwin, and the South Africans, many of them with Cornell training, but including Frankel, and also Schapera whose more purely anthropological works are well known.

Yet although grateful for all this, we who wish to see rational decisions about the agrarian problems of the present day cannot be satisfied. Indeed we cannot avoid being genuinely anxious when we contemplate the problems that loom large for the future in Africa, blown in and swollen as they are by the "winds of change"—demographic, commercial, social, and political.

This surprises many people who greatly oversimplify Africa's position as under-populated, reasonably richly endowed by Nature, and able and willing to develop. It surprises, too, those who, often subconsciously, bury their concern in a superficial pride in "progress to self-government" and in United Nations' activities. And naturally there are those who, wearing their own professional blinkers and blowing their own professional trumpets, cannot see what we agricultural economists see, nor willingly agree to many research pennies being thrown our way. And, finally, there are those deeper thinkers like Frankel who see all social and economic problems not as technical and mathematical problems, but as challenges arising from human aspirations and requiring not so much "solutions" as work and endeavour in detail—and continuously and flexibly, because aspirations themselves change. Such penetrating concepts must command much respect and may gradually defeat much of the over-mechanical, over-generalized "development economics" of the 1950's and 1960's. But they are concepts that may lead some superficial thinkers to counter our sound purposes in agricultural economics. And we must make more allowance for their doubting, for at times we do not all make crystal clear that we are not all-seeing, omnipresent decision makers chasing only mathematical solutions. We have yet fully to establish that our purposes are rather (a) to clarify by methodical observation the economic and social decisions that individuals and small and large groups must face if they are to make the best use of their opportunities, and (b) to show, in quantitative terms if possible, the results of alternative decisions. We must freely admit that this is particularly difficult in societies in which culture-contracts have had, and are having, major effects on scales of value and therefore on demands for goods and, through demands for incomes, on supplies of labour and enterprise. But if no quantitative measures of these matters are attempted, if we do not assemble much relevant experience within Africa and from elsewhere, if we do not look ahead with men of medicine and demographers, and those anthropologists who have sufficient interest in culture change—then we shall be avoiding our professional responsibilities in relation to a whole continent to which we could contribute much of real value.

There is indeed much wisdom for us in Confucius' ideas concerning Truth: ". . . not having it, to admit the fact; having it, to use it." To serve Africa well we must obviously remember the first part of this, but also dare to work and advise on the basis of the second part.

Among the first duties of any student of Africa's agrarian problems is to understand how and to what extent the *factors of production* differ from those in the economies and societies with which he is familiar, or on which his textbooks and other readings are based. And climate with all its sweeping and subtle variations should undoubtedly have early attention. It has largely determined the soil types, the natural vegetation, what man has done with these, and the consequences. It is basic to all considerations of choice of products because it largely determines the *normal* production possibilities and directly and indirectly the year-to-year variations therein. Usually it dominates the labour situation seasonally. With soils, it largely controls supplies of water for man and his farming. More often than not it determines, when tillage areas are expanded, what choices must be made if soil fertility is to be maintained. It largely determines the pest and disease situations. Seasonally, too, it determines the shortages of fresh food and grazing and so the whole conservation and storage problem. How elementary this may seem; yet how often has it been forgotten.

Then soils. Compared with those in countries where studies in agricultural economics have been most fully developed, tropical and sub-tropical soils have been formed under very different water and temperature régimes: they react differently to tillage practices: input-output relations for various fertilizers, mulching, and irrigation can be very different from those in temperate areas. Many tropical soils in high rainfall areas are liable under cropping to lose fertility fast owing to oxidation of the organic matter, erosion, and leaching. Many in low rainfall areas also suffer erosion early in the rainy season and are short of phosphates, but have a low economic capacity for additional phosphates. In the middle belts, the low forest and high savannah lands, nitrogen may be especially short but soil management is difficult for other and more complex reasons. Over very wide regions, too, rain water and gravity have sorted out soil particles into contour strips which differ widely in natural fertility and capacity for labour and other inputs. So problems in layout and enclosure, mechanization, integration of livestock with crop activities, and farm planning generally are complicated. And not least important in over-all planning is the recognition that it is the soils that yield most for the inputs allocated to them that are now most used. African farm families "pick the eyes out of the countryside." The usual statistics of man-land ratios are therefore especially misleading for the optimists: as population pressures rise, and demands for land to grow commercial crops increase, much land with lower capacities for inputs must be used.

Having studied soils and climates, an agricultural economist will have an increased respect for African farm families, the third great group of production factors. Their conditions are so harsh over much of Africa that their thriving at all is good reason to have optimism about their fortitude and energy and basic ability to learn from experience. To ignore their accumulated knowledge and traditions gathered in their own local conditions is worse than foolish.

Yet we must also recognize the limitations of the labour force and of the supply of entrepreneurial and other skills. They are those imposed by almost universal lack of more than two or three years of primary schooling, and by the fact that where later stages of formal schooling and college work are reached, they are too little related to rural needs. The parrot system which Tagore so rightly opposed is still all too prevalent at these stages as well as in the primary schools. Then there is the lack of anything like enough local trials and experiments: the technical, and therefore the economic, basis of sound advice is too narrow. And lack of schooling and the formal experimental approach tend to aggravate public health problems: farm families are less able for physical and mental work than they could be—an important matter where so many tasks are heavy and highly seasonal and where even short delays can so greatly affect outputs (e.g., lateness in weeding). Further, there are limits due to social organization and traditions that were evolved—tribal area by tribal area—for demographic, economic, and military circumstances very different from those of the present or future. Ideas about the division of labour between the sexes, about the proper work of young men, about the use of labour for soil conservation, about what "time horizons" to consider in other connexions, and so on—all these ideas differ widely between different races and tribes, and are in many areas inconsistent with present-day conditions and aspirations. Those emergent individuals who, as a result of schooling or other forms of cultural contact, may wish to bring about changes capable of fulfilling new aspirations, may have serious social obstacles in their paths (e.g., the young work groups of indifferent efficiency in Lake Province, Tanganyika, who oppose the freer market for labour that appears to be essential to more intensive farming; or those of Eastern Nigeria who impose communal harvesting of wild oil palms and oppose greater individual enterprise with greatly improved palms). Other serious obstacles to enterprise are the disease and other conditions that have through the decades kept many tribes from integrating crop and livestock husbandries, and led them to considering livestock more as display and reserve capital and currency than as productive medium-term capital. Those limitations on enterprise due to lack of experience with complex tools and machinery are likewise serious although somewhat easier to remove gradually with proper training.

Apart from land—which itself is now in some areas so limited in relation to population that the creeping paralysis of over-population of an Asiatic type is already very obvious—the supplies of capital available to farm families in Africa are so restricted that they deserve attention next amongst the factors of production. In the past, the accumulators of capital generally have been those of high social position including the older men. But their accumulations were largely short-term because they had also many obligations to provide "social security." And, as in all poor countries, lesser men and women also have had to face demands from their poorer relatives and friends that in effect have been very steeply progressive income tax and capital levies. Polygamy has also been an effective means of spreading about such productive capital as there was, and turning it into consumption goods. Now, when there may be somewhat more opportunity to invest in productive assets, there is also a greater propensity to consume and this is by no means always accompanied by that foresight and enterprise that reflects it in a more immediate propensity to invest. Thus, such additional productive assets as are now being added to the small stock are those that arise almost entirely from the investment of more manual labour and often that of farm families themselves—more coffee, cocoa, or tea bushes, more acres sown to cotton or ground-nuts, better weeding, and so on. But not, in many areas, more draft bulls and implements, carts, flood control, water conservation, and irrigation requiring outside skills and machinery; not fencing and livestock sheds requiring purchased materials. The exceptions, closely fostered by governments, prove the rule. This is true also in the whole wide field of pest control: the highly sophisticated controls of cotton pests in the Gezira Scheme of the Sudan, in the coffee plots of Kenya, and the cocoa plots of Western Nigeria are spectacular, but they are the exceptions.

It must not be forgotten, of course, that price relationships are far more unfavourable to the use of complex inputs such as tractors and modern machinery than in temperate areas. Such inputs have to be imported and serviced by scarce and expensive or comparatively inept labour, while the labour they would displace, or the additional export products they would produce, are comparatively cheap. Moreover, the location of repair facilities in relation to the small and often scattered demands for them must inevitably pose serious difficulties. In a few areas these obstacles appear to have been overcome, and local contractors, able to draw on trained mechanics, put up a brave performance. But many have yet much to learn about depreciation and replacement costs.

Other limitations on the proper use of capital arise from the nature of the markets for land, land leases, and credit. These cannot be understood without the realization that the transition from rights and transactions based on social status to those based on contracts is hazardous and far from complete. Where pressures of human population on farm land have risen most and where special opportunities to develop cash cropping have been greatest, there communal land tenures have given way to individual rights in land. And there loans, from being personal, interest free, and often not repayable in any directly related amount or form, have become interest-bearing and not clearly defined. But this does not ensure that the enterprising now have the benefit of a good market for land, and sound arrangements for tenure and credit. There largely remain barriers to mobility of land between users that are related to racial, tribal, clan, and other social divisions but, in addition, within these barriers the slow development of sound land tenure and credit arrangements also retards mobility. This can thus be far slower than where the demands for

TABLE 22.1

ORDINARY FARM AND COMMERCIAL FARM*
(Karatina area, Kikuyu Reserve, Kenya, 1957)

Measure	Units	Ordinary Farm	Commercial Farm
Land area......................	in acres	2.5	19.6
Total output, gross..............	in £	36	856
Choice of Products			
Output sold..................	per cent of total output	13	94†
Perennial crops................	per cent of total area	2	19
Improved pasture.............	per cent of total area	0	51
Combination of Factors			
Total land acres...............	per 300 days labour	2.0	2.0
Perennial crop acres...........	per 300 days labour	‡	0.5
Livestock (cow units)..........	per 300 days labour	0.8	2.0
Feedingstuffs bought...........	£ per £100 total output	0	9
Pesticides bought..............	£ per £100 total output	0	6
Seeds, tools, etc. bought........	£ per £100 total output	1	3
Hired labour costs.............	£ per £100 total output	0	24
Family labour, manual.........	£ per £100 total output	53	1
Capital use, management, and profit..................	£ per £100 total output	46	57
Net Output and Its Distribution			
Total........................	£ per acre	14	36
Of which to: hired labour.......	£ per acre	0	10
farm family........	£ per acre	14	26

* Source: Unpublished data from "Survey of African Agriculture," by J. R. Raeburn and R. J. W. Johnson.
† Including a small increase in inventory.
‡ Less than 0.05 acres.

land have not risen much and allocations can be on a comparatively free basis by the traditional authorities. Occupation of farm land, where land has considerable value, is by no means always sufficiently secure. Some son of a lender to the occupant's father, or some step-brother of the occupant may claim possession. Farmers may even fear to rest land in bush and grass fallows because it would be "sold" to strangers by head-men. Compensation for improvements or disturbance appears seldom to be considered, although recognized rights can be established through clearing of bush or forest, or in tree crops by

TABLE 22.2

ORDINARY FARM AND BETTER FARM
(Genieri, Gambia, West Africa)*

Measure	Units	Ordinary Farm	Better Farm
Size of family..................	in total persons	18	7
Land area cropped..............	in acres	27.2	8.6
Total output gross†.............	in £	245	102
Choice of Products			
Output sold..................	per cent of total output	23	32
Rice, swamp.................	per cent of cropped area	27	20
Rice, upland.................	per cent of cropped area	10	10
Other grain..................	per cent of cropped area	31	30
Ground-nuts..................	per cent of cropped area	32	40
Combination of Factors			
Land cropped, acres:...........	per 300 days labour average-day tasks‡	2.7	2.2
Women's grain crops.........	per woman	165	152
Men's grain crops...........	per man	32	29
Men's ground-nuts...........	per man	49	47
Skills and labour per acre as indicated by crop yields:			
Women's grain crops.........	§	124	127
Men's grain crops...........	§	58	204
Men's ground-nuts...........	§	102	139
Seeds, tools, etc. bought........	£ per £100 gross output	‖	‖
Hired labour costs.............	£ per £100 gross output	1	1
Net Output			
Total.......................	£ per acre cropped	9	12
Of which to: hired labour.......	£ per acre cropped	+	+
family labour......	£ per acre cropped	9	12

* Source: Based on data for 1949 (compounds M and P) in Haswell, M. R. (1953). *Economics of Agriculture in a Savannah Village*, Col. Research Studies, No. 8, H.M.S.O.
† Excluding a very small output from goats, sheep and poultry, and fuel, etc. from the bush. Rice valued at £50 a ton; other grains at £25 a ton; ground-nuts, undecorticated, at £35 a ton.
‡ Based on areas of crops. For fuller definitions, see: Haswell, *ibid.*
§ Yield an acre in per cent of local average yields. The average yield of paddy rice was 0.39 tons per acre of swamp, and that of ground-nuts (undecorticated) was 0.22 tons per acre.
‖ Probably less than 1.

planting them. Sound mortgage credit is almost non-existent. Lack of fencing and enclosure—the traditional freedoms to graze—are prevalent obstacles to integration of livestock and crop husbandries.

In this short chapter illustrations of possible improvements in farming can be few. The two chosen (Tables 22.1 and 22.2) are widely different in that the first, from the highlands of Kenya, depends essentially on the introduction of an intensively produced export crop (coffee), on the integration of dairy husbandry, grazing control, and rotational pastures with improved tillage crop production, and on improved selection of tillage crop enterprises. Table 22.2, on the other hand, is from the Gambia at a low elevation and is much simpler, depending on elementary care in the production of subsistence grain crops and ground-nuts for sale. Here having sound seed, and enough of it, planting early on well chosen and prepared ground, and controlling weed competition sufficiently energetically at the right time—these together substantially raise yields per acre and per unit of labour. Such improvements can be spread as fast as farm families can come to recognize their net benefits and to provide the mental and physical energy to secure them. They therefore are grounds of hope for the future even when we recognize the obstacles that everywhere cause a skewed distribution of farmers in relation to measures of accomplishment.

The improvements in the "commercial farm" in Kenya (Table 22.1) are less easy to achieve because they depend not only on improvement in entrepreneurial skills and energies but also land reform (including much amalgamation and enclosure), substantial initial capital, intensive advisory services, and even some strict regulations about, for example, coffee bush establishment, erosion control, and spraying cattle at very frequent intervals. Comparatively few areas have soils and climates so favourable to intensive production. Even so, what has been done by African farmers in the Highlands of Kenya with skilled guidance and help is indicative of the direction in which opportunities lie—economic farming within the context of the fullest technical knowledge, and the most effective tenure and other institutional arrangements that can be contrived.

Some observers, and not least the families on the smaller holdings, will balk at the social changes and redistribution of land that the contrast in Table 22.2 implies. In 1957 the landless labourer who worked for farmers could obtain only about 1 shilling a day while the smallholder with 2 to 5 acres of land had an income of about 2 shillings a day. The resistance to becoming landless was (and is) therefore enormous. And this was a main cause of the Mau Mau troubles of the area, which became a conflict as much between the "haves" and "have nots" amongst the Kikuyu as between Africans and Europeans. Clearly some rise in wages as against returns to capital and management on the "commercial farm" would be desirable and would be fostered if the non-agricultural sectors of the economy were expanded to drain off more than the natural increase in human population. But the question still remains: how far can the gains possible from good management be secured without agrarian unrest and social turmoil?

In Eastern Nigeria in the Palm Belt, and in other high-forest areas with dense population and important cash crops, this question is increasingly urgent and is aggravated by past unbalance and inadequacies in education. In Ghana and Uganda and other areas where population pressure is not yet so great it is a question that should, for the sake of the next and succeeding generations, be squarely faced and intelligently dealt with now.

It is inevitable that Africa will increasingly ask for and expect investment and aid in various forms from the rest of the world. One form of help that is quite fundamental, but often little thought about, is a willingness to permit her agricultural and pastoral produce a reasonably free access to the markets of the richer countries. Without this, economic and social progress would be largely stifled. Another type of help, on the other hand, is a willingness to admit the validity of arguments in favour of protection by African countries of infant industries where and when these arguments are in fact probably valid. Without this, labour tends to remain on the land, urban domestic markets are curbed, and the various stimuli to intensive commercial agriculture are limited.

But, given these two types of help, together with further investment in economic non-agricultural activities such as mining, Africa greatly needs improvements in farming and these must for many years remain a major part of the basis of general development. Only when they are well perceived can we see in correct perspective the related social, land reform, marketing, credit, advisory, research, and other matters of State concern. Yet who would judge that the supplies of new farming, research, and administrative skills and energies now being devoted to African agriculture make up more than a pittance in relation to what, twenty years from now, will be seen to have been desirable.

23

Post-war Changes in Farm Structure and Farming Population in Sweden

ÅKE SAMBERGS

and

ALLAN ANDERSSON

**Agricultural Economics Research Institute,
Stockholm, Sweden**

APART FROM a few minor set-backs, the Swedish national economy has enjoyed a boom period since the end of World War II, a period of continuous development unparalleled in the earlier history of the country. The demand for labour has been strong from both the industrial and service sectors, and the increased supply, which has been due to the natural increase in the economically active age groups and the greater participation of married women, has proved insufficient. There has also been a considerable flow into the country of refugees from countries ravaged by war and of people from the other Scandinavian countries and Finland. But in spite of this considerable growth of the labour force, employment has at times been not only full but over full (i.e., a shortage of labour).

The most important source for the expanding industries in their search for labour has been agriculture. The farming population is estimated to have dropped from around 2.0 million to 1.2 million between 1945 and 1960. In any account of the changes that have taken place in farm structure and farming population since the war, it must be clearly emphasized that it is this competition or pull from other sectors of the labour market that has played a major role.

By "farm structure" we mean first of all the number of farm units, broken down by the size of the area farmed. We shall be considering thereafter the structure of enterprisers in respect to different categories of owner as well as different types of farmer. The concept

[*240*]

of structure could be approached also in other ways. We could discuss production policy (e.g., crops v. livestock, changes in use of area), production structure, and market conditions, or the composition of different production factors (e.g., the replacement of labour by capital, the degree of mechanization, or the use of fertilizers), but none of these more differentiated forms of structure are discussed here.

In modern agriculture, the most suitable basis for measuring the size of a farm would seem to be one of pure business economy, especially figures about the turnover. Swedish agricultural statistics, however, use area—above all, the area of arable land—as the measure of size. This is partly for historical reasons and partly because of the great difficulties associated with organizing statistics on farms by true economic size. In view of the great importance of forestry in Swedish agriculture, however, particularly in the forest areas and the northern parts of the country, the size of a farm should preferably be measured, not only by its arable land but by the extent of its forest land.

In the population statistics, the population is broken down not only by the traditional headings of age, sex, and marital status but also into earners and non-earners. The latter consist of members of earners' families and "retired and other independent persons." When attempting to delimit the farming population it is natural to ascribe to it first of all the earners whose main work is in agriculture and dairy farming, both enterprisers and employees. The next step is to include their dependent family members. Finally, it used to be customary to divide the "retired and other independent persons" (who consist for the most part of ex-earners and their families) into sectors, including agriculture. This procedure, however, has now been abandoned.

The concept "farming population" is frequently broadened by the addition of persons working in or dependent on forestry, fisheries, etc., making the sector called "agriculture, forestry, and fishing." In this study it has proved, for technical reasons, impossible to keep strictly to one and the same definition of farming population.

AGRICULTURAL POLICY AND FARM STRUCTURE

By a decision of the Riksdag in 1947, Swedish policy on agriculture is based on a combination of a rationalizing programme and price support in the form of tariff protection. The aim was to make it possible for the farming population to reach equality in income with other groups of the population. More concretely, a person working a rationally operated family farm, i.e., with 10 to 20 hectares of arable land, should, as a result of the pricing of agricultural produce, command the same income as an industrial worker. In practice, however, the calculations for price policy purposes since 1956 have been based on 10 to 20 hectare farms in the plains districts. Three years later a new programme, with the same aim, was adopted for the period 1959–65.

In this programme, however, the comparison, by the end of the period, was to be in respect of farms in the 20 to 30 hectare group. It was considered that as a result of technological development a farm of less than 20 hectares would be unable to provide a family with full employment by the end of the period.

A large-scale state commission, the *1960 års jordbruksutredning* (the Agricultural Committee of 1960) has now been given the task of drafting a new agricultural policy to come into force in 1965 when the present agreements terminate.

The large-scale rationalization programme adopted by the authorities aims at promoting the development of larger, more rational units. Special state county organs have been set up which, by purchasing and selling land and by loans and financial assistance, are to promote the fusion and enlargement of farm units, and to support rationalizing in the form of better buildings and of tile draining improvement of pastures, etc.

Apart from a few good years in the early 1950's, it has been impossible to reach the goal of equality of income, and the income gap in recent years has widened more and more, to the disadvantage of agriculture. The reasons for the low profitability are many, and only a few can be listed here. It has been impossible to eliminate the effect of the fall of prices of agricultural products in the world market. Also, wage increases in manufacturing have been unusually high, which has affected both the cost situation in agriculture and the comparison with industrial workers. Farm workers over a succession of years have been recovering part of their wage lag in relation to other groups of workers, and this has increased agricultural costs. Finally, bad weather in recent years has led to small harvests, poor quality, and extra costs.

CHANGES IN FARM STRUCTURE 1944–61

Three different sources have been used to throw light on structural changes in agriculture since the war:

1. The Swedish Censuses of Agriculture of 1944, 1951, and 1956
2. The Agricultural Register of the Swedish Farmers' Union (R.L.F.)
3. The Agricultural Economics Research Institute's survey of the farming structure and population.

The most important source for a survey of the structure of Swedish agriculture can be said to be the censuses. These are calculations of all the farm units in the country, now made every fifth year, giving a detailed description of conditions in agriculture referring to a certain point in time (15 September), also with a detailed division into regions. Unfortunately, no figures from the 1961 census are available at the time of writing.

Since 1954 the Agricultural Register has covered all agricultural real estate in the country, i.e., not only that belonging to members of the Farmers' Union. The Register is kept up to date, and has been transferred to a punched card system which facilitates its use for statistical purposes. The Agricultural Economics Research Institute, for instance, and certain state authorities use the Register as a framework for sampling, and it is also a valuable initial and control material for the Census of Agriculture. Finally a considerable increase in information on the farming population can be obtained from the 1960 Census of Population, in that results from the census forms can be processed in a data machine together with information on area taken from the Register, making it possible to present the census data broken down by size of farm.

The third of the sources listed—the Agricultural Economics Research Institute's survey of the farming structure and population— which is financed entirely by the farmers' two big central organizations (The Federation of Swedish Farmers' Associations and the Swedish Farmers' Union), makes numerous studies of economic and social questions. The survey in question is an example of one of the many random sample surveys made by the Institute, but is much wider in scope than those previously made.

With a view to making the collection of information in such surveys as effective as possible a permanent field organization of contact men has been built up, whose job is to prompt those who are slow to report information, and to supplement the details provided. These contact men, who are entirely unpaid and reimbursed only for their direct expenses, are elected by the Swedish Farmers' Union (R.L.F.), one man being elected annually for each local R.L.F. association. Their number is slightly over 2,300.

In the survey on structure and population, these contact men functioned as quasi-interviewers. They visited the farms selected in their district, and together with the farmers they filled in the extensive questionnaires. The survey is based on a selection that covered originally more than 9,000 farms chosen at random from the 1951 Census of Agriculture. In the first stage the development of these farms between 1951 and 1956 was studied. In the second, the same farms were followed up to 1961. This has made it much easier to study the content of the structural changes than was the case with the usual point-of-time calculations. It was also found that this material showed much greater changes than did the official statistics.

As shown by Table 23.1, the number of farm units with 2 to 20 hectares dropped by more than 40,000 between 1944 and 1961. This is roughly one farm in every seven. The drop is greatest in the two

TABLE 23.1

NUMBER OF FARM UNITS AND CHANGES, 1944–61, IN DIFFERENT SIZE GROUPS,
BY AREA OF ARABLE LAND
(1944 Census of Agriculture and the R.L.F. Agricultural Register, 1961)

Size Group, Hectares of Arable Land	Number of Units		Change, 1944–61	
	1944	1961	Number	Per Cent
2 to 5	107,800	80,800	−27,000	−25.0
5 to 10	94,100	76,400	−17,700	−18.8
10 to 20	58,500	57,000	− 1,500	− 2.6
20 to 30	17,000	18,500	+ 1,500	+ 9.1
30 to 50	10,700	12,100	+ 1,400	+12.6
50 to 100...............	5,100	5,600	+ 500	+10.0
100 and over.............	2,300	2,200	− 100	− 6.2
Total......................	295,500	252,600	−42,000	−14.5

TABLE 23.2

PERCENTAGE DISTRIBUTION OF THE NUMBER OF FARM UNITS IN 1951 BY STATUS IN 1961
(Survey made by the Agricultural Economics Research Institute)

Size Group, Hectares of Arable Land in 1951	Discontinued 1951–61	Moved Down 1951–61	No Change 1961	Moved Up 1951–61	Total
2 to 5	31.6	....	58.1	10.3	100.0
5 to 10	16.6	6.5	65.2	11.7	100.0
10 to 15	14.4	10.1	59.3	16.2	100.0
15 to 20	9.5	12.0	60.5	18.0	100.0
20 to 30	8.3	12.3	67.5	11.9	100.0
30 to 50	7.7	8.9	74.5	8.9	100.0
50 to 100..........	8.0	10.4	76.1	5.5	100.0
100 and over........	6.1	12.2	81.7	....	100.0
Total..............	19.6	5.8	62.6	12.0	100.0

TABLE 23.3

CHANGES OF AREA IN FARMS SURVIVING THROUGHOUT THE PERIOD 1956–61
(Survey made by the Agricultural Economics Research Institute)

Type of Change	Hectares of Arable Land	Per Cent
Additional land purchased...............	44,600	1.4
Additional land leased..................	138,300	4.2
Land put under cultivation..............	8,200	0.3
Total................................	191,100	5.9
Land sold............................	16,300	0.5
Land leased out.......................	62,300	1.9
Transferred to pasturage................	29,100	0.9
Transferred to forest land..............	11,900	0.4
Transferred to other ground............	9,500	0.3
Total................................	129,100	4.0

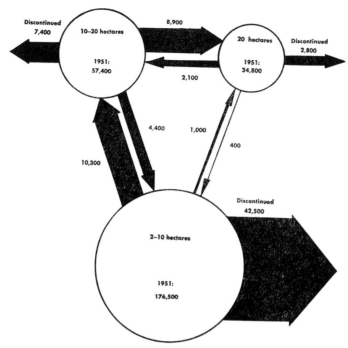

Fig. 23.1. Changes in farm structure in Sweden, 1951–61.

lowest size groups. In the 2 to 5 hectare group every fourth, and in the next highest group every fifth farm dropped out during the period. In the 10 to 20 hectare group, which is very important from the point of view of agricultural policy, development has alternated, with an increase between 1944 and 1951, followed by a decline. The number of farms in the 20 to 100 hectare groups have all increased, although not to any great extent. The big farms, with over 100 hectares of arable land, have slightly decreased. This is largely due to certain large farms having incorporated tenanted farms of over 100 hectares.

The extent of the changes given in the table is really too low.[1] Checks made from other material, such as the Institute's own survey on structure, have shown that the official statistics underestimate the number of units. It is mainly the increasingly common "joint units," i.e., when two or more farms are run as one, that the censuses have difficulty in recording. For the period 1951–61 the Institute's survey shows a drop of about 50,000 units.

Table 23.2 and the Figure 23.1 show displacements between the different size groups in the 10-year period, 1951–61. We find that the moves upwards predominate, but that moves downwards also occur. Also, that the relative mobility is greatest in the 10 to 20 hectare

---

[1] The 1961 Agricultural Census, the results of which were not known when this chapter was written, has given a total account of farm units of 232,000 (a decrease of 21.2 per cent between 1944 and 1961). The large difference between the two figures for 1961 depends mainly upon different definitions of what is meant by a farm unit.

TABLE 23.4

Average Size of Farm Units in Different Major Regions 1944–61, in
Hectares of Arable Land Per Unit
(1944 Census of Agriculture and the survey of the Agricultural Economics
Research Institute)

Major Region	Hectares Arable Land				Percentage Increase 1944–61
	1944	1951	1956	1961	
Plains of southern and central Sweden...........	19.4	20.3	21.9	23.5	21.1
Forest districts of southern and central Sweden........	9.3	9.8	10.2	10.6	14.8
Northern Sweden...........	6.0	6.4	6.9	7.2	20.1
Whole of Sweden...........	12.1	12.6	13.5	14.3	18.5

group. Of the farms belonging to this group in 1951, 18 per cent increased their area to pass into another group, while 12 per cent declined. Stability increases in the larger size groups.

Some of the "moves down" are perhaps the result of minor adjustments due to abandoning remote or poor arable land. In most cases, however, some real estate included in the farm had been sold or leased. An illustration is provided by Table 23.3, which shows certain changes of area in farms which survived throughout the period 1956–61.

It is apparent from Table 23.3 that a certain increase of area takes place by the purchase or lease of arable land from other farms that continue to exist. The remainder is obtained from farms that cease to exist as independent units. According to the survey almost 200,000 hectares of arable land were on farms which were discontinued between 1956 and 1961. In 1961, 131,000 hectares or 65 per cent of this area was still used as arable land, of which 125,000 hectares were on units with more than 2 hectares.

Table 23.4 gives an idea of the structural changes (expressed in average area of arable land farmed) during the post-war period, in different parts of the country.

The figures for 1944 are not entirely comparable with those of the other three years as they are taken from the 1944 Census of Agriculture. A comparison between the censuses of later years and the survey made by the Institute shows that the figures on average are lower in the censuses. The reason is probably the over-estimation in the censuses of the number of units. This means smaller averages since the total area of arable land remains roughly constant. It can be taken, however, that the error was smaller in 1944 than in later years.

The average area has increased most in the farms in the plains districts, while the smallest relative change is shown by the forest districts in southern and central Sweden.

SWEDEN'S AGRICULTURE AND ITS FOREST LAND

The country's total forest land, according to the 1956 Census of Agriculture, amounted to 22.5 million hectares. Private persons owned 11.3 million hectares. Just under 8 million hectares were worked by farmers with more than 2 hectares of arable land.

According to the same source, over 75,000 of the country's 268,000 farms had no forest land. This number included all the tenanted units at that time. Only 17,000 units had more than 15 hectares of arable land plus forest land in excess of 25 hectares.

That farmer-managed forestry has played, and still plays, an important role for agriculture in forest districts cannot be denied. In the winter half of the year, when agriculture in certain places cannot give the farmer full employment, forestry provides a reinforcement to his income. It can be particularly important at times when agriculture provides insufficient livelihood, owing to bad crops or a general low level of profits. Also, it is valuable for the farmers to have work available not only in their own forest land but also in other forests, private or public.

Table 23.5 illustrates the importance of forest ownership for the continuity of a farm. It shows the percentage change in number of farm units from 1951 to 1961 in different size groups, in respect to arable land farmed and forest land owned (according to the Institute's own survey).

The figures show with relatively few exceptions that the probability of a farm's surviving increases with the greater area owned, whether this is arable or forest land. No such correlation can be found, however, in the larger farms, over 30 hectares. The majority of farms in this group are in the plains districts, where forest land cannot play any great role.

TABLE 23.5

PERCENTAGE CHANGE IN NUMBER OF FARM UNITS, 1951–61, IN RESPECT TO ARABLE LAND FARMED AND FOREST LAND OWNED
(Survey made by Agricultural Economics Research Institute)

Size Group, Hectares of Arable Land	Size Group, Hectares Forest Land				Total
	0 to 25	25 to 50	50 to 100	100 and over	
2 to 10............	−31.3	−19.5	−14.7	−19.3	−27.1
10 to 20............	−12.7	− 5.0	− 0.9	+33.7	− 8.0
20 to 30............	+ 2.7	+ 7.3	+19.3	−20.0	+ 4.0
30 and over..........	+10.7	+ 4.4	± 0.0	− 6.6	+ 6.9
Total............	−22.5	−15.6	− 8.3	− 8.4	−18.8

The current rationalizing of forest operations is hindered by the fact that the land is spilt up into numerous small units, often with an inefficient configuration. To counteract such disadvantages in the private sector, voluntary co-operation in the form of *forestry areas* has been arranged. Such areas are formed within the organization of associations of forest owners, and a trained forester is employed in the administration. The owners associated in such an area thus receive advantages in forms of expert help in planning operations, access to machines used jointly in the area, and recruitment of labour which can be guaranteed continuous employment. Although this sort of scheme has been tried for a period of only 7 or 8 years, it has increased rapidly in scope. At present some 165 forestry areas have been established, with about 10,000 associated owners, representing an area of 700,000 hectares of forest land.

OWNER CATEGORIES

As is clear from Table 23.6, the greater part (85 per cent) of the arable land is in private hands. Between 1951 and 1961 the total area of arable land has decreased by about 8 per cent or 266,000 hectares. These figures are from the Institute's survey (the figures from the Census of Agriculture are smaller). It is noticeable that companies and the state show higher rates of decrease. This is due to the discontinuing of a large number of smaller farms, which had mostly been leased by forest workers employed in forests belonging to these owner categories.

The increase in the area owned by unpartitioned estates is remarkable. When a person dies in Sweden his estate can be jointly ad-

TABLE 23.6

Area of Arable Land 1951 and 1961, by Owner Categories
(Institute's survey)

Category of Owner	Area of Arable Land, in Hectares			Percentage Change		
	1951	1956	1961	1951–56	1956–61	1951–61
Private persons	2,879,000	2,758,000	2,646,000	− 4.2	− 4.1	− 8.1
Of which: joint owners	......	174,000	195,000	....	+12.1	....
Unpartitioned estates	177,000	198,000	183,000	+11.9	− 7.6	+ 3.4
Companies and foundations	111,000	103,000	93,000	− 7.2	− 9.7	−16.2
Central govt.	71,000	59,000	54,000	−16.9	− 8.5	−23.9
Local govt. authorities	46,000	42,000	45,000	− 8.7	+ 7.1	− 2.2
Church	95,000	94,000	91,000	− 1.1	− 3.2	− 4.2
Other owners	13,000	15,000	14,000	....	....	....
Total	3,392,000	3,269,000	3,126,000	− 3.6	− 4.4	− 7.8

ministrated by a *Sterbhus* of his heirs before the estate is partitioned. This theoretically transitional period can last an indefinite length of time. The increase in such unpartitioned estates was very strong between 1951 and 1956, but has since given way to an increase instead in the area jointly owned by several persons. We can thus trace a certain disinclination to partition estates or to transfer ownership to individuals. This is due, certainly, to difficulties in financing, but also to a flight to real property such as is natural in times when the value of money is steadily decreasing. Instead of selling a farm, the part-owners prefer to retain it and rent it out to one of themselves or to an outside tenant.

TENANCY

Over 900,000 hectares, just under a third of the area of arable land on farms of over 2 hectares, is farmed by tenants. Over the course of the years, this area has declined both absolutely and relatively. However, the proportion of such land has decreased only very slightly. It is more interesting to study the increase in "mixed farms" (units farmed by people who are part tenants and part owners). Farmers can be divided thus into three categories, namely owner farmers, tenant farmers, and mixed farmers. The following table gives the percentage distribution of farms by category of farmer.

	Owner farmers	Tenant farmers	Mixed farmers	Total
1951	72.3	16.8	10.9	100.0
1956	71.7	15.5	12.8	100.0
1961	71.8	14.7	13.5	100.0

One explanation of the increase in mixed units is to be found in the farms that have been discontinued. When a farm has ceased to be an independent unit, the ex-farmer and his family continue to live there. There is a marked reluctance also to sell forest land. A suitable arrangement then is to lease the arable land to a neighbour, and it is in this way that mixed farms are formed. Where a shortage of capital is an obstacle to an increase in area by means of purchase, an increase can be achieved instead by tenancy.

CHANGES IN FARMING POPULATION

The main materials for a study of the post-war development of the farming population are provided by the 1945, 1950, and 1960 Population Census figures. At the time of writing, however, there is available only relatively scanty information from the 1960 statistics on the division of the population in industries. Certain information can be gathered from the Institute's survey on the farming structure and population.

At the end of the World War II about 40 per cent of the population lived in sparsely populated areas, while by 1960 this proportion had dropped to just over 27 per cent. In the statistics, all those domiciled outside built-up areas with 200 or more inhabitants are classified as living in sparsely populated districts. The structural changes in agriculture already discussed have gone hand in hand with a dwindling of the population in this sector.

The farming population (in the sense of "agriculture, forestry, and fisheries") is predominant in these areas, but the proportion has declined over the years. In 1945 the farming population accounted for about 77 per cent of the total population in sparsely populated districts, while the figure for 1960 was 58 per cent. Here, however, the very small proportion of the farming population living in densely populated areas has been included for technical reasons.

The following table shows the decline of the population in agriculture, forestry, and fishing.

Year	*Number (in thousands)*	*Percentage of total population*
1945	1,995	29.9
1950	1,729	24.6
1960	1,200	16.0

The figures for 1960 are estimated, owing to the fact that the 1960 census does not break down the population group, "retired and other independent persons," into sectors. It has been necessary, therefore, to make an approximate calculation of the numbers in this group that should be ascribed to agriculture. We find that the number of persons in agriculture, forestry, and fishing dropped by almost 800,000 or 40 per cent during the 15-year period. From having comprised 30 per cent of the total population it dropped to just over 15 per cent in 1960.

The development of the economically active (earning) population between 1945 and 1960 is illustrated in Table 23.7, which also shows the distribution as between agriculture, forestry, and fishing. The table gives both absolute figures and percentage of total population.

TABLE 23.7

DISTRIBUTION OF POPULATION BETWEEN AGRICULTURE, FORESTRY, AND FISHING, 1945–60
(Census of Agriculture)

Year	Agriculture		Forestry		Fishing		Total	
	Number	Per Cent	Number	Per Cent	Number	Per Cent	Number	Per Cent
1945	623,000	20.8	93,000	3.1	17,000	0.6	733,000	24.5
1950	540,000	17.4	77,000	2.5	15,000	0.5	632,000	20.4
1960	354,000	10.9	83,000	2.6	10,000	0.3	447,000	13.8

TABLE 23.8

EARNING POPULATION, DISTRIBUTED BY SECTORS
(1960 Census of Agriculture)

Sector	Number of Earners (in thousands)	Number of Family Members (in thousands)	Total (in thousands)	Per Cent of Earners
Agriculture, forestry, fishing.....	447	477	924	46
Mining, manufacturing, handicrafts................	1,463	1,447	2,910	50
Commerce and communications..	680	546	1,226	55
Services, etc.................	654	345	999	65
Total......................	3,244	2,815	6,059	54

The largest relative decline has been in the fishing population, a group which is numerically unimportant. The agricultural population proper has been reduced by about 43 per cent. In forestry, on the other hand, the number of earners has fallen more moderately. Between 1950 and 1960 there was actually an increase. This is bound up with the fact that the number of permanently employed forest workers has slightly risen in recent years. It should be noted, however, that the line drawn between agriculture and forestry is not entirely satisfactory.

As apparent from Table 23.7, those active in agriculture proper in 1945 answered for a good fifth of the total earning population. In 15 years the figure sank to about 10 per cent. Comparing the two tables, we find that agriculture, forestry, and fishing answer for a smaller proportion of the earning population than of the total population. This is due to the fact that this sector has a relatively large proportion of non-active old people and children at home.

Table 23.8 shows the earning population and their families, i.e., wives and children under 16 living at home, distributed by sectors, according to the 1960 census. The group "retired and other independent persons" has here been ignored.

Agriculture is the only sector where the economically active persons are in the minority. The proportion of earners there is 46 per cent, while in services, for instance, it is as much as 65 per cent.

According to Table 23.9, enterprisers account for almost half the earning population in agriculture, forestry, and fishing. In agriculture alone the proportion is greater.

Comparing Tables 23.1 and 23.9, we find little correspondence between the number of farm units and the number of enterprisers in agriculture, forestry, and fishing, even if we allow for there being few enterprisers in the two latter categories. The classification into the vocational and occupational sector in the census, however, is in re-

TABLE 23.9

EARNERS IN AGRICULTURE, FORESTRY, AND FISHING, 1945, 1950, AND 1960
(Census of Agriculture)

Category	1945	1950	1960	Of Whom Women 1960
Enterprisers.................	375,000	347,000	228,000	9,000
Assisting members of family.....	122,000	96,000	62,000	18,000
Other employees.............	236,000	188,000	157,000	13,000
Total......................	733,000	632,000	447,000	40,000

spect to a week in October. Many part-time farm workers at that time
quite naturally appear as employees in other sectors. On the other
hand there are a number of farmers with less than 2 hectares of
arable land who have been classified as enterprisers. In this chapter
only the units with at least this area have been included.

The number of enterprisers has fallen by about 40 per cent since
World War II, while the numbers of family members assisting have
dropped to almost half. It may seem surprising that the number of
other employees has not fallen more sharply than by a third. This is
due to the fact that the number of earners in forestry has remained
more or less unchanged over the same period. Of other employees in
agriculture (forestry and fishing), some 50 per cent are estimated to
have been in forestry in 1960.

Just under 40,000 women, of whom 9,000 are enterprisers, are
reckoned as earners in agriculture. It should be mentioned here in
passing that it is very difficult to draw the line between domestic work
and work in agriculture in the case of female labour. The principles
used in classification have varied from one census to another so that
comparison over time is impossible.

The skewness in age distribution, with the emphasis towards the
higher age groups, that characterizes the population of Sweden, is
much more marked in the sparsely populated areas than in the densely
populated. The reason is the current move to built-up areas. This is
mainly in the 15 to 50 age groups, as is clear also from the fact that in
1960 the densely populated areas had 41 per cent of their total population in these groups, as opposed to 34 per cent in the sparsely populated. The latter, on the other hand, had a correspondingly larger
proportion in the higher age groups.

If we compare the farming population with other sectors, the
difference is even greater. Only 35 per cent of the earners in agriculture are under 40 years of age, while the corresponding figure for
other earners is 51 per cent. On the other hand, 32 per cent of the
farming population are in the age groups over 55, while the figure in

TABLE 23.10

PERCENTAGE NUMBER OF ENTERPRISERS IN AGRICULTURE IN 1945–60 AND OF FARMERS
IN 1960, WITH DISTRIBUTION BY AGE GROUPS
(Census of Agriculture)

| Age | Enterprisers | | | Farmers |
	1945	1950	1960	1960
Up to 34	12.3	11.6	10.7	7.7
35 to 44	22.0	21.3	20.6	18.5
45 to 54	25.7	26.0	27.4	26.7
55 to 64	22.5	23.2	26.2	26.4
65 and over	17.5	17.8	15.1	20.7
Total	100.0	100.0	100.0	100.0
Median age	51	52	52	54

the other sectors is only 17 per cent. The median age for the farming population is 46, compared with 39 for urban occupations.

Table 23.10 shows the development towards increasingly older enterprisers in agriculture during the period 1945–60. It also shows the age distribution for those farming in 1960. The latter figures include a considerable number of farmers, particularly on the small units, who did not have their main work in agriculture, but worked in other sectors. There are included also a number of older persons who were not classified as able-bodied at all.

We see that the proportion of enterprisers under 35 decreased, and that the median age increased slightly. The change is quite small, however. On the other hand, the right-hand column shows a quite

TABLE 23.11

DISTRIBUTION OF FARMERS BY AGE IN RELATION TO SIZE OF UNIT FARMED
(Figures from Agricultural Economics Research Institute)

| Size Group, Hectares of Arable Land | Median Age of Farmer | | Percentage of Farmers Over 70 Years of Age | |
	1956	1961	1956	1961
2 to 5	54	56	11	13
5 to 10	52	53	7	7
10 to 15	49	51	3	5
15 to 20	47	50	4	5
20 to 30	46	48	3	2
30 to 50	47	48	3	3
50 to 100	45	45	2	2
100 and over	47	49	9	6
Total	51	52	7	7

different age distribution. This is due to the circumstances discussed above. It is interesting to study the connexion between the age of the farmer and the area of arable land worked. Table 23.11 has been taken from the Institute's survey on the farming structure and population.

The farmers in the 2 to 5 hectare group had a very high median age, which also increased in the 5-year period. This is due to the fact that very often there were, as now, no successors to these farms. The present farmer runs his farm as long as he can. We find also that the number of farmers over 70 increased markedly in the smallest farms during the period. The age of the farmer declined with the size of the farm. For the medium and large units the median age was somewhat under 50.

According to the same survey, the number of part-time farmers was increasing. While in the 1950's only about 25 per cent of the farmers worked outside the farm to any extent, more than 30 per cent do so today. Over 10 per cent of farmers work at least 150 days a year outside the farm.

There is a clear connexion between the size of farm and the existence of a successor. According to the Institute's survey, more than half the farm units under 15 hectares in 1961 had no young male member of the family to take over the farm. In the smallest farms the figure was under 40 per cent. With the larger farms, there was more frequently a potential successor, e.g., on over 60 per cent of the farms in the 20 to 30 hectare group. A comparison between 1956 and 1961 shows that the situation in respect to successors was different on farms of less than 15 hectares of arable land from what it was on larger units. The percentage of farms with young male members of the family dropped about 10 points over the five years on the former and remained unchanged on the latter.

SUMMARY

The number of farms in Swedish agriculture has dropped considerably since World War II. According to the official statistics the number of farm units has fallen by over 40,000. Other sources show an even greater fall. The total area of arable land farmed has also decreased, in that areas lying a long distance away, or otherwise unsuitable, have been planted with forest or used for other purposes. The decrease in farmed area, however, has not been as great as the drop in the number of farms, which means that the remaining farms have become larger and more rational. The increase in average area of arable land farmed thus rose by almost 20 per cent between 1944 and 1961.

While the areas of arable land leased out and the purely tenant farms have decreased in recent years, the mixed farms, where the farmer owns a part of the land and rents the remainder, have increased in importance.

The farming population has shrunk since World War II to an even greater extent than the number of farms. The number of persons has dropped from 2 million to about 1.2 million, i.e., by 800,000. In 1960, it was calculated that only 15 per cent of the total population belonged to the agriculture, forestry, and fishing sector. The earning population in agriculture proper in the same year comprised approximately only just over 10 per cent of the total economically active population.

The age distribution of the farming population is very unfavourable compared with other sectors. For the earners, the median age is 47, as opposed to 39 in other sectors. Certain tendencies towards a shift upwards in the age distribution of agricultural enterprisers are also evident. In recent times it has been found also that there is uncertainty on more and more farms about what will happen when the present owner finally becomes inactive. In many cases there is no young male member of the family to take over.

24

Farm Management and Credit Guidance as a Tool for Achieving Successful, Well-balanced Systems of Farming

NATHANIEL B. TABLANTE

Agricultural Credit and Cooperatives Institute,
University of the Philippines

A PRIMARY GOAL of the national policies of economically backward nations is to increase agricultural production and the incomes of farm families and of rural people generally, and to improve their way of life. The thinking of economic planners and policy makers in these countries has always been directed towards measures to achieve lasting agricultural progress and rural development. These have taken the form of programmes to eliminate rural poverty, or to correct "inherent distortions in the roles of the factors of production."[1] Education and agricultural extension, basic and applied research, subsidies and price supports, credit and marketing, irrigation, land reform, community development, and so on are means to this end.

General concern for agricultural development grows out of the strategic position of agriculture in the total economic structure of backward countries. Considering that agriculture continues to be their basic industry and that a high percentage of the population lives in rural areas and depends upon farming for its livelihood, these programmes can be expected to have the greatest impact in the task of nation building.

In recent years many countries have started to assault the prob-

---

[1] U. Aziz, "The Interdependent Development of Agriculture and Other Industries," *Proceedings of the Tenth International Conference of Agricultural Economists.* Oxford University Press, London, 1960, pp. 335–48.

lem of low production and low farm incomes by the use of supervised agricultural credit, a programme based largely on experiences in the United States during the depression involving farm production plans and budgeting. This has been found to be workable in Paraguay, Brazil, Venezuela, Peru, Honduras, Mexico, Chile, and Taiwan, and their experiences should prove valuable to others in a similar stage of economic development.

Being a comparatively new concept in agricultural development, supervised farm credit is not clearly understood even by those who strongly advocate it. This chapter aims therefore at providing for a fuller understanding of how supervised credit or, more specifically, farm management and credit guidance, can be used for achieving successful, well-balanced systems of farming, and ultimately for improving levels of agricultural production and rural living.

Before going into the details of the mechanics and philosophy of the system, let us first examine the nature of the problem to which the programme may be directed.

BACKGROUND OF THE PROBLEM

The basic problem which farm management and credit guidance (or supervised agricultural credit) is expected to solve is the state of rural poverty engendered by low production and low income per farm family. This is common to practically all backward nations, particularly in Asia. As such, while the data given here specifically refer to Philippine conditions, it is reasonable to assume that they could well apply without material alteration to any other country in this part of the world.

In a 1955 study of 5,195 farms in 25 provinces in the Philippines, by the College of Agriculture, University of the Philippines,[2] the average family farm labour earnings was reported to be 375 pesos[3] and family income from all sources, 982 pesos. Nearly one-half of this income was derived from non-farm sources and only slightly over one-third came from farm labour and management. With an average size of six persons per farm household, this means that the per capita income from all sources was only 164 pesos. The net cash farm income per farm family was 184 pesos (the difference between cash farm receipts of 321 and cash farm expenses of 137).

The low income of farm families was the result of the interaction of many closely related factors, the most important being the following:

---

[2] Horst and Judith von Oppenfeld, J. C. Sta. Iglesia, and P. R. Sandoval, *Farm Management, Land Use and Tenancy in the Philippines.* Central Experiment Station Bul. 1, Univ. of the Philippines, 1957.

[3] The official rate of exchange at the time of the study was 2 pesos to $1; under the present free-market rate, it is about 3.96 pesos to $1.

Uneconomic Organization of Individual Farm Units

A major cause of low productivity and low incomes of farm families is the inefficient organization of farms, characterized by small uneconomic size, seasonal utilization of land, general lack of supplementary enterprises, and the concomitant under-employment of labour. According to reliable estimates, about 40 per cent of the 2.4 million farms in the Philippines are less than 2 hectares in size, 36.6 per cent between 2 and less than 5 hectares, and only about 4.0 per cent are 20 hectares or more. The national average is about 3.5 hectares. (One hectare equals 2.471 acres.)

Large areas of farm land are not utilized fully during the year. Owing to a lack of irrigation or drainage, many farms are operated under a mono-culture, one-crop system of farming for only a few months of the year. The absence of other cash crops and of livestock enterprises is conspicuous. As a consequence, the labour is not productively employed. According to the 1955 study, of the total potential farm labour force of 28.3 months supplied by the operator and his family for the year, 8.9 months were spent in productive farm work, 6.2 months in off-farm employment, and 13.2 months in virtual unemployment. There are few places in the world today where farmers who are idle during a large part of the year and who produce only one crop annually are able to give their families a decent standard of living.

Capital Shortage and Inadequacy of Credit Institutions

Lack of capital is perhaps the most serious limiting factor in the development of Philippine agriculture. Of the average capital of the farmers included in the 1955 study, 92 per cent consisted of land and buildings, 4 per cent of semi-fixed assets such as work animals, and 4 per cent as operating capital for productive livestock, tools, equipment, and supplies. On tenant-operated farms, about 88 per cent of the average capital (mostly land) was supplied by the landlord. Of the 12 per cent supplied by the share-tenant, a large portion was tied up in small buildings (including the dwelling) in the home lot and in semi-fixed assets generally unproductive most of the year, leaving very little available as working capital. On the average, the share-tenant's working capital was usually not more than 200 pesos (often borrowed from private moneylenders), to cover the minimum needs for tools, small animals, and supplies.

With a small cash return derived from the one-crop system of farming, the typical Filipino small farmer has little or no savings. Rarely does he accumulate enough from his low income to meet even the barest subsistence from one harvest to another. Under these conditions, he has to rely greatly on credit to finance either family living expenditures or farm operations, or both. In a survey of 5,144 farmers in 1955,[4] it was revealed that only 26 per cent did not use any form of credit that year. Those who borrowed did not apply the credit funds for productive purposes. In another study conducted in 1958,[5] it was shown that about 71 per cent of the loans were used to finance family living expenses.

Unregistered private moneylenders, including landlords, rural moneylenders, merchants, stores, relatives, and friends, who charge high rates of interest, are still the principal source of credit. Of the 2,412 short-term loans studied by de Guzman, 88 per cent came from private individuals at an average interest rate of 55 per cent per annum. Certain usurious lending practices in the rural areas, with interest rates reaching as high as 300 per cent in some cases, were still in existence. Lack of acceptable mortgageable property to use as collateral and the general remoteness of credit institutions from the type of socio-economic organization in the rural areas account for the inadequacy of institutionalized, registered, credit sources to cope with the small farmers' needs for capital. Handicapped by low income, the small farmer (one with small holdings) cannot secure the necessary capital to improve his operations, and he is thus prevented from using better seeds, more fertilizers, equipment, and improved techniques of production.

Lack of Technical and Economic Information

Basic information about improved farm practices, management, effective production methods, marketing, and the wise use of credit and co-operative facilities have not been made available sufficiently to the people who need them most. This is due to ineffective communication between the researchers and the farmers. While there may be a stockpile of technical information based on research findings, and while there may be a large number of competent technicians who can help to improve farming methods, the farmers and the rural people in general have not benefited much from them. One reason is that the technical and business information needed by the farmers is generally not in transferable or acceptable forms. Another reason is the low level of education of the farmers. The average education of the small farmers in the 1955 study was four years in the elementary school. So long as the farmers remain uneducated and illiterate, the adoption of new ideas and improved techniques cannot make much headway.

Exploitation of the Small Farmer

With a low level of literacy, many farmers are exploited: First, by a pernicious tenancy system which provides no security of tenure and equitability in sharing the produce; there is no incentive, there-

[4] L. P. de Guzman, "An Economic Analysis of the Methods of Farm Financing Used on 5,144 Farms: 1955," *The Philippine Agriculturist*, XLI (1958), pp. 460–78.

[5] J. P. Gapud, "Financing the Farm Business of 100 Lowland Rice Farms in Muñoz, Nueva Ecija," *The Economic Research Journal*, Vol. 6 (2), Sept. 1959.

fore, for the farmers to make improvements. Secondly, they are exploited by powerful landlords who charge high rents, by unscrupulous moneylenders who exact their usual exorbitant interest rates, and by middlemen (mostly aliens) who control the marketing and pricing systems.

Social Values and Cultural Institutions

One other factor that contributes to the low income of rural families may be categorized under the heading, social and cultural patterns in the villages. Customs, beliefs, superstition, social obligations, and negative attitudes on the part of the rural people tend to maintain primitive systems of farming and low levels of living. So long as these traditional institutions and set ways are not overcome by effective education, there will be little likelihood for rural progress.

FARM MANAGEMENT AND CREDIT GUIDANCE— AN INTEGRATED APPROACH

If agricultural progress is to be achieved, if farm production is to be increased, if the net farm incomes and the living standards of the rural families are to be improved, the structural defects and perversions in the system need to be corrected. The urgent need is for a basic tool that will attack the root causes of poverty. As a means to achieve it, the system commonly referred to as supervised farm credit is proposed to enable low-income farm families to acquire the necessary resources and technical knowledge and so to become soundly established in well-balanced systems of farming.

Objectives of Farm Management and Credit Guidance

The basic objective of a programme of this kind is to promote rapid change by providing low-income farm families with an incentive for improvement and an opportunity for well-balanced farming. The instrument for this is adequate and timely credit on reasonable terms backed up by intensive supervision or farm management guidance. Once the farmers have acquired the necessary resources and the know-how for successful farming, they will be required to proceed from supervised to conventional sources of credit and technical information, within a reasonable period of time depending upon the term of loan. Supervised credit is intended to be merely a transition to bring the farmer to the level where the efficiency of the farm family has been sufficiently improved and has acquired enough equity in chattels to enable it to carry on by itself. According to Dr. Horace Belshaw of the F.A.O.,[6] the objectives of this approach are essentially the same as those of community development—promoting over-all improvement in rural life by stimulating the efforts of the people and

---

[6] Horace Belshaw, *Agricultural Credit in Economically Underdeveloped Countries.* F.A.O. Agricultural Studies No. 46. F.A.O., Rome, 1959, pp. 199–210.

increasing their capacities to help themselves, though there is special emphasis in supervised credit on the credit aspects and on the individual farmer and his family.

The following objectives of the supervised credit programme in Paraguay, as mentioned by Pane (1952)[7] may be considered as more or less typical of the goals of a system of farm management and credit guidance:

1. To teach improved farm and home practices to the small farmers, their wives and children through supervisors, both men and women, who have been trained by STICA *(Servizio Tecnico Interamericano de Co-operacio Agricola)* and who work directly with these farm families.

2. To place adequate credit facilities within the reach of these farmers. This credit is to be extended upon a production capacity basis as determined by a previously prepared farm management plan, and not upon a collateral basis. The interest rate is to be modest and the period of repayment extended over sufficient time to facilitate amortization.

3. To assist farmers to select and obtain those implements, seed, and necessary supplies that most adequately serve their needs at the most reasonable prices possible.

4. To promote and assist, first, in the development of agricultural co-operatives, small informal machinery and study co-operatives; and later, agricultural purchasing and marketing co-operatives.

5. To assist in the redistribution of land and adjustment of families to the land through leases, in loans for the purchase of additional land, and possibly through colonization of new areas by farm families now living in congested areas.

6. Above all, to teach farm families how to improve their farming programs in order to produce sufficient food to satisfy their own and their country's needs.

The Concept of Supervised Farm Credit

Supervised credit is the technical term applied to a particular system of credit provision which integrates adequate and timely credit with practical farm and home management guidance under intensive supervision by technically trained personnel. Adequate credit facilities on reasonable terms are made available to eligible farmer-borrowers on a production capacity basis as determined by a previously prepared farm management plan and budget developed jointly by the supervisor, or technician, and the farm family concerned. Execution of the plans is closely supervised or guided by the technician. On the basis of this definition, it would be appropriate to use the term "farm management and credit guidance" rather than "supervised credit."

Other authorities also recognize the dual aspect of a system of supervised credit in terms of technical farm management guidance and

---

[7] Victor Pane, "Supervised Credit in Paraguay," *Proceedings of the International Conference on Agricultural and Cooperative Credit,* Vol. I, pp. 595–603. Univ. of California Printing Department, Berkeley, 1952.

the provision of adequate and timely credit. Belshaw[8] referred to it as a system "which coordinates credit provision with extension services and aims at effective supervision, but usually goes further, for example, in making improved provision for marketing and other ancillary services."

A noted authority on supervised credit, Dr. Dario Brossard, believes that combined credit and education services for the farmer and his family are the basis on which to increase production and improve living conditions for rural families. Instead of referring to it as supervised credit, he would prefer to call it a "rural welfare service," for credit is only a part, though an essential part, of the system. The basis of any supervised credit programme is education, not only in better farming practices, but also to educate the farmer's entire family.[9]

An agricultural credit seminar in Ceylon in 1961,[10] pointed out that supervised credit embraces both the granting of credit and the technical supervision thereafter. It is regarded as an educational process premised on the idea that the combination of agricultural credit and technology, if properly applied, can be many times more effective than either credit or education alone.

Principal Components of the Programme

The two major components of supervised agricultural credit are (1) adequate and timely credit and (2) intensive supervision in the form of practical farm management guidance based on a farm plan and budget jointly developed by the technician and the farm family.

ADEQUATE AND TIMELY CREDIT

This kind of credit is a loan extended to a financially responsible farmer at a time that it is needed and in an amount sufficient to enable him to make the most efficient use of his available resources to adopt proven farm practices, to increase his production, and otherwise to improve his ability to operate his farm profitably in accordance with a farm production plan. It also means enough credit given at the proper time to enable the farm family to realize enough income from the farm business to support a good living and to have reasonable reserves for unforeseen expenditures.

Too little or too much credit, relative to what is actually required for a realistic farm plan and budget, may seriously affect the repaying capacity of the borrower and, therefore, may also indirectly affect the lender. If the loan is insufficient to meet a well-laid-out programme, or if it is not released on time, the borrower is hampered in effecting

[8] Horace Belshaw, *op. cit.*

[9] Dario Brossard, "Features of Supervised Credit in Latin America," *Proceedings of the International Conference on Agricultural and Cooperative Credit*, Vol. I, pp. 298–304. Univ. of California Printing Department, Berkeley, 1952.

[10] *Proceedings of the First Near East–South Asia Agricultural Credit Seminar*, The Nadaraja Press, Colombo, 1961, pp. 13–15.

the necessary improvements. He may tend to borrow more funds elsewhere, or he may be tempted to misapply the inadequate loan proceeds. In a study conducted by the College of Agriculture, University of the Philippines, it was revealed that three-fourths of the farmers whose loans were late, borrowed outside. Also, no less than 38 per cent of the cases of misapplication were a direct result of late loan releases. On the other hand, if a loan exceeds the amount really required by the plan, the borrower may not be able to repay on time, and this may result in foreclosure on his property.

INTENSIVE SUPERVISION

Intensive supervision is the key to a programme of farm management and credit guidance.

The term supervision as an element of supervised credit, carries a more fundamental connotation than the mere checking and control used by lending institutions to ensure that the proceeds of a loan are used for the purposes for which they were granted. It refers to the assistance and guidance provided by the trained technician to the borrower in developing short-range and long-range farm plans and budgets in analysing problems and progress; in establishing efficient farm management and marketing practices; in making wise use of credit; and in executing the farm management plans which they have jointly developed earlier. Assistance given by the technician to farmers eligible for loan includes analysing the adequacy of available resources and the development of a sound farm plan; determining any adjustments and improvements needed on the farm; wise use of income, or money management; keeping farm and home records; making periodic analyses of the business; marketing the produce; and following up the execution of the plan and budget.

Mr. Rene Cruz of the National Bank for Development of Honduras, in discussing supervised credit as practiced in Honduras, stated:[11]

> More important than just the credit is the supervision, not only of how the farmer is going to spend the money that he receives from the lending institution, but of seeing that this man betters his condition, that he lives better, that he eats better, that he educates his children, that he introduces a better system of farming, that he uses tools, machinery, and implements.

Intensive supervision, according to Mr. Frate Bull, one-time Land Tenure Adviser of the former Foreign Operations Administration (now Agency for International Development), is reflected in the practical guidance given to the farm family who obtains a loan. To quote his statements:[12]

---

[11] Rene Cruz, "Problems of Supervised Credit: Honduras," *Proceedings of the International Conference on Agricultural and Cooperative Credit,* Vol. I, pp. 291–97. Univ. of California Printing Department, Berkeley, 1952.

[12] Frate Bull, "Supervised Agricultural Credit." A talk given to the Agricultural Economics Seminar, U.P. College of Agriculture, Sept. 22, 1956. (Mimeographed.)

It means actually showing and teaching them to successfully manage their farm and home business. It means assisting them to recognize and solve their own problems. It means finding the major improvements needed to be made in the farm operations and convincing the husband and wife that they would profit by making such improvements. It means advancing credit to finance improvements, but only after the farmer recognizes the need for such and agrees to put the improvement into effect. It means that a farm management supervisor follows up to give the farmer the required know-how and continuously encourages him to follow his farm plan to a successful end. It means that the farmer and his wife are taught to wisely spend their money.

In the country report of Ceylon presented to the Seminar in 1961,[13] it was stated that supervision:

a. Helps the cultivator to estimate and assess correctly the various types of loan and the quantum of credit for a particular farming season;
b. Advises him how to use such credits effectively to the best advantage;
c. Suggests improvements in his farming techniques;
d. Induces him to follow improved farm-and-home-management practices;
e. Furnishes him with the latest market information so that he may buy cheap and sell dear to the best of his ability;
f. Chalks out a time-schedule for repayment of his loan punctually and with ease and therefore in the sum total;
g. Raises his money income and standard of living.

ESSENTIALS OF AN EFFECTIVE FARM MANAGEMENT AND CREDIT GUIDANCE PROGRAMME
Trained Farm Management Supervisors

Of vital importance to the successful implementation of an effective supervised credit programme is the development of a staff of adequately trained technicians who will be responsible for giving the kind of supervision or guidance envisaged in the programme. It should be oriented towards the development of competence in the management of the entire farm business and in rural leadership. The supervisors should be able to acquire the knowledge and skills needed for carrying out the programme. This would normally include a basic knowledge of agriculture, decision making in management, preparation of farm plans and budgets, book-keeping and accounting, working and dealing with rural people, co-operative organization, problem solving, business analysis, and money management.

The College of Agriculture, University of the Philippines, has started to train farm and home development workers. The training period is about a year to provide a complete view of the farm situation and of the activities involved in the operation of a farm business for a given year. The trainees undergo a rigorous screening process. One qualification is that they should be agricultural college graduates. They are required to live and work with the co-operating farmers in

---

[13] "The System of Supervised Credit," *Proceedings of the First Near East–South Asia Agricultural Credit Seminar, op. cit.,* pp. 13-15.

the villages, so that they can establish good rapport with the farm families.

Carefully Selected Borrowers To Be Assisted

The greatest benefits of farm management and credit guidance go to those farmers who, because of technical and/or economic limitations, do not have acceptable collateral to offer. They may not be eligible for credit of ordinary kinds, but they may have a good potential capacity for repaying loans. With the right kind of assistance under a supervised credit programme, they would be enabled to stand on their own and move on from intensive to extensive types of supervision. The problem is one of selecting the types of borrower who could benefit most from the programme.

Criteria for the selection of beneficiaries have been established in many countries. These include moral character, experience in farming, size of farm, and willingness and desire to progress. In Paraguay, the following requirements must be met by a farmer wishing to benefit:[14]

a. That he be head of the family;
b. That he shall have worked permanently on the farm, for a period of time sufficient to provide experience in agriculture;
c. That farming be his principal occupation;
d. That he be honest and of good conduct;
e. That he have the desire to improve his standard of living, so that with credit assistance he may be able to achieve economic progress and cancel his loan within the required term.

In the United States, the following personal qualifications of applicants for loans under the programme of the Farmers Home Administration are considered:[15]

a. The applicant rents or owns enough good land to support a comfortable living for the family, plus at least enough to meet all payments on necessary loans;
b. He has had experience or special training in farming;
c. He is willing to work and shows interest in farming better and in having a better living for his family;
d. He has a reputation of honesty and of always trying to meet his debt payments.

In countries where supervised credit programmes are in operation, local advisory or consulting committees play an important role in determining the eligibility of borrowers. As the name implies, these committees or councils are only advisory in nature, with no authority to participate in the administration of the programme itself. Usually the members of such a committee are respected citizens of the community who are in a good position to analyse the personal qualifications of prospective borrowers and their moral standing in the com-

[14] Victor Pane, *op. cit.*, pp. 595–603.
[15] Frate Bull, *op. cit.*

munity. They are appointed by the institution administering the programme. In Paraguay, the rural consulting committee or community council in each district also reviews the farm and home plans before they are transmitted to the central office for final approval and action. In some areas, co-operatives are used instead of community advisory committees to advise on the eligibility of borrowers and to ensure that loans are not misapplied.

Jointly Developed Farm Plans and Budget

The farm production plan and budget is the product of the collaborated efforts of the farm family and the farm management supervisor. It is worked out jointly before the loan is granted. The plan includes an estimate of income and expenses, resource availability and needs, crop and livestock enterprises to be carried on the farm during the year, estimated production and sales of farm products, estimated subsistence and production costs, proven farm practices to be adopted, adjustments and improvements to be made, and provisional conditions for repayment of loans.

Once the farm plan and budget has been completed and the credit has been granted, the farmer should endeavour to follow it and conform to the conditions within his capacity. Otherwise, the lending agency may demand full payment of the loan even long before its maturity date. The supervisor makes frequent visits to the farm to see to it that the plan is being carried out and to provide further technical guidance. In the course of the loan period, the plan may be changed to conform with changes in conditions. But the farmer-borrower should not change the plan without the knowledge and consent of the supervisor. Inasmuch as conditions differ from one farm to another, the budget should be adapted to individual problems and needs. There cannot be any single plan that would fit the requirements of all types and systems of farming, much less all farmers.

Appropriate Loan Policies and Procedures

The very nature of the programme suggests that policies and procedures as well as terms and conditions of the loans must differ from those required for ordinary agricultural credit. They should be formulated with due consideration of the objectives. On this basis, the terms are generally more liberal than those of conventional credit. The basis commonly used for determining the amount and term of a loan and the scheduling of repayments is the farm and home plan and loan budget. Since the loan budget indicates the amount of credit required and the time or approximate date when credit funds will be needed, loan releases should be made, where appropriate, only in such amounts and at such times as the need arises, and for the purposes contemplated in the plan. Where practicable, the loans should not be given to the farmers in cash but in kind in accordance with the farmer's purchase needs.

Loan repayment schedules should have the element of flexibility, that is, payments can be made at any time, even ahead of schedule, depending upon the financial ability of the borrower. The credit agency, however, can foreclose the loan if there is clear evidence of misapplication, lack of co-operation with the supervisor, or failure by the borrower to carry out the plan. The programme in Paraguay incorporates this feature of flexibility to wit:[16]

> Loans do not have exact due dates; the borrower is expected to repay as he can. Loan payment must be made in cash. The borrowers are not compelled to market their produce nor to pay the amortized amounts of their debts when market prices are not reasonable nor convenient to their interests. Rural supervisors are instructed to help the farmer store his goods for sale later if prices are not reasonable when his loan falls due.

In view of the fact that the low economic status of the type of borrower whom the programme is especially designed to benefit does not permit him to have material assets that could be offered as adequate security for loans, policies on collateral requirements have to be somewhat more relaxed than in regular credit disposition. According to a leading authority,[17] ". . . in all cases the most important bases of security are careful selection of borrowers, effective preliminary planning before loans are given, adequate advisory services and supervision." Dr. Brossard[18] expressed the same thinking that ". . . the security lies in a well-thought-out plan and in the supervision . . . ." itself. While security must be required, he said, ". . . it must have essentially an educational function, in order to accustom the farmer to assume and fulfil obligations."

In Honduras, Mr. Cruz[19] reports that they give short-term credit to 18 months, and intermediate credit for between four and seven years. Mortgage on real estate is not accepted as security. Farmers give chattel mortgages on their crops and on the implements, tools, cattle, and livestock that they may own, or are going to buy with the loan, up to 80 per cent of the value of the security. In Paraguay, according to Dr. Pane,[20] loan guarantees required of borrowers under the programme include mortgages on real estate and chattel mortgages on movable goods, with the latter lasting until the farmer's debt is cancelled up to 100 per cent of the value of the object.

---

[16] Victor Pane, *op. cit.*
[17] Horace Belshaw, "Supervised Credit," *Agricultural Credit in Economically Underdeveloped Countries,* F.A.O. Agricultural Studies No. 46, F.A.O., Rome, 1959, pp. 199–210.
[18] Dario Brossard, *op. cit.*
[19] Rene Cruz, *op. cit.,* pp. 291–97.
[20] Victor Pane, *op. cit.,* pp. 595–603.

Adequate Financing

A vital factor for the success of a supervised credit programme is the provision of adequate funds needed by the implementing agency for credit expansion or for integrating its capital and for administrative expenses including operational overhead and cost of supervision. Funds for these purposes may be obtained either through a long-term, interest-free loan from an international financial organization, or by direct government appropriation. The funds so obtained would be loaned to the farmers eligible to borrow. The income derived from interest collected may be used to cover part of the operating expenses and administrative overheads of the institution and partly to pay for the costs of training the necessary farm management technicians, as well as the conduct of research on agricultural credit.

It is estimated that in Honduras the cost of supervision in the early stages is equal to about 40 per cent of the amount of the loans, of which 8 per cent represents interest.[21] The balance of 32 per cent has to be provided by the institution out of its own funds. In the Pilot Project on Supervised Agricultural Credit in the Philippines,[22] for the first year the cost of supervision amounted to about 10 per cent of the total loans granted. The estimated cost of supervision per borrower was 93.45 pesos for one year.

Farm management and credit guidance should be subsidized by the government, for no regular banking institution can afford to carry the cost of supervision indefinitely. It should not be charged against the borrower in the form of interest on the loans extended. If the funds for financing not only the administrative expenses but also the cost of supervision had to be derived from interest income, the rate of interest that would have to be charged would be exorbitant and would defeat the purpose of the programme. The cost should be treated as normal government expenditure for an essential public service in the same category as education, health and social services.

Research and Experimentation

Research is a necessary adjunct of a system of this kind. It is needed for gathering data that will be useful in establishing benchmarks against which progress may be measured, and in developing sound policies for agricultural credit. It is needed for testing new techniques and for sharpening existing tools. Continuing research is needed to provide farm management technicians with up-to-date information that would enable them to do their work more effectively and more efficiently. And it will provide a useful basis for analysing

---

[21] *Ibid.*, pp. 291–97.
[22] "A Pilot Project on Supervised Agricultural Credit." Preliminary Report (July 1961–Sept. 1962). Agricultural Credit and Cooperatives Institute, Univ. of the Philippines. (Mimeographed; 38 pp.)

the problems and needs of rural families so that appropriate measures may be taken towards solving them. Furthermore, research will be needed to evaluate the programme in the course of its implementation.

For countries proposing to adopt a supervised credit programme, it is necessary first to determine whether it will work well in conditions and socio-cultural patterns that may be substantially different from those where it has been tried. It is not advisable to transplant a system from one country to another merely on the basis of apparently similar problems. This is because economic, social, political and other conditions are not necessarily the same. The programme should be tried out first on a small scale in selected areas. It is primarily for this reason that the Agricultural Credit and Cooperatives Institute of the University of the Philippines, in collaboration with the Development Bank of the Philippines, established a pilot project in the area served by the Cabanatuan City Branch of the Bank, starting in July, 1961. Through this project we hope to gain the necessary information and experience that will guide us in a programme on a bigger scale. We want to test the workability of the supervised credit system used by the Farmers Home Administration in the United States under conditions existing in the Philippines, and to adjust it as may be necessary to our socio-economic and cultural patterns.

Under this project four agricultural technicians consisting of an agronomist, a farm management technician, an animal husbandryman, and a plant protection technician, under a leader, are assigned to provide farm management and credit guidance to small agricultural loan borrowers of the Bank. After about a year and a half of operation, some encouraging results have already been obtained. It is expected that at the completion of the 3-year term of the project, valuable data will be available to justify certain changes in loan policies and procedures to make them more suitable for rural areas.

SUMMARY AND CONCLUSION

Rural poverty is still the basic problem of agricultural development in many economically backward countries of the world today. Measures have been developed to increase agricultural production and farm incomes so that the standard of living of rural families may be improved.

A programme that has been tried and found effective in a number of Latin American countries and in Taiwan and which strikes at the root causes of low income is supervised agricultural credit or, more appropriately, farm management and credit guidance. This is an integration of practical farm management guidance and adequate and timely credit on reasonable terms to enable low-income farmers to acquire the necessary technical know-how and resources for successful well-balanced systems of farming.

The beneficent results of the scheme cannot be over-emphasized. It affords farmers the opportunity and incentive to advance their status. It helps those farmers who through no fault of their own cannot secure credit from conventional sources, to improve their financial status and make them eligible for loans from regular sources.

Through intensive supervision, farmers are assisted to make the necessary adjustments in their farming operations and to adopt scientific methods of production. Our experience in the Philippines shows that farmers who have adopted the practices recommended by the technicians have been able to increase their incomes by at least 100 per cent. Such increases in production and in buying power could revolutionize in an orderly manner the social and economic development of backward nations.

A cadre of adequately trained farm management and agricultural extension technicians will be developed.

Farmers assisted under this programme are educated in farm management and in the wise use of credit. From a long-term point of view, one significant result will be a change in the attitudes and values of the farm families. For the remaining years of their productive lives they will tend to follow the improved farm management practices and sound credit principles taught by the technicians. The greatest impact will be on the next generation.

Farm management and credit guidance also complements and reinforces other developments such as land reform, crop and livestock improvement, irrigation, co-operatives, and others. It plays a strategic role in making the other parts of a socio-economic development programme more effective.

Supervised credit, however, has also its weaknesses and limitations. It is costly and the coverage is not as broad as that of agricultural extension or community development programmes. It cannot be expanded rapidly owing to a lack of competent, well-trained technicians.

In spite of these limitations, there are good prospects that it can be a very effective instrument in improving the economic status of the rural population. It is not a panacea for solving all their problems, but is one of several tools for use in achieving that end. It can go a long way towards alleviating the misery, poverty, and exploitation of the millions of people living and working in rural areas.

REFERENCES

1. "A Pilot Project on Supervised Agricultural Credit." Preliminary Report (July 1961—Sept. 1962). Agricultural Credit and Cooperatives Institute, Univ. of the Philippines. (Mimeographed; 38 pp.)
2. Aziz, U., "The Interdependent Development of Agriculture and Other Industries." *Proceedings of the Tenth International Conference of Agricultural Economists.* Oxford University Press, London, pp. 335–48.
3. Belshaw, Horace, *Agricultural Credit in Economically Underdeveloped*

Countries. F.A.O. Agricultural Studies No. 46. F.A.O., Rome, 1959, pp. 199–210.

4. Brossard, Dario, "Features of Supervised Credit in Latin America," *Proceedings of the International Conference on Agricultural and Cooperative Credit,* Vol. I, pp. 298–304. Univ. of California Printing Department, Berkeley, 1952.

5. Bull, Frate, "Supervised Agricultural Credit." (A talk given to the Agricultural Economics Seminar, U. P. College of Agriculture, Sept. 22, 1956. (Mimeographed.)

6. Cruz, Rene, "Problems of Supervised Credit: Honduras," *Proceedings of the International Conference on Agricultural and Cooperative Credit,* Vol. I, pp. 291–97. Univ. of California Printing Department, Berkeley, 1952.

7. de Guzman, L. P., "An Econmic Analysis of the Methods of Financing Used on 5,144 Farms: 1955," *The Philippine Agriculturist,* XLI (1958), pp. 460–78.

8. Gapud, J. P., "Financing the Farm Business of 100 Lowland Rice Farms in Muñoz, Nueva Ecija," *The Economic Research Journal,* Vol. 6 (2), Sept. 1959.

9. Pane, Victor, "Supervised Credit in Paraguay," *Proceedings of the International Conference on Agricultural and Cooperative Credit,* Vol. 1, pp. 595–603. Univ. of California Printing Department, Berkeley, 1952.

10. "The System of Supervised Credit," *Proceedings of the First Near East-South Asia Agricultural Credit Seminar,* pp. 13–15. The Nadaraja Press, Colombo, 1961.

11. von Oppenfeld, Horst and Judith, J. C. Sta. Iglesia, and P. R. Sandoval, *Farm Management, Land Use and Tenancy in the Philippines.* Central Experiment Station Bul. 1, Univ. of the Philippines, 1957.

25

The Impact of Modern Development on Farmer Co-operatives

CARL THOMSEN
Institute of Agricultural Economics, Copenhagen, Denmark

THE BASIC PURPOSE of farmers' co-operatives has always been to assist the members in improving the economic results of their holdings. Some of the most spectacular periods of expansion have in fact coincided with times of important technical and economic change as farmers came to appreciate that the co-operatives would make them better able to meet the new conditions.

In order to fulfil their task it is necessary, however, for the co-operatives constantly to adapt their functions and organization to the changing situations in which they operate. What at one time proved to be an optimum solution may today be completely outmoded, and the risk of lagging behind is particularly great in years of rapid development, such as the period after the last war.

In Denmark, the need to keep abreast of developments is particularly pronounced, as the Danish farmer in spite of his co-operative traditions will generally sell his products where he obtains the best price, and buy where the cost is the lowest. Even in the pioneer years, the primary motive to create and join the co-operatives lay in the economic advantages they could provide by way of improved bargaining power and large-scale operations in processing, marketing, and purchasing.

This kind of attitude among farmers presents a constant challenge to directors and managers of farmers' co-operatives. Only by living up to it will they be able to maintain, let alone expand, their share of the trade. In the present situation it is much more difficult than in the early days to demonstrate the economic advantages of the co-operatives to the farmer. He must be shown what the position would be if there were no co-operatives.

An examination of the changes imposed on farmers' co-operatives by modern development is not just a matter of academic interest but may have very practical significance. It will be a *sine qua non,* in fact, for responsible co-operators if the co-operatives are to serve the farmers as well in the future as they did in the past. At the same time, there would appear to be a case for more theoretical analysis of the problems involved, and agricultural economists might well make a valuable contribution to developments in this respect. The following survey attempts to trace some of the main features and problems on the basis of Danish experience.

THE FARMER CO-OPERATIVE–FIRM AND ASSOCIATION

From an economic point of view, a farmer co-operative like other co-operatives performing business functions presents the dual features of a firm—a business enterprise—and at the same time an organization or association of independent farmer members running their own businesses. For purposes of analysis, it may be useful to make a distinction between the aspects which are related to the business functions of the co-operative, and those related to the co-operative as an organization. To these two categories we may add the aspects related to developments on the individual farms of the members and in the farming industry at large.

As a business enterprise the farmer co-operative has to face the same problems of technical and economic development as private undertakings performing the same kind of business. In this category is the tendency towards integration and specialization, extended processing and sales promotion, to satisfy the needs of the modern consumer. In addition, the co-operative must be concerned with the special problems of its organizational structure: e.g., democratic control, the sense of solidarity, the delegation of authority and decision making, and the necessary adaptations to modern conditions, as far as these matters are concerned. Furthermore, the farmer co-operatives will have to be alert to the increasing need of farmers to delegate functions to separate undertakings outside the farm and, in another vein, they must take an active part in the industry's negotiations with government authorities and quite often in the implementation of government policy.

AN ACCOUNT OF DANISH EXPERIENCE

By way of introduction, the figures in Table 25.1 give a picture of the proportion of national turn-over which is handled by some of the more important types of farmer co-operatives in Denmark. It is clear from these figures that these undertakings have a decisive role to play

TABLE 25.1

THE RELATIVE IMPORTANCE OF FARMER CO-OPERATIVES IN DENMARK,
IN PERCENTAGES OF NATIONAL TURN-OVER

Kind of Co-operative	Percentages of National Turn-over		
	1960	1950	1940
Co-operative dairies, milk handled................	90	91	91
Co-operative bacon factories, pigs slaughtered........	88	90	85
Co-operative egg packing, eggs handled.............	41	32	26
Feedingstuffs purchasing co-operatives, turn-over by number of cows...........................	59	54	49
Fertilizer purchasing co-operatives, quantity.........	40	38	40

in the farming industry and in its adaptation to modern conditions. The preponderant position of farmers' processing, marketing, and purchasing co-operatives compared with other branches of co-operation in Denmark is brought out further by the fact that they represent together almost 75 per cent of the total turnover by value of Danish co-operatives, including the consumers' co-operatives.

The Co-operative Dairies

Most of the co-operative dairies were set up before 1900 and represented at that time a revolutionary development from the point of view of both specialization and scale of operation. The handling and processing of milk was transferred from a large number of member farms to the co-operative which, although it was very small by to-day's measure, had an optimum size for the limited capacity of the dairy machinery at the time and the slow means of transport available.

Through the co-operative dairies the small farming enterprises were able to take advantage of the economies of scale in the processing and marketing of milk and dairy products. Their bargaining position was further strengthened, as the local co-operative dairies formed secondary regional associations for the export of butter, etc. The process of concentration went even further and resulted as early as 1912 in the creation of one central national organization. During the same period, the dairy associations also formed a secondary co-operative for purchases of materials and machinery as well as a factory for dairy machinery.

This short flash back will suffice to show that a large part of the present problems are of the same nature as before. The principles are still fundamentally the same, but their implementation now-a-days is a much more complex undertaking and asks for highly competent leaders and managers.

The question of *integration* is a case in point. Modern development has increased the relative advantage of the large dairies, as is clearly demonstrated by the difference in working costs per 100 kilos of milk between the large and the small dairies. In addition, modern transport has made it possible for one dairy to cover much larger areas of production.

The national organization has put much effort into promoting the merging of small dairies by preparing plans and providing assistance locally. This effort has been successful to some extent, as shown by the reduction in the number of dairies (see Table 25.2). During the last 10 years more than 200 dairies have disappeared, but many more will have to follow. The important investments connected with the introduction of modern machinery is a strong argument in favour of this, but it must be admitted that the speed of progress is severely hampered by the organizational structure. Local and personal interests on the part of members, directors, and managers often prove to be a serious obstacle in spite of the obvious economic advantages. Sometimes, however, a compromise solution can be found by linking integration with a certain amount of specialization or division of

TABLE 25.2

DEVELOPMENT OF FARMERS' CO-OPERATIVES IN DENMARK

	Years		
Kind of Co-operative	1960	1950	1940
Co-operative Dairies			
Number of dairies...................	1,132	1,309	1,399
Number of members.................	155,600	180,000	189,900
Number of employees...............	6,950	6,410	5,500
Milk handled per dairy, 1,000 tons......	3.8	3.6	3.2
Co-operative Bacon Factories			
Number of factories.................	62	61	61
Number of members.................	182,300	201,300	193,500
Number of employees...............	10,540	6,070	4,100
Pigs slaughtered per factory, 1,000......	131	63	43
Number of joint specialized plants.	17	14	9
Number of employees in these..........	2,700	1,360	580
Co-operative Egg-packing Branches			
Number of branches.................	1,440	1,005	800
Number of members.................	85,000	58,000	42,600
Eggs handled per branch, tons..........	35	32	24
Feedingstuffs Purchasing Co-operatives			
Number of local co-operatives..........	1,776	1,684	1,565
Number of members.................	104,400	100,000	95,100
Number of employees...............	1,420	1,130	720
Fertilizer Purchasing Co-operatives			
Number of local co-operatives..........	1,759	1,656	1,508
Quantity handled per co-operative, tons...	390	240	190
Total Number of Farms in Denmark.......	196,100	208,000	209,100

tasks between a few of the existing dairies in a given region. It should also be recognized that the contact between directors and members of a large integrated co-operative will be facilitated if attempts are made to maintain as much as possible of the local organizational structure.

In spite of the present difficulties, there can be no doubt that the number of dairies will have to be reduced rather drastically if the co-operative dairy industry is to take full advantage of the possibilities offered by modern techniques. This is the only way to meet the increasing competition from large-scale private dairies. And here the question of *quality* is highly important, as the smaller units have difficulties in satisfying the standards required. To assist on this point the national organization has recently decided to set up a number of regional laboratories, which are to serve the dairies of each region by providing facilities that would be beyond their means individually. Advisory assistance on questions of hygiene and handling techniques is also provided to an increasing degree.

So far as *marketing* is concerned, the national organization has increased the scope of joint activities by setting up a factory for packaging material, which forms part of a programme to stimulate the marketing of butter in packets, carrying the mark of the *lur-brand*. Another characteristic feature has been the introduction of a limited number of well-defined standard types of cheese.

The initiation of more intensified *advertising* both at home and abroad has meant a break away from the traditional attitude towards costs of this nature. In addition, the national organization has a general programme of *sales promotion,* including *inter alia* a consultative service for food retail shops. Mention should also be made of the fact that the dairy co-operatives, through their secondary and central organizations, have played an important part in the regulation of supply to export markets.

Recent developments on the export markets and the ensuing economic difficulties have lead to the introduction of a number of measures to support the agricultural industry. As part of this framework, the national organization has become responsible for the implementation of *price policy* measures for dairy products on the home market.

Before leaving the dairy sector, it is of interest to note that the problem of the small-scale milk producer has given rise recently to heated discussions touching the principles of co-operative organization. The fact that the very small producer gives rise to higher costs of operation in the dairy, has pointed to the need of a reconsideration of the traditional policy of collecting the milk at the cost of the co-operative, no matter the distance and quantity involved. More generally, this raises the question of allocation of costs in proportion to the costs actually incurred.

It is generally recognized that it is a fundamental duty of a co-operative to serve the small as well as the large-scale producer. But the question of cost allocation cannot be dismissed *sine die*. Those who advocate a change in this respect put forward the claim that the co-operatives will not be able to serve the small producer in the future if all the larger producers leave the co-operative because they get better terms elsewhere. It should not be the task of the co-operatives to protect clearly uneconomic units at the cost of the viable.

The Co-operative Bacon Factories

Unlike the dairies, the bacon factories covered rather wide areas from the beginning, partly because of the need to assure a reasonable supply of pigs as a basis for regular operation. The question of *scale* has therefore had very little significance in this sector up to the present, when the importance of new investments are beginning to pose problems of this nature. On the other hand, co-operative statistics have for years shown a constant superiority of the largest factories as far as costs per pig are concerned. But the great fluctuations in the number of pigs, and thus in the utilization of capacity over the years, have been a deterrent to adaptations in this respect.

A certain degree of *specialization* started very early with the creation of joint specialized factories for the utilization of various by-products, and this tendency has been accentuated in recent years, as appears from the figures in Table 25.2. More recent examples of this development are the co-operative canning factories, which have enabled the bacon factories to take an active and direct part in the expanding exports of canned meat.

Attempts are now being made to replace the traditional exports of "Wiltshire" sides by more processed meat products, and one of the latest developments in this direction has been the introduction of sliced bacon in plastic parcels. The co-operative bacon factories are determined to push processing further along the way to the consumer's table—in so far as this will result in economic gains to their members.

The remarkable improvements in bacon *quality* have been closely connected with the system of grading, which has been made more and more rigorous lately in order to satisfy the changes in taste and demand. The successful results are due, to a large extent, to the very significant quality premiums connected with the grading system. In order to take full advantage of the standard quality, a new system of marking the bacon sides continuously from one end to the other has been introduced and quite recently a common brand mark for all canned meat was adopted.

Like the co-operative dairies, the bacon factories long ago created a central organizational framework and, after a long period of government control, the central organization was extended to cover a central selling organization. In addition to the management of markets through the regulation of supplies, this organization has initiated an important programme of active advertising and sales promotion both at home and abroad.

With modern development, the *training of personnel* has become still more important, and the same applies to research for the development of new techniques and improved quality control. For these purposes, the bacon factories have set up a central research institute, including a training school for butchers and an experimental slaughterhouse.

So far as the organizational aspects are concerned, the central organization in this sector is now also directly engaged in the implementation of price policy measures on the home market. On the internal front, the main problem has been to persuade members of the need to prepare for changes in demand and to increase the degree of processing as well as the appropriations for advertising and sales promotion. The delegation of more functions to specialized undertakings has also met with opposition in some cases.

The Co-operative Egg-Packing Stations

The egg sector has always been one of the weaker links in the chain of farmer co-operatives. This is explained partly by the fact that the investments involved in the setting up of a packing station have been relatively small, as the amount of processing was negligible. In this respect the situation has changed with the advent of more complicated machinery for grading and control, and the tendency towards *centralization* is also favoured by the development of transport. At the same time a certain amount of *specialization* is taking place in so far as the bacon factories, which formerly had egg packing as a subsidiary activity, are now handing it over to the egg co-operatives.

The problems connected with the large number of small-scale producers, who give rise to high costs of collection and handling, are even more marked than in the dairy sector. In fact, the discussion on a more proper allocation of costs, perhaps even in the form of price discrimination, started among the egg co-operatives, which are subject to very keen competition from the private trade.

The arguments in favour of a more flexible price system have a very real economic background, but they represent a challenge to the principle of solidarity, which is one of the pillars of co-operation. There is an urgent need, therefore, for widespread dissemination of factual information among members before they can be expected to accept a change of this nature. The future of egg co-operatives may well depend on the success of such a campaign.

The Purchasing Co-operatives

The purchasing co-operatives up to the present have comprised a large number of small units. The business functions were mostly limited to the operation of a small warehouse as a depot for joint consignments from the secondary associations. The small amount of clerical work involved was often done at very low cost by the chairman or one of the members.

This kind of organization is no longer able to satisfy the needs of the progressive farmer. To mention a few points, the introduction of combine-harvesters has created a rapidly growing demand for grain silos and drying facilities, and the shortage of labour results in a demand for fuller service, including the preparation of ready food mixes delivered in bulk to a farm silo. The development has moved so quickly, however, that the purchasing co-operatives are liable to miss the bus, compared with the private trade which has been subject recently to a drastic process of integration in order, *inter alia,* to finance the very important investments involved.

The co-operatives are increasingly aware of this situation, and many of them have taken steps to keep pace. But the amount of investment needed will normally make it a condition of economic operation that a number of local co-operatives integrate into one large unit. Distances no longer present any hindrance to such a development, but local interests in this case also have proved to be a serious obstacle which can be overcome only by more intensive information for members. In some parts of the country the secondary associations endeavour to stimulate developments by providing assistance of a more-or-less direct nature. On the other hand, the capital needed often gives rise to important difficulties. Members have been traditionally hesitant to increase the working capital of the co-operatives, and the taking up of important new loans is seldom popular and not always possible. The setting-up of a central credit institution for these purposes has been the subject of serious discussion at the national level for some time, but so far without concrete results.

In spite of the difficulties, the last couple of years have seen a large number of small local societies being merged into larger units. Most of them are of so recent a date, however, that they have not been reflected in the figures of Table 25.2. Several plans are at the point of execution, but there is still a long way to go, and it must be admitted that in some cases the process of integration is not carried far enough from an economic point of view owing to the resistance from local interests.

It may have serious consequences for the future if the co-operatives fail to keep pace with private trade. There will then be a risk of farmers becoming dependent on merchants in connexion with the debts they are likely to get into should the present economic difficulties persist. This might eventually force them into some kind of contract farming.

At the regional and national levels, modern development has resulted in a considerable expansion of the technical installations to provide the local societies with the more complex mixes of food and fertilizers. In the case of fertilizers, the central organization is participating in the construction of a factory for new types of nitrogenous fertilizers, including anhydrous ammonia. The particular nature of this new fertilizer has made it necessary also to set up a system of distribution with regional depots constructed for the purpose. At the local level, many co-operatives undertake its actual distribution in the field as a service to their members.

A REVIEW OF THE ORGANIZATIONAL ASPECTS

Experience has shown that the democratic control of farmer cooperatives make it difficult to achieve the *integration* of local units which modern development has made necessary. This problem will have to be overcome if the co-operatives are to compete with private trade in future, and it can be overcome only by putting a vast amount of effort into the dissemination of information among members and local leaders. The need for education is particularly pressing, as the members of to-day have no experience or personal remembrance of the difficulties of the pioneer period, but have come to take for granted the existence of co-operatives and the results thereby obtained.

Another important consideration is the growing distance between members and directors. The small local co-operative has the advantage of a close contact between all members *inter se,* including the elected directors. As the size of the co-operative increases, it is necessary to take special steps to maintain this contact, which is indispensable if the co-operative *organization* is to function properly. This is even more important as the growing size of the units increases the need to delegate authority and important decisions, if the co-operative is to succeed as a *business undertaking.* Both these aspects emphasize the need for training directors, managers, and potential leaders. The large-scale operation of to-day thus presents a challenge to the co-operative system in many ways.

In modern society the large organizations exercise a considerable political influence. As a consequence, the central co-operative organizations have to take an active part, sometimes against their own wishes, in the general negotiations between representatives of the farming industry and government authorities. They have been engaged also in the implementation of price policy measures. This development has created a new type of organizational problem, often of a far-reaching nature, with very little experience in the past to support the important decisions which have to be made.

Farmer co-operatives have strengthened the bargaining power of the many small agricultural enterprises and have enabled them to take advantage of economies of scale in processing, marketing, and purchasing. In fact, they are largely responsible for the fact that Danish farmers were able to obtain incomes comparable with other sectors of the economy. At present this is no longer possible, but the farmer co-operatives will continue to play an important role. Their existence is a precondition to the viability of the family farm though they must adapt their organization and structure to meet the challenges of modern development if they are to live up to expectations.

REFERENCES

Andelsselskaber i Danmark (reprints from Andelsbladet).
Dansk Mejeribrug, 1962.
Farmers' Marketing Organization, O.E.E.C./E.P.A., 1961.
Landbruget, D.A.G., 1961.
A. Axelsen Drejer, "Andelsvineslagterierne i Danmark 1887–1962," 1962.
"The Scope of Farmer Co-operatives," *Journal of Farm Economics,* May 1962.

26

Some Aspects of Rural Population in the United Arab Republic

A. A. EL TONBARY

Department of Agricultural Economics,
Faculty of Agriculture, University of Ain Shams, Cairo

and

M. S. ABOU EL EZZ

Department of Geography, Faculty of Arts, University of Cairo, Giza

THE OBJECT of this chapter is to outline the major characteristics of rural population in the U.A.R. It is true that its structure differs but slightly from that elsewhere, yet in Egypt it has unique traits which give it a special significance that is worthy of study. We divide the subject into three main parts: trends, structure, density and relevant problems.

A number of criteria are often adopted to distinguish between rural and urban population. In the Egyptian censuses urban population means all those who reside permanently in the *chefs lieux,* and district capitals, whilst the rural population embraces all those who live otherwise. Sometimes a numerical criterion is used on the grounds that urban areas include all settlements of over twenty thousand inhabitants. A third measure for defining urban population is based upon the functional differences between various settlements (e.g., urban settlements mainly practise administrative functions). The fourth measure is based upon occupational differentiation. Accordingly, rural population comprises all persons engaged in farming plus the members of their households dependent on them. The Egyptian censuses, however, enumerate only the persons gainfully employed.

Owing to a lack of relevant statistics the following analyses rely mainly on the definitions adopted by the official department of statistics which distinguish between two sectors, one entirely urban, the other residing permanently in the countryside and depending for its livelihood, one way or another, on agriculture.

[282]

TABLE 26.1

Increase in Total Population by Number and Percentage, U.A.R.*

Census	Total Population	Rate of Increase	
	(in thousands)	(in thousands)	(per cent)
1897.................	9,715		
1907.................	11,287	1,572	1.6
1917.................	12,750	1,463	1.3
1927.................	14,217	1,467	1.1
1937.................	15,932	1,715	1.2
1947.................	19,022	3,090	1.9
1960.................	26,089	7,067	2.7

* Source: Dept. of Statistics and Census, Population Census, Govt. Press, Cairo.

TRENDS

It is a known demographic fact that Egypt witnessed a veritable demographic revolution at the outset of the present century. The irrigation revolution which accompanied the construction of the Aswan Dam and the other Nile control projects was the trigger which caused the population explosion. Within a period approximating half a century from 1897 to 1947 the total population leaped from 9.7 millions to slightly over 19 millions. This was a mean annual increase of 186,000. Nevertheless, this increase was inflated more than threefold during the period from 1947 to 1960 as shown in Table 26.1.†

The greater part of the increase was recorded in urban areas, a feature which is logically on a par with the tremendous development which has taken place in such areas (see Table 26.2). The rate of increase of rural population on the other hand has decelerated in almost all provinces of the Republic. To illustrate this more vividly it is enough to cite the following example. The annual rate of increase of the population of Cairo accelerated from 1.5 per cent during the decade 1897–1907, to 4.6 per cent in 1947–1960. The rate of population increase in Menoufia Province diminished throughout the corresponding period from 1.3 per cent to 1.1 per cent. In the last three censuses the share of rural population in the total population has declined from 76 per cent in 1937 to 63 per cent in 1960. This is mainly attributed to the continuous influx of rural migrants to the urban centres which represent the main geographical foci of attraction. Nevertheless, the trend of rural population varies in the different provinces. Table 26.3 portrays the following three features:

1. All provinces have witnessed a decline in their rural population. Giza Province particularly stands on its own with a remarkable decrease of 25 per cent of its rural population in the period from 1937

---

† Tables accompanying this chapter are of necessity abbreviated, so certain data used in the text do not appear in a single table, although all are from authentic sources of population count.

TABLE 26.2

TOTAL PERCENTAGE OF INCREASE IN POPULATION FROM 1897 TO 1947
IN URBAN AND RURAL AREAS, U.A.R.*

District	Annual Rate of Increase		Total Increase
	1896–97	1946–47	1897–1947
Urban			
Cairo..................	1.5	5.9	272
Alexandria.............	1.2	3.4	191
Canal Zone.............	2.2	5.0	390
Suez..................	.6	11.6	530
Damietta..............	.7	3.3	70
Rural			
Behira.................	2.2	1.8	99
Dakahlia...............	1.8	1.6	90
Sharkia................	1.8	1.7	84
Gharbia................	1.5	1.1	80
Kaliubia...............	1.7	1.0	75
Menoufia..............	1.3	.8	35
Giza..................	1.5	1.9	116
Beni Suef..............	2.0	.9	98
Fayoum................	1.9	1.1	80
Minia..................	2.5	1.2	100
Assuit.................	1.6	1.4	81
Sohag.................	1.6	1.5	88
Kena..................	0.9	.9	57
Aswan.................	1.3	.5	40
Kafr El Sheik...........	...	....	...
All Provinces.............	1.6	1.9	130

* Source: Dept. of Statistics and Census, Population Census, Govt. Press, Cairo.

to 1960. Such a considerable loss is ascribed to the fact that, owing to its geographical proximity to Cairo, Giza has acquired the functions of a metropolitan satellite. Hence a considerable percentage of its population has come to be classified as urban.

2. The provinces of Gharbia, Kaliubia, and Aswan form a special category with a decrease in the percentage of their rural population ranging from 10 to 15 per cent. As regards Gharbia Province the decrease is due mainly to administrative boundary changes which have ceded some districts previously included within it to the newly formed province of Kafr El Sheik (in the north-western part of Mid-Delta), or to either the new Damietta Province (in the extreme north-eastern corner of Mid-Delta) or to Dakahlia Province. Such changes in the administrative boundaries of Gharbia have caused the amputation of ten districts which were previously included within its domain. As regards Kaliubia Province, its rural population has also diminished by some 13 per cent. This is understandable since a considerable percentage of the migrants drawn into Cairo originate from the nearby

TABLE 26.3

Percentage of Rural Population in 1937, 1947, and 1960, U.A.R.*

Province	Percentage			Percentage Decrease From 1937 to 1960
	1937	1947	1960	
Behira...................	87	86	82	5
Gharbia..................	85	80	72	13
Kafr El Sheik.............	..	..	83	..
Dakahlia.................	88	85	82	6
Damietta.................	..	..	75	..
Sharkia..................	90	88	84	6
Menoufia................	91	90	86	5
Kaliubia.................	88	86	75	13
Giza....................	93	89	68	25
Beni Suef................	88	86	79	9
Fayoum..................	85	84	81	4
Minia...................	88	85	83	5
Assuit...................	87	83	79	8
Sohag...................	87	84	82	5
Kena....................	90	88	86	4
Aswan...................	87	84	75	12
Whole U.A.R.............	76	70	63	13

* Source: Agricultural Economics Bul., Dept. of Agricultural Economics and Statistics, Ministry of Agriculture, Cairo, S.O.P. Press, Vol. 13, No. 1, 1962, pp. 6–7.

province of Kaliubia. Aswan Province also loses quite a number of its rural inhabitants owing to a complexity of factors. Paramount amongst these are: its southernmost setting, the encroachment of the desert on its narrow cultivable tracts, the relatively high level of the cultivated fringes on both sides of the Nile with the consequent lack of water supply during the drought period, and finally the submergence of all the lands above Aswan after the construction and heightening of the Aswan Dam.

3. The remaining twelve provinces of the Nile Valley and the Delta constitute a third category with a decline of their rural population of less than 10 per cent.

It is thus noticeable that the rural areas of the U.A.R. are now suffering from a serious depopulation on account of urban attraction. Urbanization has proceeded since the dawn of the present century at a pace which cannot be compared with that of any other part of the Middle East. It is natural, therefore, that urban growth was in point of fact at the expense of the countryside. Yet the paradoxical feature is that a tremendous rate of natural increase is simultaneously recorded. It even exceeds that of urban districts. However, it is now admittedly true that rural population movements swallow up a considerable fraction of the natural excess of the rural population.

As regards the directions of the rural-urban population movements it is possible to postulate that, in general, congested provinces lose larger proportions of their rural population than provinces with low population densities. All provinces of the U.A.R. with the exception of Giza and Damietta can be considered the main regions of population expulsion. Foremost amongst these come Kaliubia, Menoufia, and Aswan. All three lose quite a proportion of their rural inhabitants to the urban centres which have acquired through their functions a centripetal force. Yet certain rural districts, particularly those with low population densities, can be considered on the other hand as regions of population attraction. This fact applies to provinces in the prairies of the northern part of the Delta such as Behira, Kafr El Sheik, Gharbia, and Dakahlia, where there exist extensive tracts of clay salty soils suitable for land reclamation. These provinces are in constant need of labour which is usually provided from the congested provinces located on or close to the Delta Apex (Kaliubia, Menoufia). Hence, the general direction of labour migration in the Delta follows a south-to-north axis. Such migration has a seasonal rhythm and is often called *tarahil*.[1] It is noticeable also that Upper Egypt with its restricted cultivated acreage together with the prevalence of basin irrigation over some 700,000 feddans of its total cultivated area, loses a higher percentage of its rural inhabitants than lower Egypt.[2]

STRUCTURE[3]

By population structure is meant the sex and age composition. Rural areas in the U.A.R. in 1960 show in general a marked excess of females over males with the exception of the eight provinces of Damietta, Kaliubia, Dakahlia, Menoufia, Sharkia, Giza, Minia, and Assuit. With the exception of two provinces, Fayoum and Beni Suef, the reverse is recorded in the urban centres, where the influx of rural migrants consists mainly of males who seek better opportunities for employment in the *chefs lieux* (see Table 26.4A).[4] This feature does not represent a divergence from the trend elsewhere, however, since it has been recorded in several other countries. This is attributed by many writers to the fact that male deaths exceed those of females and also because women are known to be more robust than men, in addi-

---

[1] A common colloquial term denoting seasonal migration of labour. Etymologically the word *tarahil* is derived from the Arabic verb *yarhal*, which means to travel.

[2] M. S. Abou El Ezz, "Some Aspects of Migration in Cairo," *Bul. Soc. Geog. d'Egypte*, T. 32, 1959, pp. 121–41.

[3] A. A. El Tonbary, *Principles of Agricultural Economics*, Dar Nashr El Sakafa Press, Cairo, 1962, pp. 17–48.

[4] Dept. of Statistics and Census, *General Statistics Bulletin*, Vol. 1, No. 12, 1962, pp. 1–2.

TABLE 26.4A

SEX RATIO PER THOUSAND MALES IN URBAN AREAS, U.A.R.*

Census Year....	1897	1907	1917	1927	1937	1947	1960
Sex Ratio......	883	889	938	906	956	965	965

* Source: Dept. of Statistics and Census, Population Census, Govt. Press, Cairo.

TABLE 26.4B

SEX RATIO PER THOUSAND MALES IN THE U.A.R.*

Census Year	Males	Females	Sex Ratio Per 1,000 Males
	(in thousands)	(in thousands)	
1897.........................	4,947	4,786	969
1907.........................	5,616	5,573	992
1917.........................	6,369	6,348	997
1927.........................	7,058	7,119	1,009
1937.........................	7,966	7,954	998
1947.........................	9,418	9,602	1,021
1960.........................	13,068	12,916	988

* Source: Dept. of Statistics and Census, Population Census, Govt. Press, Cairo.

tion to other factors. As regards the trend of the sex ratio in Egypt as a whole, Table 26.4B portrays an increase of the sex ratio from 969 per thousand males in 1897 to 1,021 in 1947. The years of 1927 and 1947 mark the excess of females over males.

The excess of males in the forementioned provinces may be ascribed to some undefinable factors amongst which are: the influence of the nomadic element in the population (as in Sharkia), the inadequacy of the registration of female births, and the remoteness of some rural areas which hinders the notification of births.

The significance of the sex composition of the population lies in its effect on the labour potentialities, since females in rural areas are considered to some extent a passive element in the cultural landscape. They gravitate to certain jobs suitable to their nature; it also points to the marital status which in turn affects population growth. It is unfortunate that the female sector of the population is not fully utilized, yet the new agricultural revolution, under the slogan of socialism, might favourably change this state of affairs by providing alternative employments.

The age structure of the rural population shows the demographic characteristics of an expanding population with the largest proportion of individuals in the lowest age group, 0 to 5 years. (See Fig. 26.1.) What is known as the age pyramid strikingly illustrates one with a wide base and a narrow attenuating top. Cleland depicted some con-

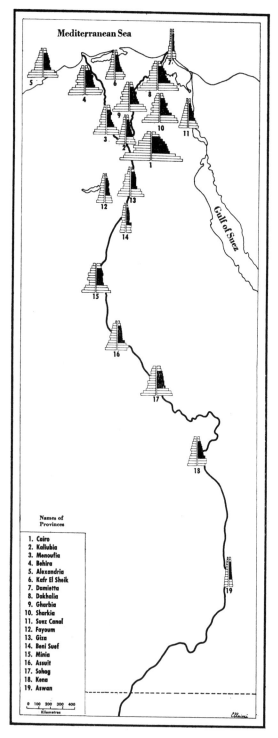

Fig. 26.1. Age pyramids by sex (female in black) in different provinces of
the United Arab Republic; with quinquennial age groups from 0 to 60 years.
Based on census returns of 1960.

fusion in the age data of the population of Egypt when he noticed that the total number of females between 20 and 29 years in 1927 exceed those between 10 and 19 in the 1917 census.[5] It is therefore necessary to tackle the data bearing on the age composition with some caution. However it is possible in this connexion to satisfy oneself by distinguishing three main categories of age: youngsters below 15 years, persons of working age, 15 to 50 years, and over-age dependents, from 50 years upwards. This tripartite division is typified in the rural areas where very high births but a low expectation of life are recorded, so that the number of young people surpasses that of old.

Urban areas on the other hand have a different age structure with a long-continued drop in birth rates, a remarkable bulge in the functional age group (15 to 50) and a greater number of old people. The increase in the middle age group is due to the continuous influx of middle-aged rural migrants.

It is possible, therefore, to divide the rural areas into the following three categories according to age composition.

1. Provinces with a preponderance of male adults (in the middle age group) such as Kafr El Sheik, Gharbia, Behira, and Dakahlia; in these provinces a considerable percentage of the inhabitants constitutes communities where men migrating without their wives are likely to settle temporarily. They are often employed as hired labourers during the cotton-picking season in the northern region of the Delta but they usually return to their native provinces afterwards. Such seasonal movements actually affect the age composition in these provinces.

2. In the extreme southern part of the country, Aswan Province, with a predominance of female adults, stands out as an exception. This is explained by the fact that the middle age group of men suffers from a serious decrease, owing to the emigration of men to other parts of the country particularly in the main urban centres.

3. The three provinces of Kaliubia, Menoufia, and Giza which lie within the sphere of influence of the metropolis (Cairo) show a marked excess of males in the middle age group. This is understandable if one takes into account the permanent movements of population in and out of the metropolis.

It is convenient in this respect to point out that the age structure of the rural population which corresponds to 39, 49, and 12 per cent for the three age groups, does not represent a departure from the structure in other developing countries. It is a vivid example of a juvenile population. The future economic development will no doubt entail a remoulding of the age composition especially when rural-urban population movements are put under control.

---

[5] W. Cleland, "A population plan for Egypt," *L'Egypte contemporaine*, 1939. A population plan in *Demographic Studies of Selected Areas of Rapid Growth*, N. Y., 1944.

DENSITY[6]

One of the more fundamental considerations in the life of any community is the analysis of the relationship of the number of inhabitants to the area of the land. This man-land ratio may be expressed in its simplest form as the number of persons per unit of area. This is sometimes known as the simple arithmetic density. The arithmetic density, however, discards the land quality and the degree of its utilization, since it portrays the relationship between the number of inhabitants and the total area whether or not it is productive. The arithmetic density for the U.A.R. is 26 persons per square kilometre. This figure is definitely misleading and fails to give an accurate picture of actual conditions since it has been computed according to the one million square kilometres composing the U.A.R. of which 96 per cent is virtually uninhabited.

Of somewhat greater significance is the physiological density which substitutes the arable area for the total area in the simple man-land ratio. This is naturally a more refined index since it omits those parts of the land which are unproductive. In Egypt, where 35,800 square kilometres are regarded as arable, the physiological density according to the 1960 census rises to 726 persons per square kilometre (Table 26.5). The discrepancy between the arithmetic and the physiological densities becomes more striking when the density is computed according to the effective area under cultivation which approximates to only 24,500 square kilometres (Fig 26.2). This gives a pronounced degree of congestion which is estimated at 1,061 persons per square kilometre. It is possible to state, therefore, that the physiological density in Egypt almost coincides with that recorded in Japan, the Netherlands, Britain, India, and China.[7]

A third concept for measuring density is provided by the agricultural density which is simply the number of rural inhabitants per unit of cultivated area. It has been mentioned that 62 per cent, approximately, of the total population is regarded as rural which accounted for 16,116,000 in 1960. Thus Egypt, which has a physiological density of 1,061, has an agricultural density of 658 which indicates that slightly over three-fifths of all the inhabitants are cultivators.

Nevertheless, more progress could be made by measuring population density according to land productivity, particularly because in Egypt the land is distinguished by a high degree of double cropping under the perennial system of irrigation. The Japanese demographer Tsurumi has made an attempt to formulate a population density in terms of the crop area which definitely includes factors of land fertility

---

[6] This discussion is based on population distribution as shown in Figure 26.2.
[7] V. C. Vinch and G. T. Trewartha, *Elements of Geography: Physical and Cultural*, McGraw-Hill, N.Y., 1950, pp. 533–36.

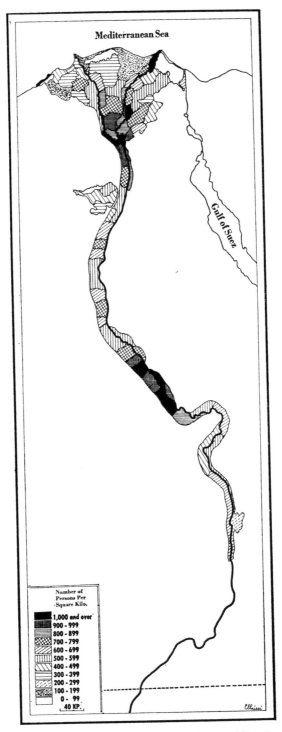

Fig. 26.2. Population density in the United Arab Republic. Based on census returns of 1960.

TABLE 26.5

DENSITY OF THE POPULATION PER SQUARE
KILOMETRE, U.A.R.*

Census Year	Population	Population Density
	(in thousands)	
1917..............	12,751	368
1927..............	14,218	406
1937..............	15,933	463
1949..............	19,022	540
1960..............	26,089	726

* Source: Dept. of Statistics and Census,
Govt. Press, Cairo.

and intensity of tillage.[8] On this basis, the population density in Egypt, when computed in proportion to the total rural population, diminishes greatly—to 367 persons per square kilometre of crop area. It can be said, therefore, that in Egypt, whilst the total cultivated area is around 6 million feddans (5,918,000)—which is the equivalent of 24,500 square kilometres—the crop area is 10,368,000 feddans representing 43,546 square kilometres. Thus the agricultural density of population as postulated by Tsurumi gives a more accurate measure of density for the rural inhabitants. It also reflects the degree of variability in land fertility particularly when one recognizes that there exists a curiously strong positive correlation between land fertility and population density. Areas with high population densities are simultaneously characterized by a high rate of land fertility which could be easily gauged by the average rental value of the land. In such areas there exists also a well-marked fragmentation of holdings to a diminutive size, notably the pygmy holdings. This is particularly noticeable in the provinces of Menoufia, Kaliubia, Giza, Assuit, Sohag, and Kena. Therefore, whenever population density increases, the rental value of the land is likely to be high correspondingly, and the diminution in the average size of holding follows in turn as a direct consequence of over-population and high soil fertility. The reverse is noticed in provinces with low population densities, such as those in the prairies of the northern Delta and in the southernmost province of Aswan.

It is worth mentioning that although the average agricultural density (according to the crop area) in Egypt does not exceed 367 persons per square kilometre, yet it is relatively high if compared with the corresponding density in other countries (98 in Bulgaria, 91 in Poland, 90 in Italy, 120 in India, and 100 in Ghana).[9]

---

[8] H. P. Fairchild, "Optimum Population," *Proceedings of World Population Conference,* London, 1927, pp. 72–85.

[9] I. Ferenczi, *The Synthetic Optimum of Population,* Paris, 1937, pp. 21–41. Also: E.C.A., *Economic Bulletin for Africa,* Vol. II, No. 2, pp. 9 and 60–63, Addis Ababa, 1962.

TABLE 26.6

PER CAPITA SHARE OF AGRICULTURAL INCOME, U.A.R., 1955–56*

Province	£E.	Province	£E.
Behira	31.5	Beni Suef	18.8
Gharbia	25.8	Fayoum	18.3
Dakahlia	24.8	Minia	23.6
Sharkia	24.0	Assuit	18.6
Menoufia	20.3	Sohag	14.7
Kaliubia	20.7	Kena	13.1
Giza	14.2	Aswan	12.1

* Source: Bulletin of the National Bank of Egypt, Cairo, 1957.

Another index of density is often termed the general economic density. The computation of this measure is subject to controversy and inexactitude. Perhaps the best measure to be adopted in this respect in Egypt is to estimate the per capita share of the agricultural income in the different provinces of the country. Undoubtedly the agricultural income is in fact considered the most appropriate measure of the standard of living, particularly because the agricultural income is influenced by a complexity of factors, the majority of which are geographic in nature. Paramount amongst them are: soil fertility, the prevailing climatic conditions which affect the kind of crop (i.e. rice cultivation is confined exclusively to the northern parts of the Delta whilst sugar cane is primarily an upper Egyptian crop), and the existing systems of irrigation and drainage. Table 26.6 indicates the per capita share of agricultural income in Egyptian pounds in 1955–56.

It is evident from this table that the four provinces of Behira, Gharbia, Dakahlia, and Sharkia attain the highest per capita share of agricultural income. Despite the fact that all the four provinces are located in the northern region of the Delta, they represent the principal areas for the production of long-staple cotton. Coupled with this, the low population density which characterizes that region also means a higher per capita share of cultivated land. On the other hand, the low rate of agricultural income which is recorded in Sohag, Kena, and Aswan is attributed to the fact that basin irrigation is responsible for it in both of the first two, whilst in Aswan—where the per capita income is the lowest—its southernmost location, the limitations of its agricultural setting, the relatively high level of its cultivated tracts, and the downstream migration of its potential labour force are all factors which account for the low standard of living.

The two provinces of Kaliubia and Menoufia which lie around the metropolis are considered to be amongst the densest regions of the country. Their proximity to Cairo together with the existence of horticultural and olericultural types of farming which cater to the daily demands of the capital (which constitutes the largest market for the consumption of the agricultural products of all the adjacent provinces) both account for the high per capita income, unexpected as it may be. The high per capita income realized in Minia Province can be attributed to the high yield of cotton per feddan and to the high fertility of its land.

An analysis of population density in the rural areas of the U.A.R. reveals some salient features:[10]

1. Land productivity is the dominant factor which underlies the high densities in: (a) the Delta Apex, (b) the Kena bend where basin irrigation is still practised, and (c) the bulge of the valley where the provinces of Assuit and Minia are located. In all the three regions, land productivity is known to be the highest according to the land classification system formulated by the Department of Agricultural Economics and Statistics.[11]

2. The peripheral parts of the Nile Valley and the Delta, whether in its northern end or in its southernmost margin, attain the lowest population density. This is as much due to their marginal locations away from the hold of the capital as to the sterility of most of their tillable tracts.

3. The low population density in Fayoum Province is due to its salt-impregnated soil, the variation in the level of land under cultivation, and the difficulty of drainage.

4. Generally speaking the Nile Valley proper has a higher population density than the Delta. Almost nowhere along its linear projection does population density fall below 350 persons per square kilometre (see Table 26.5), although the Delta exceeds the Valley in the number of settlements (there being 2,375 in the former and only 1,582 in the latter). This feature is ascribed to the high percentage of waste land in the Nile Delta which approximates to almost one-third of its total acreage.

5. The high population density recorded in the above-mentioned provinces is due to a complexity of factors such as high land productivity, the prevalence of basin irrigation which prevents the depletion of soil fertility, the potential width of the flood plain itself, the availability of irrigation waters, and the level of the cultivated tracts.

6. Agriculture in provinces with high population densities is characterized by some unique features amongst which are the increased prices and higher rents of agricultural land which has a high

---

[10] M. S. Abou El Ezz, and Others, *Studies on the Geography of Egypt*, Misr Library, Cairo, 1957.
Also:
A. Farah, "Rural Population in the U.A.R." Unpublished Article, Dept. of Statistics and Census, Cairo, 1962.
[11] A. Z. Sheira, *Economic Classification of Agricultural Lands in the U.A.R.*, Dept. of Agricultural Economics and Statistics, Ministry of Agriculture, Cairo, 1959.

TABLE 26.7

Average Size of Land Ownership, U.A.R.*

Year	Average Size of Holdings in Feddans
1899	5.77
1909	4.01
1919	3.05
1929	3.66
1939	2.35
1949	2.18
1959	2.09

* Source: Dept. of Statistics and Census, General Annual Statistics, Govt. Press, Cairo.

capital investment, the predominance of fragmented and small holdings, the existence of a considerable labour surplus, and an emphasis on a subsistence rather than a commercial type of farming.

Provinces with low population densities on the other hand have a lower level of rents and many relatively large holdings, and give priority to cash crops such as long-staple cotton and rice.

Thus, one might reach an axiomatic conclusion that the actual value of the land depends considerably on the density of population. If for the sake of argument Egypt is divided into provinces with high population densities and low population densities, the two regions are practically complementary. Population movements are often directed from the congested areas to provinces with lower populations. This, in fact, is an instinctive attempt on behalf of the rural population to rectify the anomalies brought about by differences in land productivity. Therefore, any future scheme for the redistribution of population will almost necessarily follow the present flow-lines of farm labour provided that rural-urban movements are put under control.

7. The influence of population pressure on the standard of living is undoubtedly due to the fact that the agricultural income per head of rural population varies with the density of agricultural population per acre. This has been illustrated previously in Table 26.6 which indicates that the level of income per head is negatively correlated with the density of population, and positively correlated with the proportion of the crop area. The rental value per acre also varies with the density of population[12] and to a lesser extent with the cash-crop acreage where the area of cultivated land per head is very small as in Giza, Menoufia, and Kaliubia, and where rents are often higher than in provinces with lower population densities as, for example, Kafr El

[12] The land reform law of 1952 decreed that the rent of agricultural land should not exceed seven times the basic land tax in the case of cash rent.

Sheik, Behira, Gharbia, Dakahlia, and Fayoum. Population pressure also manifests itself in the continuous decline of the average size of holding (Table 26.7).

CONCLUSION

This review of the rural population of the U.A.R. has outlined some of its major characteristics particularly as regards its numerical trend, structure, and density. The economic behaviour of the rural inhabitants of the country, however, has been treated in the narrowest possible sense. Time might allow a more thorough tackling of this subject in future when relevant statistics come more to hand. The main feature of the demographic position of the country is undeniably the rapid rate of population growth on a small land area which is cultivated almost to capacity. Thus, each acre of land must support more than four people. If we accept 2,500 calories a day as a reasonable standard intake for health[13] which is equivalent to the produce of one acre of cultivated land to feed one person on a world average, we instantly grasp the basic problem which confronts us. The annual population increase in U.A.R. is of the order of 520,000 in the last 13 years. Even if the High Dam Scheme is completely fulfilled it will not allow for land reclamation at the rate of over a thousand acres a day since the scheme will add only 1.3 million acres to the present area under cultivation. This is why it is very imperative to seek for projects which may add more land for cultivation such as the Wadi El Gedid in the Western Desert.

The rate of population increase now outstrips the rate of agricultural production. The rural population of the country, which is 16,116,000, produces 4.5 million tons of grain and 350 thousand tons of cotton, whilst in Syria, for example, a rural population of between 1.5 and 1.75 million produces 1.3 million tons of grain and 50 thousand tons of cotton.[14] This shows the vast difference between conditions in Egypt and Syria since the latter, compared with Egypt, has twenty times as much arable land per head of rural population.

To remedy the present disequilibrium between agricultural production and population, Egypt has no alternative but to divert the rural population to other economic activities particularly when it is recognized that there is now a surplus population on the land of over 5 millions, or 30 per cent of the total rural population.[15]

The High Dam above Aswan not only represents a long-term programme for agricultural expansion but is also the mainstay of in-

---

[13] L. D. Stamp, *Our Developing World*, Faber and Faber, London, 1960, pp. 69–79.

[14] D. Warriner, *Land Reform and Development in the Middle East*, Royal Institute of International Affairs, London, 1957, p. 73.

[15] Dept. of Statistics and Census, Govt. Press, Cairo.

dustrial development. Industrialization, no doubt, will absorb a considerable fraction of the surplus labour and eventually permit a noticeable increase in the total national income. This vast project could be rightly regarded as the pivot of our future economic development since all the problems resulting from the unique structure of the rural setting will be partially solved.

Other measures must also necessarily be adopted to relieve population pressure on the land, but the scope of this chapter does not allow their discussion.

Index